Mathematics
—— LEVEL 6 ——

JEAN HOLDERNESS

CAUSEWAY PRESS

Published by Causeway Press Ltd
PO Box 13, Ormskirk, Lancs L39 5HP

First published 1991

British Library Cataloguing in Publication Data
Holderness, Jean
   Mathematics: Level 6.
   1. Mathematics
   I. Title
   510

   ISBN 0-946183-69-4

Other titles by Jean Holderness published by
Causeway Press:
Mathematics: Level 5
GCSE Maths: Higher Level
GCSE Maths: Intermediate Level
GCSE Maths: Foundation Level
Pure Maths in Practice

Typesetting and printing by
The Alden Press Oxford

Preface

Mathematics: Level 6 has been written for pupils in secondary school and it follows on from the work covered in the book **Mathematics: Level 5**. It is based on covering the programme of study for level 6 of the National Curriculum, but it also provides consolidation for earlier levels, and some additional topics from higher levels have also been included.

For many pupils, the book could be used as a basis for a year's work, but for others there is sufficient material included for it to be used for more than a year. The teacher can decide how best to use the book with a particular class. (There are some notes for teachers on page *x*.)

As usual, my family and friends have given me support and encouragement while I have been planning and writing this book, and I would like to thank them for this. I should also like to thank those who have helped with the production of the book, Sue and Andrew, my brother Jim, and the staff at Alden Press. From Causeway Press I have had support from everyone, and especially from Fred, David and Mike, and I thank them for all their help.

Jean Holderness

Acknowledgements

Artwork, page design and cover Susan and Andrew Allen

Photography © Jim Holderness and Andrew Allen

Programme of Study: Level 6 pages *xiv–xv*,
from *Mathematics in the National Curriculum*,
reproduced with the permission of the Controller
of Her Majesty's Stationery Office

Copyright photographs
British Aerospace pp. 183 (top right), 213 (top)
Camera Press p. 265 (middle left)
Daily Telegraph Colour Library p. 253 (bottom middle)
Ed Buziak pp. 37 (bottom), 243 (middle), 274 (bottom left), 274 (bottom right)
Hulton–Deutsch Collection pp. 205, 222
Intercity p. 182 (middle)
Jim Nettleship p. 96
John Mills–Citizen Newspapers p. 138
Lancashire County Council p. 219
Liverpool Daily Post and Echo pp. 244, 253 (bottom left)
Network p. 114 (top)
Peter Newark's Western Americana pp. 108, 275 (bottom)
Picturesport Associates p. 182 (bottom)
Popperfoto pp. 24 (middle left), 88 (middle), 89 (bottom), 183 (middle left),
         212 (top), 275 (top), 304
Royal Mint p. 115 (top)
Science Museum pp. 153, 180, 183 (top left), 262, 209, 310
Topham Picture Source pp. 36 (middle), 123 (top left), 167 (middle left),
             167 (bottom left), 167 (middle right), 167 (bottom right), 182 (top),
             190, 243 (bottom), 265 (middle right)
United Nations p. 275 (middle)
United States Information Service p. 183 (bottom)

Contents

Chapter 1   Numbers

Thinking about numbers   1
Tables and mental arithmetic   2
Prime numbers, dividing by numbers   3
Further calculations, multiplication and division   6
Using negative numbers   8
Sequences of numbers   13
Difference methods   16

Chapter 2   Algebra

Thinking about Algebra   24
Rules for addition, subtraction, multiplication, division   26
Making expressions, substitution, solving simple equations   27
Collecting terms, removing brackets   29
Equations involving terms with brackets or fractions   30

Chapter 3   Decimals and Measurements

Thinking about decimals and measurements   36
Decimals   38
Putting decimal numbers in order of size   39
Calculations with decimals   40
Correcting a number up to a certain number of decimal places   41
Measurements, tables   43
Accuracy of measurements   44

Chapter 4   Quadrilaterals

Thinking about quadrilaterals   50
Sum of angles, perimeter   52
Special quadrilaterals   52
Diagonals   53
Facts about angles and triangles   53
A kite   55
A trapezium   57
A parallelogram   58
A rhombus   59

A rectangle 60
A square 60
Definitions and properties of special quadrilaterals 61
Symmetry 62
Properties of diagonals 68

Chapter 5 **Fractions and Percentages**

Thinking about fractions and percentages 70
Fractions 72
Changing fractions to decimals 72
Multiplication with fractions 73
Fractional changes 74
Percentages 76
Fractions into percentages 77
Percentages into fractions 77
Percentage of a sum of money or a quantity 78
To increase or decrease by a percentage 78
To express one quantity as a percentage of another 79
Addition and subtraction of fractions 82
Division of fractions 83

Chapter 6 **Collecting information**

Thinking about collecting information 88
Statistics, statistical diagrams 90
A line-graph 90
Pictogram, bar chart, pie chart, bar-line graph, histogram 91
Mean and range of a set of data 93
Statistical investigations 95
Questionnaires 96

Miscellaneous Section A

Aural practice exercises 102
Revision exercise 104
Activities 107

Chapter 7 **Ratio**

Thinking about ratio 114
Ratios as fractions, decimals or percentages 116
Using ratios 116

Chapter 8   **Polygons**

Thinking about polygons   122
Polygons, regular polygons   124
Sum of the angles in a polygon   125
Size of each angle in a regular polygon   126
Exterior angles of a convex polygon   126
Geometric patterns, tessellations   130
To construct regular polygons   135

Chapter 9   **Probability**

Thinking about probability   138
Formula for probability   140
Mutually exclusive events   141
Independent events   143
Tables, lists and tree diagrams   144

Chapter 10   **Functions and Coordinates**

Thinking about functions and coordinates   152
Functions represented by mapping diagrams, tables,
   pairs of numbers   154
Representing functions by graphs   156

Chapter 11   **Solid Figures**

Thinking about solid figures   166
Names of solid figures   168
Practice in drawing solid figures   169
Faces, vertices and edges   171
Nets of solid figures   172
Making models of solid figures from cardboard   172
Plans and elevations   179
The regular solid figures   180

Chapter 12   **Speeds**

Thinking about speeds   182
Speed and average speed   184
Finding distance   185
Finding time   186
Time in hours and minutes   186

Miscellaneous Section B

Aural practice exercises	192
Revision exercise	194
Activities	197

Chapter 13 Bearings

Thinking about bearings	212
3-figure bearings	214
Alternative notation for bearings	220

Chapter 14 Perimeter, Area and Volume

Thinking about perimeter, area and volume	222
Perimeter	224
Area, areas of rectangle and square	225
Areas of triangle, parallelogram and trapezium	230
Volume, volumes of cuboid and cube	233
Surface area	233
Density	235

Chapter 15 Scatter Graphs

Thinking about scatter graphs	242
Scatter graphs	244
Relationship between variables, correlation	246

Chapter 16 Reflection and Enlargement

Thinking about reflection and enlargement	252
Reflection	254
Enlargement, similar figures	256
Scale factor of an enlargement	257

Chapter 17 More Equations

Thinking about more equations	264
Linear, quadratic and cubic equations	266
Simple quadratic equations	266
Simple cubic equations	268
Finding cube roots by trial and improvement	269
Some other equations	270

Chapter 18   Circles

Thinking about circles   274
Names of parts of a circle   276
Symmetry   277
To draw a tangent   277
Drawing patterns using compasses   278
Constructions using ruler and compasses   282

Miscellaneous Section C

Aural practice exercises   290
Oral practice   292
Revision exercises   293
Activities   301

Index   312

Answers   315

Topics for Activities (included in the miscellaneous sections)

A booklet about measuring and weighing, 107
A garden patio, 301
A maths poster display, 307
A year's work, 199
Bearings, 308
Buttons, 303
Buying a tool-kit, 197
Diagonals of polygons, 203
Feed yourself for £1, 197
Inside a quadrilateral, 107
Make a guess-the-number game to puzzle your friends, 112
Moebius bands, 111
Paper sizes, 302

Planning for Christmas, 109
Probability experiments, 202
Reflection using mirrors, 306
'Roll-a-penny', 304
Seven, 108
Stars for Christmas decorations, 110
Sums and differences, products and squares, 107
The Fibonacci Sequence (4), 206
The Fibonacci Sequence in Nature, 309
The laws of growth or decay, 198
The semi-regular solid figures, 208
Using a network map, the London Underground, 204
Using the computer, 113, 211, 311

To the teacher

Mathematics: Level 6 has been planned for use in secondary schools. It follows on from the work in the book **Mathematics: Level 5**, and it contains all the topics mentioned in the Programme of Study and the Attainment Targets for Level 6.

Although the main focus is on level 6, the book contains substantial links with earlier levels, allowing for consolidation of work which may not have been understood completely at a younger age.

There are also some topics from higher levels included, and these, together with extended work on other activities, give an opportunity for some pupils to make further progress beyond level 6.

The book is organised as follows:- For each chapter there is an introductory section called 'Thinking About . . .' You could use these sections, or parts of them, for class discussion, for group work or for individual work. They could take a brief few minutes or several lessons. You might find that by extending the ideas there you are covering the work of the chapter quite adequately and very little follow-up work will be needed.

The main part of the chapter consists of bookwork and worked examples, followed by straightforward exercises. There should be no need for most pupils to have to work through the whole of any of these exercises. They are there in case practice is needed, and to give the pupils confidence in using the mathematical techniques. It is useful to have the bookwork available for reference. If the teacher has planned a good lesson then it may be unnecessary to use the bookwork at all, but children are not always present in every lesson, and the absentees need some text to help them later.
In addition, some of the essential bookwork from *Level 5* has been reproduced here, because the pupils may no longer have a copy of that book. In many topics, especially in the earlier chapters, there is quite a bit of overlap with the work of *Level 5*. For those pupils who did not fully understand it last year it gives a second chance. If the pupils already know it confidently then they can go quickly on to new work and spend more time doing that in greater depth.

The last exercise of each chapter is more varied, giving ideas for applications and activities of various lengths. Some are purely mathematical and some relate the mathematics of the chapter to real-life applications. The teacher can best plan how to use these activities with the class, whether to use them for individual work, group work or as a whole class activity, and deciding how much time can be spent on them. If the pupils can be allowed to make their own choice of an activity that interests them, they can produce very satisfactory work to match their own levels of ability.

The book has 18 chapters, giving roughly 6 for each term if the book is to be used for a year. After every 6 chapters there is a miscellaneous section with aural questions, revision questions and more suggestions for activities. There are puzzle questions fitted in at the ends of chapters where there is space. These are in no particular order and are there to give further interest.

The chapters are arranged in an order which interlinks Arithmetic, Geometry, Algebra, Statistics and Probability, so that there is a variety of maths in each part of the book, but there is no need to keep to the exact order of topics.

I have again started the book with a short section on tables because even if these were known a year ago it does not follow that everyone still knows them. If everyone in the class **can** do mental arithmetic quickly and correctly then a check-up will not take very long. But if some pupils are not too good at it then more time and effort will be needed so that they are encouraged and helped to improve. Those who know the basic number facts will take a more confident part in aural work and discussion, will do written work quickly and accurately, and will find Maths more enjoyable. This will have a cumulative effect on their progress in future years.

I think that applications or activities which are related to everyday life are very useful, and many have been included in the book. However, the best topics are those which apply directly to the interests of the class, to topics currently being studied in other subjects, to what is happening in your school or neighbourhood, or to what is currently in the news. So it is hoped that the teacher will think of the mathematical connections and introduce them.

I have avoided introducing social issues in the questions. A teacher can decide whether it is appropriate with a particular class at a particular time to include discussion of such matters as health topics, sex discrimination, government spending, etc.

I have also avoided use of statistics such as road accidents or deaths. I think these must be introduced with care, by a teacher who knows the class. (I like Maths lessons to be cheerful, not depressing.)

Here are some notes about particular topics:

Chapter 6, Statistics. I have shown examples of diagrams and graphs used in *Level 5*, as well as revising the line-graph, the mean and the range. All these will be needed for making summaries of the results of pupils' own investigations.

Chapter 7, Ratio. I have not stressed scales of maps because this was done in some detail in *Level 5*.

Chapter 8, Polygons. I have shown two ways of splitting the polygons into triangles, so that you can use whichever method you prefer. It would be ideal if the pupils could discover a method for themselves.

Chapter 9, Probability. This chapter does not take the idea of probability much further, as the addition rule for mutually exclusive events belongs to level 7 and the multiplication rule for independent events belongs to level 8. The pupils may discover these rules for themselves, or you may like to introduce them.

Chapter 10, Graphs. When plotting functions involving whole numbers only, squared paper is quite adequate, and is simpler to use than graph paper. But when graph paper is used I am assuming it has 2 mm squares. Graph paper with 1 mm squares is much more difficult to use, especially for those with poor eyesight.

Chapter 15, Scatter graphs. The first type of graph is only suitable for discrete data with a small range, and has very limited use. All continuous data, and discrete data when the range of values is large, are plotted on the second kind of graph, where crosses are plotted on points, not inside squares. Most of the questions use this sort of graph. I have concentrated on the idea of correlation in this chapter, as lines of best fit belong to level 7. You may like to introduce them here.

The following topics do not belong to level 6, so they can be omitted at this stage if you do not want to include them:

Negative numbers. I did not find the work included in *Level 5* was helpful enough for use in checking negative solutions in equations or for finding values of functions involving negative numbers. So I have included more formal work on negative numbers in Chapter 1, although it really belongs to level 8. Neither topic needs division by negative numbers, so I have not stressed this.

Fractions, chapter 5. Multiplication of fractions seemed essential for dealing with fractions, percentages and ratios so I have included it. As optional activities I have also included addition and subtraction of fractions because this is useful for probability questions, and division of fractions so that times in hours and minutes can be used with fractions of hours in the formula for speed, chapter 12. These topics also belong to level 8.

Areas and volumes, chapter 14. There is a jump from level 4 (areas by counting squares and volumes by counting cubes) to level 8. Yet practical work could involve areas and volumes, density is mentioned in level 6 and areas will be needed for Pythagoras' theorem in level 7. So this seemed a good place to revise previous work and take it a stage further.

Circles, chapter 18. I am not too sure at which level this should come in, but I think many children enjoy drawing compass patterns, so I have included 'circles' as the last chapter of the book. The constructions are useful and will link with locus questions in level 7. The other discoveries are only intended to be for activities, the angle properties are not needed until level 10 and the other properties are not needed at all.

Calculators. I am aware that calculators do not all work in the same way. To mention several variations in the text would be too confusing to everyone, so I have to leave it to the teacher to sort out any particular problems with the particular calculator being used.

Computers. Where, a few years ago, pupils could be encouraged to write their own programs, the emphasis now seems to be on using commercially-produced programs, except for very simple applications. Even with those, the differences in language among the different machines have discouraged me from listing even simple programs in this book.

I hope that the programs listed in *Level 5* were useful in giving some examples for those people interested in programming.

In this book, I have mentioned computers in a general way, and I hope that you have got the necessary software to work on your own computers.

Answers. To produce a book without answers as well as an edition with answers would increase the costs. (This is the publisher's problem, not mine.) I have tried to compromise by giving the answers to the straightforward questions, but not always giving answers to the activities questions, where it is important that the pupils make their own discoveries. The puzzle answers are not given, either. I have arranged for the answers to begin on a right-hand page, so that if you do not want the class to have them, they can be cut out of the book.

I hope you and your pupils find this book useful and interesting. Enjoy your Maths.

Jean Holderness

Level 6   Programme of Study

To achieve level 6 within the attainment targets pupils should be:

Using and applying mathematics

- designing a task and selecting the mathematics and resources; checking information and obtaining any that is missing; using 'trial and improvement' methods.
- presenting findings using oral, written or visual forms.
- making and testing generalisations and simple hypotheses; defining and reasoning with some precision.

Number

- reading, writing and ordering decimals and appreciating place values.
- understanding and using equivalence of fractions and ratios.
- working out fractional and percentage changes.
- calculating using ratios in a variety of situations.
- converting fractions to decimals and percentages.
- using estimation and approximation to check that answers to multiplication and division problems involving whole numbers are of the right order.

Algebra

- determining possible rules for generating sequences.
- using spreadsheets or other computer facilities to explore number patterns.
- solving linear equations; solving simple polynomial equations by 'trial and improvement' methods.
- using and plotting Cartesian coordinates to represent simple function mappings.

Measures

- understanding and using compound measures, *e.g. speed, density*.
- recognising that measurement is approximate and choosing the degree of accuracy required for a particular purpose.

Shape and space

- classifying and defining types of quadrilaterals.
- using angle and symmetry properties of quadrilaterals and polygons.
- using 2-D representation of 3-D objects.
- using computers to generate and transform 2-D shapes.
- understanding and using bearings to define direction.
- reflecting simple shapes in a mirror line.

- enlarging a shape by a whole number scale factor.
- devising instructions for a computer to produce desired shapes and paths.

Handling data

- designing and using observation sheets; collating and analysing results.
- surveying opinions, using a questionnaire (taking account of bias).
- creating scatter graphs for discrete and continuous variables.
- constructing and interpreting information through two-way tables and network diagrams.
- identifying outcomes of two combined events which are independent.
- knowing that the total sum of the probabilities of mutually exclusive events is 1 and that the probability of something happening is 1 minus the probability of it not happening.

1 Thinking about numbers

Everyday numbers

Numbers play a large part in our lives. Certain numbers we can recognise immediately.
What is . . .
the number of your house,
your phone number,
the number of the bus route to go to school, or to town,
your parent's car registration number (consisting of numbers and letters) ?

What numbers are shown here ?
Can you think of other numbers suggested by this scene ?

Official numbers

Ask an 'old soldier' if he remembers his army number. Even though it is many years since he needed it, he probably remembers it.

Other numbers which adults need are . . .
National Insurance number,
National Health number,
Bank account number,
Secret PIN number, for using at cash machines.
Can you suggest others ?
The list of numbers we use seems endless.

Why has a PIN number to be kept secret ?

Do you know ?

What are these numbers used for ?
999,   071 or 081,   0800.

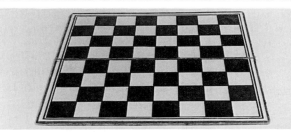

Puzzle questions

Here are some numbers in a popular quiz. Can you supply the missing words, whose initial letters are given ?

3 BM (SHTR)
11 P in a FT
13 L in a BD
18 H on a GC
24 H in a D
29 D in F in a LY
32 DF at which WF
57 HV
76 T in the BP
90 D in a RA

Sequences

'2, 4, 6, 8,
Who do we appreciate ?'
This is an example of a sequence of numbers.
How would you describe the numbers in the sequence ?

How many squares are there on a chessboard ?
No, there are more than 64!
How many squares are there **altogether** ?

Begin by counting the complete square, that makes 1.
Then, how many squares are there consisting of 7 of the small squares each way ?
Continue by working out how many squares there are consisting of 6 of the small squares each way.
Now you should have 3 numbers making the beginning of a sequence.
How would you describe the numbers in the sequence ?
Continue the sequence until you can find the answer for the total number of squares.

1 Numbers

Tables and mental arithmetic

You should know certain number facts so well that you can give the answers almost without thinking.
Write down the answers to these questions, seeing how quickly you can do them.
Work downwards in columns.

6 × 6	3 × 11	6 × 8	2 × 1	7 × 3
7 × 2	4 × 6	4 × 7	7 × 12	9 × 0
5 × 0	8 × 10	3 × 10	12 × 9	5 × 5
8 × 4	2 × 5	1 × 12	8 × 3	1 × 7
6 × 3	1 × 8	7 × 1	9 × 4	4 × 9
11 × 9	5 × 2	2 × 8	8 × 7	11 × 10
10 × 8	6 × 5	11 × 6	4 × 3	12 × 5
11 × 5	7 × 8	3 × 7	0 × 9	9 × 8
7 × 7	1 × 6	8 × 6	2 × 2	6 × 9
0 × 2	6 × 7	12 × 1	6 × 0	12 × 3

Now try these mixed questions.

8 + 1	60 ÷ 5	5 + 5	8 + 0	23 + 16
10 × 10	2 + 7	3 × 5	9 − 3	6 × 4
5 − 1	12 × 6	10 × 5	28 + 9	44 ÷ 4
5 + 6	18 + 3	77 ÷ 11	3 + 8	7 − 7
3 × 12	8 × 7	17 − 9	0 × 13	14 × 1
15 − 6	8 + 6	54 − 5	18 − 9	39 − 19
16 + 4	30 ÷ 5	9 + 3	2 × 3 × 4	5 × 7
6 − 0	4 − 2	40 + 60	7 + 7	14 − 7
27 ÷ 9	45 ÷ 9	56 ÷ 7	10 × 4	20 × 1
67 − 7	10 − 5	47 + 7	35 − 9	9 + 9

Now, decide whether you need further practice. It is important **to you** that you can do basic arithmetic accurately and quickly. Otherwise you will waste so much time on working things out, time which could be better spent.
Perhaps you have a computer program which will give you practice by asking questions at random. On page 22 there is a number game which you can try with your friends.
You should think of other ways to get more practice, so that you improve.

When you know that 4 × 6 = 24, you also know that
4 + 4 + 4 + 4 + 4 + 4 = 24
6 + 6 + 6 + 6 = 24
24 ÷ 4 = 6
24 ÷ 6 = 4
Since 4 = 2 × 2 and 6 = 2 × 3, 24 = 2 × 2 × 2 × 3, so 24 also divides by
2, 3, 2 × 2 × 2 (=8) and 2 × 2 × 3 (=12). Since 24 does not have any prime
factors except 2 and 3, it will not divide by any other prime numbers, such as
5, 7, 11, or their multiples.
You may notice some other facts about 24, such as
1 × 2 × 3 × 4 = 24
7 + 8 + 9 = 24
3 + 5 + 7 + 9 = 24
In a similar way, find out some facts about these numbers; 30, 32, 35, 36, 40.

Prime numbers

A number which has no factors, except 1 and itself, is called a **prime number**.

Dividing by numbers

A number divides by 2 if its last figure is 2, 4, 6, 8, 0.
A number divides by 5 if its last figure is 5, 0.
A number divides by 4 if its last two figures divide by 4.
e.g. For 1792 just check the last two figures, 92. (92 divides by 4 so 1792 does also.)
A number divides by 3 if its digits add up to a multiple of 3.
e.g. For 46137 use 4 + 6 + 1 + 3 + 7 = 21 (and for 21 use 2 + 1 = 3). This divides
by 3 so 46137 does also.
A number divides by 9 if its digits add up to a multiple of 9.
e.g. For 567 use 5 + 6 + 7 = 18 (and for 18 use 1 + 8 = 9). This divides by 9 so 567
does also.

In exercise 1.1 there is more practice in using numbers. Do the questions without using
a calculator, and if possible do them in your head.

Exercise 1.1

1. Write in figures the numbers
    1   Three hundred and ninety-six thousand, two hundred and forty-one.
    2   Nine thousand and six.
    3   Four million, three hundred and eighteen thousand, and ninety-two.
    4   Three million, three thousand and thirty.
    5   Two and a half million.
    6   Ninety-six thousand.
    7   Seven thousand and twenty-two.
    8   Seventy thousand.
    9   One thousand and one.
    10 One-quarter of a million.

2. Write down the values of
    1 5×6 **6** 30×3
    2 $3 + 8$ **7** $56 \div 8$
    3 $50 \div 2$ **8** $20 - 9$
    4 7×0 **9** 15×1
    5 $99 + 5$ **10** 11×11

3. Write down the answer and the remainder in these questions.
    1 $60 \div 8$ **6** $18 \div 6$
    2 $20 \div 3$ **7** $68 \div 7$
    3 $50 \div 10$ **8** $32 \div 4$
    4 $80 \div 11$ **9** $100 \div 8$
    5 $100 \div 9$ **10** $27 \div 5$

4. **1**   Find two numbers whose sum is 11 and whose product is 24.
    2   Find two numbers whose sum is 12 and whose product is 20.
    3   Find two numbers whose sum is 15 and whose product is 56.
    4   Find two numbers whose sum is 13 and whose product is 30.
    5   Find two numbers whose sum is 29 and whose product is 100.

5. 1   What must be added to 4 × 8 to make 40 ?
    2   What must be added to 5 × 9 to make 50 ?
    3   What must be added to 6 × 11 to make 70 ?
    4   What must be added to 7 × 3 to make 30 ?
    5   What must be added to 8 × 2 to make 20 ?

6. 1   8 + 7 − 5 =
    2   What are seven 7's ?
    3   What is the product of 9 and 6 ?
    4   By what must 8 be multiplied to make 40 ?
    5   What is 20 less than 64 ?
    6   How many 4's added together will make 48 ?
    7   What number multiplied by itself makes 81 ?
    8   What is 23 doubled ?
    9   How many times does 7 go into 42 ?
   10   What is ten times 30 ?

7. From the numbers 62, 64, 65, 69, 70, 72, 75:
    1   Which numbers divide exactly by 2 ?
    2   Which numbers divide exactly by 5 ?
    3   Which numbers divide exactly by 3 ?

8. 1   Which numbers between 40 and 50 are prime numbers ?
    2   Which of these numbers, 67, 77, 87, 97, are prime numbers ?

9. **Square numbers** are 1^2, 2^2, 3^2, 4^2, . . . which worked out are 1, 4, 9, 16, . . .

    Cube numbers are 1^3, 2^3, 3^3, 4^3, . . . which worked out are 1, 8, 27, 64, . . .

    From the numbers 23, 27, 31, 36, 42, 45, 49, 50, 55, 64, name
    1   the square numbers,
    2   the cube numbers,
    3   the prime numbers,
    4   the numbers which divide exactly by 5,
    5   the numbers which divide exactly by 3.

10. 1   Write down any number less than 10, double it and add 4. Multiply the
         result by 5 and subtract 10. Divide by 10 and subtract the number you
         started with. What is your answer ?
    2   Write down any number less than 10, add 3 and multiply the result by 4.
         Then subtract 6 and multiply by 3. Add 12 and divide by 6. Subtract 5 and
         divide by the number you started with. What is your answer?

Further calculations

Even when numbers are larger, you can still work out straightforward calculations
without your calculator, although you may need to write down some working.

Examples

1 $200 \times 50 = 2 \times 100 \times 5 \times 10$
$= 2 \times 5 \times 100 \times 10$ } do this in your head
$= 10 \times 1000$
$= 10\,000$

2 $6000 \times 80 = 6 \times 1000 \times 8 \times 10$
$= 6 \times 8 \times 1000 \times 10$ } do this in your head
$= 48 \times 10\,000$
$= 480\,000$

3 $7200 \div 90 = \dfrac{720\cancel{0}}{9\cancel{0}} = 80$

4 $3000 \div 500 = \dfrac{30\cancel{0}\cancel{0}}{5\cancel{0}\cancel{0}} = 6$

5 $212 \times 57 = 12\,084$

$$
\begin{array}{r}
212 \\
\times \quad 57 \\
\hline
1484 \\
10600 \\
\hline
12084 \\
\hline
\end{array}
\qquad \text{or} \qquad
\begin{array}{r}
57 \\
\times \quad 212 \\
\hline
114 \\
570 \\
11400 \\
\hline
12084 \\
\hline
\end{array}
$$

or you may use a different method if you prefer to.

One thing you can do, after working out such a question, is to use approximate
numbers to check that your answer is about the right size.

212 is 200, to 1 significant figure,
57 is 60, to 1 significant figure.
$200 \times 60 = 12\,000$, and your answer is just over $12\,000$, so it seems to be the right
size.

6 $3910 \div 34 = 115$

$$
\begin{array}{r}
115 \text{ Ans} \\
34\overline{)3910} \\
\underline{34} \\
51 \\
\underline{34} \\
170 \\
\underline{170}
\end{array}
$$

Again, checking the answer,
3910 is 4000, to 1 significant figure,
34 is 30, to 1 significant figure.

$$4000 \div 30 = \frac{400\cancel{0}}{3\cancel{0}} = \frac{400}{3} = 133, \text{ to the nearest whole number.}$$

However, 34 is quite a bit larger than 30, so you would expect your answer to be a bit smaller than 133.

$$\text{Try } 4000 \div 40 = \frac{400\cancel{0}}{4\cancel{0}} = 100.$$

34 is quite a bit smaller than 40, so you would expect your answer to be a bit larger than 100.
So the answer 115 seems to be about the right size.

You can also check by multiplication.

If $3910 \div 34 = 115$,

then $115 \times 34 = 3910$.

$$
\begin{array}{r}
115 \\
\times \quad 34 \\
\hline
460 \\
3450 \\
\hline
3910
\end{array}
$$

Exercise 1.2

1. Work out the answers to these questions, without using your calculator.

1	80×70	**6**	$320 \div 40$
2	600×400	**7**	$4200 \div 70$
3	3000×90	**8**	$3600 \div 900$
4	100×5000	**9**	$56\,000 \div 80$
5	70×200	**10**	$6000 \div 500$

2.   Work out estimated answers to these calculations, without using your calculator.

    1 $317 + 240 + 775$ **6** 140×31
    2 $1331 - 285$ **7** 73×19
    3 $132 + 250 + 379$ **8** 320×82
    4 $2103 - 519$ **9** 650×28
    5 52×47 **10** 61^2

3.   Find the exact answers to the calculations in question 2, without using your calculator. Compare them with the estimated answers to check that they are about the right size.

4.   Work out estimated answers to these calculations, without using your calculator.

    1 $357 \div 21$ **4** $1953 \div 63$
    2 $1386 \div 33$ **5** $34\,710 \div 89$
    3 $25\,480 \div 49$

5.   Find the exact answers to the calculations in question 4, without using your calculator. Compare them with the estimated answers to check that they are about the right size.

6.   Work out the estimated answers to these calculations, without using your calculator, and then use your calculator to find the exact answers. Compare these answers with the estimated answers to check that they are about the right size.

    1 542×37 **4** 2150×41
    2 5260×103 **5** 697×880
    3 $28\,700 \times 52$

7.   Work out the estimated answers to these calculations, without using your calculator, and then use your calculator to find the answers, correct to 1 decimal place. Compare these answers with the estimated answers to check that they are about the right size.

    1 $714 \div 52$ **4** $321 \div 87$
    2 $500 \div 75$ **5** $840 \div 33$
    3 $4730 \div 46$

Using negative numbers

You have used negative numbers already. Now your are going to work out calculations involving them, as you are going to need to use these in later chapters.

Use your number line for counting up, when the sign is +, or down, when the sign is −.

Examples

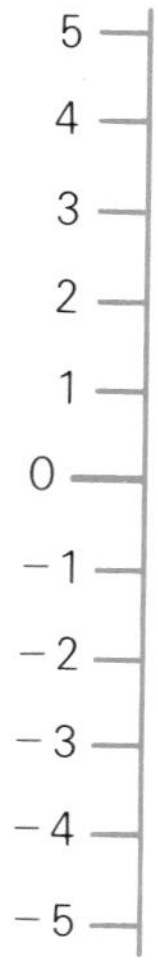

4 + 2 = 6
Start at 4 and go up 2, getting to 6

4 − 7 = −3
Start at 4 and go down 7, getting to −3

(−3) + 5 = 2
Start at −3 and go up 5, getting to 2

(−3) + 1 = −2
Start at −3 and go up 1, getting to −2

(−3) − 6 = −9
Start at −3 and go down 6, getting to −9

```
5 ─┤
4 ─┤
3 ─┤
2 ─┤
1 ─┤
0 ─┤
−1 ─┤
−2 ─┤
−3 ─┤
−4 ─┤
−5 ─┤
```

Now do these questions:

1.	3 − 6	6.	(−11) − 9
2.	(−6) − 3	7.	6 − 12
3.	(−6) + 7	8.	0 − 3
4.	5 − 8	9.	1 − 2
5.	(−1) + 2	10.	(−3) + 5

Sometimes you may have to work out expressions such as (−4) − (+3) or 5 − (−6). These are best done by changing the middle two signs into one according to rules.

> + + should be replaced by +
> + − or − + should be replaced by −
> − − should be replaced by +

+ + means 'keep going up', and can be replaced by +

(go up) (keep in the same direction)

e.g.   4 + (+3) = 4 + 3 = 7
       (−2) + (+6) = (−2) + 6 = 4
       (−7) + (+1) = (−7) + 1 = −6

+ −, means 'go down', and can be replaced by −

(go up) (go in opposite direction)

e.g. $4 + (-3) = 4 - 3 = 1$
      $(-2) + (-6) = (-2) - 6 = -8$
      $1 + (-5) = 1 - 5 = -4$

− + means 'go down' and can be replaced by −

(go down) (keep in the same direction)

e.g. $(-3) - (+6) = (-3) - 6 = -9$
      $2 - (+1) = 2 - 1 = 1$
      $5 - (+7) = 5 - 7 = -2$

− − means 'go up' and can be replaced by +

(go down) (go in opposite direction)

This is the result which seems strange, but it is correct.

e.g. $2 - (-1) = 2 + 1 = 3$
      $(-4) - (-5) = (-4) + 5 = 1$
      $(-7) - (-3) = (-7) + 3 = -4$

So there are two stages to working out such questions.
If two signs follow each other, replace them by one sign. Then use the number line to work out the answer.
Here are a few more examples:

$(-5) + (+1)$ Replace + + by +, which means 'go up'
$= (-5) + 1$ Start at −5 and go up 1, getting to −4
$= -4$

$(-5) - (+3)$ Replace − + by −, which means 'go down'
$= (-5) - 3$ Start at −5 and go down 3, getting to −8
$= -8$

$5 + (-7)$ Replace + − by −, which means 'go down'
$= 5 - 7$ Start at 5 and go down 7, getting to −2
$= -2$

$5 - (-1)$ Replace − − by +, which means 'go up'
$= 5 + 1$ Start at 5 and go up 1, getting to 6
$= 6$

Now do these questions.

1. $5 + (-2)$ 6. $(-3) - (-1)$
2. $1 - (+2)$ 7. $1 + (-1)$
3. $(-4) - (-9)$ 8. $2 - (-5)$
4. $(-2) - (-1)$ 9. $(-5) + (+4)$
5. $7 + (+2)$ 10. $(-2) - (-5)$

Multiplication

$(+4) \times (+3)$ is the same as 4×3 and equals 12
$(+4) \times (-3)$ is the same as $4 \times (-3)$ and equals -12
$(-4) \times (-3)$ is the tricky one. It equals 12 (not -12)

+	×	+	=	+
+	×	−	=	−
−	×	−	=	+

These results are shown in this multiplication number pattern, where you can follow the patterns backwards from right to left and then downwards from top to bottom.

	−4	−3	−2	−1	0	1	2	3	4
4	−16	−12	−8	−4	0	4	8	12	16
3	−12	−9	−6	−3	0	3	6	9	12
2	−8	−6	−4	−2	0	2	4	6	8
1	−4	−3	−2	−1	0	1	2	3	4
0	0	0	0	0	0	0	0	0	0
−1	4	3	2	1	0	−1	−2	−3	−4
−2	8	6	4	2	0	−2	−4	−6	−8
−3	12	9	6	3	0	−3	−6	−9	−12
−4	16	12	8	4	0	−4	−8	−12	−16

Now do these questions.

1. $(+8) \times (-3)$ 6. $(+7) \times (-2)$
2. $(+6) \times (+5)$ 7. $(-5) \times (+11)$
3. $(-4) \times (-2)$ 8. $(-8) \times (-2)$
4. $(-9) \times 7$ 9. $(-3) \times 0$
5. $0 \times (-6)$ 10. $20 \times (-9)$

You are not so likely to need division involving negative numbers yet, but the rules follow those for multiplication, and are

$(+12) \div (+3) = \ \ 4$
$(+12) \div (-3) = -4$
$(-12) \div (+3) = -4$
$(-12) \div (-3) = \ \ 4$

+	÷	+	=	+
+	÷	−	=	−
−	÷	+	=	−
−	÷	−	=	+

If your calculator has a $\boxed{^+/_-}$ key, then you can enter negative numbers, and you can do calculations with the calculator, although it is better just to use the rules and manage without the calculator.

e.g.   For $(-4) + (-3)$ press $4 \boxed{^+/_-} \boxed{+} 3 \boxed{^+/_-} \boxed{=}$ and you will get the answer -7.

      For $(-4) - (-3)$ press $4 \boxed{^+/_-} \boxed{-} 3 \boxed{^+/_-} \boxed{=}$ and you will get the answer -1.

      For $(-4) \times (-3)$ press $4 \boxed{^+/_-} \boxed{\times} 3 \boxed{^+/_-} \boxed{=}$ and you will get the answer 12.

It is not so straightforward if your calculator does not have a $\boxed{^+/_-}$ key. You can put -3 in the memory by using $0 - 3$, and then get -4 on the calculator by using $0 - 4$, in order to do the same calculations. Again, it is easier just to use the rules, instead of relying on the calculator.

Exercise 1.3

Work out the answers to these calculations.

1.   **1** $4 + 2$ **11** $1 - 7 + 6$
     2 $4 - 3$ **12** $4 + 2 - 5$
     3 $(-2) + 1$ **13** $(-6) + 10 - 5$
     4 $(-2) - 1$ **14** $(-2) - 1 + 6$
     5 $4 - 8$ **15** $0 - 8 + 4$
     6 $(-4) + 3$ **16** $6 - 12 - 2$
     7 $(-2) - 3$ **17** $(-5) + 3 - 1$
     8 $(-2) + 11$ **18** $(-5) - 2 + 3$
     9 $0 - 5$ **19** $(-1) + 6 - 5$
    10 $(-8) - 3$ **20** $4 - 5 + 2$

2.   **1** $4 - (+3)$ **11** $2 - (+3)$
     3 $(-5) + (-2)$ **12** $(-10) + (-6)$
     3 $0 - (-6)$ **13** $(-3) + (+5)$
     4 $(-1) + (+1)$ **14** $7 - (+2)$
     5 $(-4) - (-2)$ **15** $(-3) - (-6)$
     6 $0 + (-5)$ **16** $9 - (-4) + (-3)$
     7 $(-3) - (+4)$ **17** $2 - (+4) - (-2)$
     8 $2 + (-5)$ **18** $8 + (-6) + (+1)$
     9 $6 - (+7)$ **19** $(-5) - (-3) - (+5)$
    10 $(-8) - (-2)$ **20** $6 - (+6) - (-4)$

3. **1** $2 \times (-3)$ **8** $6 \times (-6)$ **15** $0 \times (-10)$
    2 $(-3) \times (+5)$ **9** $(-7) \times (-7)$ **16** $(-3) \times (-1)$
    3 $(-3) \times (-6)$ **10** $(-1) \times (+1)$ **17** $(-2) \times 5$
    4 $(+9) \times (-4)$ **11** $(+2) \times (-1)$ **18** $(-5) \times (+7)$
    5 $(-1) \times 4$ **12** $(-9) \times (-9)$ **19** $(-6) \times (-4)$
    6 $(-8) \times 0$ **13** $3 \times (-3)$ **20** $8 \times (-2)$
    7 $(-5) \times (-3)$ **14** $(-1) \times (-2)$

Sequences

Exercise 1.4

1. Copy and continue these sequences for 3 more terms. Describe the rule for
   continuing the sequence in each case.
   1   3, 10, 17, 24, . . .
   2   3, 6, 12, 24, . . .
   3   3, 9, 27, 81, . . .
   4   3, 2, 1, 0, . . .
   5   3, -2, -7, -12, . . .
   6   3, 1, $\frac{1}{3}$, $\frac{1}{9}$, . . .
   7   3, 0.3, 0.03, 0.003, . . .
   8   3, 4, 6, 9, 13, . . .
   Write down the first few terms of some other sequences which begin with the
   number 3.

2. You can define sequences by different rules. Here are some examples, starting in
   each case with the number 10. Give the next 3 terms in each case.
   1   Add 3 each time.
           10, 13, 16, . . .
   2   Subtract 4 each time.
           10, 6, 2, . . .
   3   Multiply by 2 each time.
           10, 20, 40, . . .
   4   Divide by 10 each time.
           10, 1, 0.1, . . .
   5   Add 1 then add 2, 3, 4, . . .
           10, 11, 13, 16, . . .
   6   Multiply by 1 then multiply by 2, 3, 4, . . .
           10, 10, 20, 60, 240, . . .

3. Unless you know the rule, you need enough terms to identify the sequence. Sometimes there is more than one possible sequence, but if one sequence is obvious, don't try to find a more unlikely one.

    The sequence beginning 1, 2, 4, . . .
    These three terms are not enough to give us sufficient information to identify which sequence it is.
    It could be 1, 2, 4, 8, 16, . . . or 1, 2, 4, 7, 11.
    What are the rules for these sequences?
    Give the next few terms in two possible sequences beginning 1, 3, 9, . . . and say which rules you are using.

4. **Geometrical representation of sequences**

    Draw the next picture in each of these sequences.

    1   **Square numbers**

    1   4   9   16

    2   **Triangular numbers**

    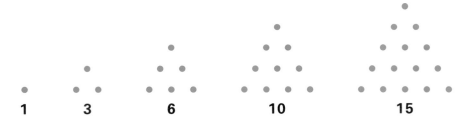

    1   3   6   10   15

    3   **Rectangular numbers**
        Here the rectangle is 2 units longer than wide.

    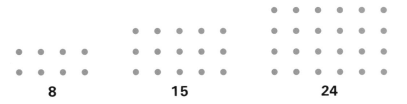

    8   15   24

4   Trapezium numbers

      9   12   15

5   Hexagonal numbers

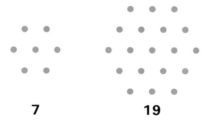

      7   19

Invent some similar designs making number patterns.

5.   **Fibonacci sequence**

1, 1, 2, 3, 5, 8, 13, . . .

Each number after the first two is found by adding the two preceding numbers.
This is a very interesting sequence of numbers. See if you can make some
discoveries about it. Some ideas will be given in the next exercise and in later
chapters.
Keep all your investigations and discoveries about the Fibonacci sequence on file
paper so that you can collect them all together.
You can have similar sequences using the same rule but starting with any two
numbers.
e.g. 10, 0, 10, 10, 20, 30, 50, . . .
Continue these sequences, which use the same rule, giving the next 3 terms in
each case.

1   1, 4, 5, 9, 14, . . .
2   2, 4, 6, 10, 16, . . .
3   7, −2, 5, 3, 8, . . .
4   −3, 3, 0, 3, 3, . . .
5   2, 5, 7, 12, 19, . . .

6. **Difference methods**

Look at the sequence   2   5   10   17   26

Find the differences between consecutive terms   3   5   7   9

Find the differences between those numbers   2   2   2

Assuming that the 3rd row is a row of 2's, you can construct the middle row and then continue the sequence on the top row.

2   5   10   17   26 ⟶ 37 ⟶ 50 ⟶ 65 ⟶ 82

   3   5   7   9 ⟶ 11 ⟶ 13 ⟶ 15 ⟶ 17

      2   2   2   2   2   2   2

Here is another example.

2   3   7   14 ⟶ 24 ⟶ 37 ⟶ 53

   1   4   7 ⟶ 10 ⟶ 13 ⟶ 16

      3   3   3   3   3

Continue these sequences for the next 3 terms, using the difference method.
1   0, 4, 10, 18, 28, . . .
2   1, 5, 10, 16, 23, . . .
3   5, 5, 10, 20, 35, . . .
4   1, 2, 7, 16, 29, . . .
5   5, 8, 13, 20, 29, . . .

Exercise 1.5   Applications and Activities

1.   If a cyclist rides, on average, 35 miles each day, how far will he ride in 6 weeks, riding every day ?

2.   What is the total cost of 300 books, 100 of which cost £6 each and the rest £8 each ?

3. How many lengths of wire fencing, each 12 m long, will be needed to fence a length of 1560 m ?

4. Mr Goodwin buys 75 similar ornaments for £700 and sells them making a profit of £650. How much does he charge for each one ?

5. A farmer has a rick of straw containing 12 tonnes (12 000 kg). How many loads of straw can he sell from it if each load contains 600 kg ?

6. A video camera can be bought for £800 cash, or for an initial payment of £100 and 24 monthly payments of £36. How much extra does it cost if paid for by instalments ?

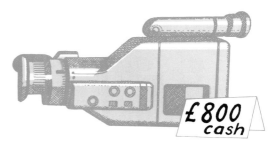

7. How many bags are needed to pack 10 000 tulip bulbs, with 25 in a bag ?

8. The seats in a hall consist of 15 rows of 34 chairs, 16 rows of 42 chairs and 11 rows of 56 chairs. How many people could the hall seat ?

9. A firm spends £240 per week on advertising. How much does it spend in a year ?

10. A dripping tap filled a litre jug in $\frac{1}{2}$ hour. How many litres of water would be wasted in a week ?

11. Here is a list of the temperatures in a Canadian town in one week, taken at noon each day.

    1 Which was the warmest day ?

    2 How much did the temperature rise between noon on Wednesday and noon on Thursday ?

    3 How much did the temperature fall between noon on Sunday and noon on Wednesday?

    4 Between Friday noon and noon on the next day, Saturday, the temperature dropped another 6 degrees. What was the noon temperature on Saturday?

	°C
Sun	−10
Mon	−11
Tues	−13
Wed	−15
Thur	−7
Fri	−6

12.   A refrigerating machine is set to lower its temperature by 5 degrees every hour.
   1   If the temperature at noon is 2°C, what was the temperature 2 hours earlier, at 10 am ?
   2   What will the temperature be at 3 pm?
   3   When will the temperature reach −28°C ?

13.   Copy and complete this number pattern to the 10th row.

$$1 \qquad\qquad\qquad = \quad 1 = 1^2$$
$$1 + 3 \qquad\qquad = \quad 4 = 2^2$$
$$1 + 3 + 5 \qquad\quad = \quad 9 = 3^2$$
$$. . .$$

Try to represent this pattern by dots in a square arrangement.
How many odd numbers are there from 1 to 99, inclusive ?
What is the sum of all the odd numbers from 1 to 99, inclusive ?

14.   **The Fibonacci Sequence (2)**

(See page 15)

1, 1, 2, 3, 5, . . .

Copy and continue the sequence until you get to a number over 1000.

Fibonacci was an outstanding mathematician of his time. He lived from about 1170 to 1250. His real name was Leonardo of Pisa, but he was the son (figlio) of Bonaccio, so he was called Fibonacci.

1   His series is usually linked to 'the rabbit problem'.
'How many pairs of rabbits can be produced from a single pair in a year assuming that every month each pair gives birth to a new pair, which starts breeding from the second month ?'

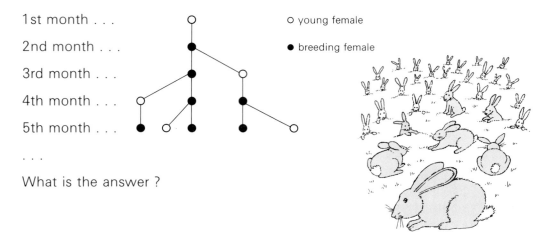

1st month . . .   o young female
2nd month . . .   ● breeding female
3rd month . . .
4th month . . .
5th month . . .

. . .

What is the answer ?

2   Paying money

If you are paying out money using only 10 pence coins and 20 pence coins, and you take into account the order in which you pay the coins, then, for example, 50 pence can be paid in these ways

10, 10, 10, 10, 10   10, 10, 10, 20   10, 10, 20, 10   10, 20, 10, 10
20, 10, 10, 10   20, 20, 10   20, 10, 20   10, 20, 20

Altogether there are 8 ways. Investigate for other amounts.

3   Number patterns

Investigations using the terms of the Fibonacci sequence 1, 1, 2, 3, 5, . . .

(1) What happens to the sequence when you use the difference method ?

(2) Take every three consecutive numbers of the sequence. Multiply the outside two and square the middle one.

e.g. $1 \times 2 =$ $1^2 =$
          $1 \times 3 =$ $2^2 =$
          $2 \times 5 =$ $3^2 =$
          . . .

What do you notice ?

Take consecutive numbers four at a time. Multiply the outside two, and the inside two, and investigate.
Do a similar investigation for five consecutive terms.

(3) Investigate the sum of squares of consecutive terms.

e.g. $1^2 + 1^2 =$
          $1^2 + 2^2 =$
          $2^2 + 3^2 =$
          $3^2 + 5^2 =$
          . . .

See what happens with differences of squares of alternate terms.

e.g. $2^2 - 1^2 =$
          $3^2 - 1^2 =$
          $5^2 - 2^2 =$
          $8^2 - 3^2 =$
          . . .

There are many other interesting facts connected with this sequence, so keep on investigating.

15. **Multiplication**

You do not always have to use the normal ways to multiply. Try the methods shown here. If you can investigate for yourself you may discover other ways which you find quicker or easier to use.

To multiply by 5, halve the number and multiply by 10. This is especially useful when multiplying even numbers.

e.g. $18 \times 5 = 9 \times 10$ $= 90$ (halving 18)
        $52 \times 5 = 26 \times 10$ $= 260$
        $37 \times 5 = 18.5 \times 10 = 185$

Multiply these numbers by 5.
1   84   **2**   36   **3**   262   **4**   27   **5**   49

To multiply by 9, since $9 = 10 - 1$, multiply the number by 10 and subtract the number.

e.g. $315 \times 9 = 2835$ $315 \times 10 = 3150$
                            subtract $\underline{315}$
                                              $\underline{2835}$

Find a similar method for multiplying by 99.

Multiply these numbers by 9.
6   64   **7**   87   **8**   476   **9**   297   **10**   384

Multiply these numbers by 99.
11   61   **12**   43   **13**   719

To multiply by 25, divide by 4 and multiply by 100.

e.g. $68 \times 25 = 17 \times 100$ $= 1700$
        $21 \times 25 = 5.25 \times 100 = $ 525

Multiply these numbers by 25.
14   24   **15**   60   **16**   76   **17**   14   **18**   31

To multiply 2-figure numbers by 11

Add the 2 figures together and put the total in the middle of the 2 figures.

$32 \times 11 = 3\ 5\ 2$ Put $3 + 2 = 5$ in the middle of 3 and 2.
$63 \times 11 = 693$

If the figures add up to 10 or more, you must carry 1 onto the left-hand figure.

$87 \times 11 = 9\ 5\ 7$ $8 + 7 = 15$. Put 5 in the middle, carrying 1 changes 8 into 9.
$68 \times 11 = 748$.

Multiply these numbers by 11.

19 81   **20** 26   **21** 43   **22** 47   **23** 85

Finally, here is a method for multiplying two numbers simply by doubling and halving. It is not recommended for normal use but it is fun to try it a few times.

'Russian multiplication' or 'Peasants' multiplication'

e.g. To multiply 1653 by 937. This method only uses the 2 times table.

	937	1653
Halve the 1st number	~~468~~	~~3306~~
each time, ignore $\frac{1}{2}$'s	~~234~~	~~6612~~
	117	13224
Double the 2nd number	~~58~~	~~26440~~
each time.	29	52896
	~~14~~	~~105792~~
Cross out the rows	7	211584
where the number in	3	423168
the 1st column is even	1	846336
		1548861

Stop when you reach 1

Add up this column, ignoring the crossed-out numbers. This gives the answer.

Use this method to work out these multiplication questions, putting the smaller number in the first column.

24 352 × 83   **25** 793 × 176   **26** 953 × 37

16. These diagrams show sheets of notepaper, divided by straight lines.

0 lines   1 line   2 lines   3 lines   4 lines

Try drawing these for yourself, including a drawing with 5 lines on. The aim is to get the most regions in each case, so avoid three or more lines going through the same point.

When there are 3 lines there are 7 regions. Count the regions in the other cases and show your results in a table.

Investigate the sequence of results, possibly using the difference method, and use it to find how many regions you could get with 10 lines.

The general formula for *n* lines is not easy to discover but maybe you can find it.

17. **A number game**

Try to race your friends in answering these questions in a certain order.
Start with **any question** on the page. Then if, for example, you get the answer
to be 8, look for the question marked 8, write down the capital letter marked
there, and do the question there next. The answer to that question will indicate
the next question to go to.
Keep all the capital letters in order on a line, so that you can check your work
later.
When you get back to the question you started with, write down the final letter,
and read the instructions below.

1.	**A**	Number of degrees in a right angle.
2.	**I**	Number of cm in $\frac{1}{2}$ m.
3.	**G**	6 × 9
4.	**T**	(4 × 4) + 4
5.	**S**	5 + 12 − 8 + 3
6.	**D**	Number of pence in £1.
7.	**C**	3^2
8.	**L**	Number of minutes in an hour.
9.	**A**	Three-quarters of 40
10.	**A**	Next number in the sequence 3, 7, 11, 15, . . .
11.	**L**	Half of half-a-dozen.
12.	**B**	The largest number which divides into both 42 and 49.
15.	**O**	Number of grams in a kilogram.
18.	**N**	25 + 6
19.	**K**	5 × 7
20.	**U**	Number of weeks in a year.
24.	**C**	Number of mm in a cm.
28.	**A**	13 ÷ 13
30.	**O**	1 × 2 × 3
31.	**N**	The square root of 25.
35.	**T**	The number of sides a square has.
37.	**R**	The smallest number into which 6 and 8 divide exactly.
50.	**A**	5 × 3
52.	**R**	2^3
54.	**U**	45 − 8
56.	**G**	24 ÷ 12
60.	**Y**	7 × 4
90.	**T**	8 × 7
100.	**N**	99 ÷ 9
1000.	**I**	3 × 6

Now, see if you can make a word from your letters, following these instructions. Write down every other letter, beginning with the letter which follows B in your list. Carry on from the end of your list to start again at the beginning, if necessary, still taking every alternate letter, until you finish with the letter just before B.

Now, you can design a similar number game. If you write the numbers and questions on cards which you place around the room you can make this into a treasure hunt. You can make the letters say where to look for the treasure.

PUZZLES

1. A farmer had 13 sheep. If all but 5 died, how many did he have left ?

2. How many triangles are there in this figure ?

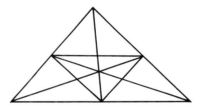

3. A greengrocer has sacks of apples weighing 48 kg, sacks of plums weighing 25 kg and sacks of pears weighing 9 kg. Mrs Kitchen wants 200 kg of fruit, including some of each kind, for bottling. Can the greengrocer supply her without having to open any of the sacks ?

4. What is the smallest number which, if you multiply it by 7, will give an answer consisting entirely of 4's ?

5. Can you draw this pattern without removing your pencil from the paper or going over any line twice ?

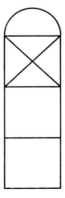

6. A farmer was in a field with a number of cows, a number of ducks and his 3-legged dog. Altogether there were 29 heads and 101 legs. How many ducks where there ?

2 Thinking about algebra

Using algebra

Expressions, formulae and equations are all very important in life today, although they are used by the experts rather than in everyday living.

Using formulae

Here are some examples of formulae which you may be using soon.

Distance = speed × time
(In symbols, this is written as
$s = vt$)

Density = $\dfrac{\text{mass}}{\text{volume}}$

$\left(\text{In symbols, } d = \dfrac{m}{v}\right)$

Mean height = $\dfrac{\text{sum of the heights}}{\text{number of children}}$

$\left(\text{In symbols, } \bar{x} = \dfrac{S}{n}\right)$

Other uses

Here are some examples of formulae which you may meet later on.

Pressure = $\dfrac{\text{force}}{\text{area}}$

$\left(\text{In symbols, } P = \dfrac{F}{A}\right)$

Why is the wearing of stiletto
heels not allowed in some buildings ?

Power (watts) = amps × volts
(In symbols, $W = AV$)

**The best speed for a car to
go round a curve**

$v = \sqrt{rg \tan a}$, where
r = the radius of the curve, in m,
g = 9.8 m/s^2,
a = the angle of the banking,
and v is the speed, in m/s.

Diophantus

He has been called 'the Father of Algebra'.

He was the first person to use algebraic symbols (of his own devising).

Although we only know that he lived in Greece, sometime between 100 AD and 400 AD, we know exactly how long he lived.

This is because a riddle, which will tell us his age, has survived.

'God granted him youth for a sixth part of his life, and adding a twelfth part to this, He clothed his cheeks with down. He lit the light of wedlock after a seventh part, and five years after his marriage He granted him a son. Alas! lateborn wretched child, after attaining the measure of half his father's life, cruel Fate overtook him, thus leaving to Diophantus during the last four years of his life only such consolation as the science of numbers can offer.'

We can show this more clearly like this:

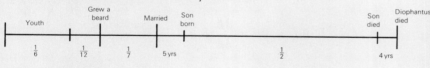

The solution

If we let his age, at death, be x years, we get an equation

$$\frac{1}{6}x + \frac{1}{12}x + \frac{1}{7}x + 5 + \frac{1}{2}x + 4 = x$$

(First we can simplify the fractions by noticing that

$\frac{1}{6}x + \frac{1}{12}x = \frac{2}{12}x + \frac{1}{12}x = \frac{3}{12}x = \frac{1}{4}x$ and $\frac{1}{4}x + \frac{1}{2}x = \frac{3}{4}x$)

Subtracting $\frac{3}{4}x$ from both sides of the equation, and adding 5 and 4, gives the simpler equation

$$\frac{1}{7}x + 9 = \frac{1}{4}x$$

Multiplying every term by 28, $\frac{1}{7}x \times 28 = 4x$, $\frac{1}{4}x \times 28 = 7x$,

$$4x + 252 = 7x$$
$$252 = 3x$$
$$84 = x$$

So Diophantus lived for 84 years.

You can check this solution in the problem.

How old was he when he got married?

2 Algebra

The rules of algebra are very exact and logical. You have already found out how to add, subtract, multiply and divide using simple algebraic expressions.

Here are some examples to remind you of the rules. Notice the differences between addition and multiplication.

Addition

$a + a = 2a$
$3a + 2a = 5a$
$a + a + a = 3a$
$3a + 2$ cannot be simplified
$3a + 4b$ cannot be simplified
$a^2 + a^2 = 2a^2$

Multiplication

$a \times a = a^2$
$3a \times 2a = 3 \times a \times 2 \times a = 6a^2$
$a \times a \times a = a^3$
$3a \times 2 = 6a$
$3a \times 4b = 3 \times a \times 4 \times b = 12ab$ (or $12ba$)
$a^2 \times a^2 = a \times a \times a \times a = a^4$

Subtraction

$8a - 5a = 3a$

$8a - 7a = a$

$8a - 8a = 0$
$8a - 4$ cannot be simplified

$8a - 3b$ cannot be simplified

Division

$8a \div 5a = \dfrac{8\cancel{a}}{5\cancel{a}} = \dfrac{8}{5} = 1\tfrac{3}{5}$ or 1.6

$8a \div 8a = \dfrac{\cancel{8}\cancel{a}}{\cancel{8}\cancel{a}} = 1$

$8a \div 4 = 2a$

$8a \div 3b = \dfrac{8a}{3b}$

Exercise 2.1 gives practice in using the rules of algebra.

Exercise 2.1

Simplify these expressions.

1.
1	$3a + 2a$	**5**	$4e - 4e$	**8**	$k^2 + 2k^2$
2	$b + b$	**6**	$2fg + 3fg$	**9**	$5m - 7n + 2m$
3	$3c - 2c$	**7**	$hj - jh$	**10**	$6p - 5p + 1$
4	$6d - 2d$				

2. **1** $2a \times 3$ **5** $2f \times 6f$ **8** $m \times 1$
    2 $0 \times 3b$ **6** $gh \times 7$ **9** $n \times n \times n$
    3 $c \times c$ **7** $3j \times 4k$ **10** $p \times 5 \times p$
    4 $d \times 5e$

3. **1** $3a \div a$ **5** $e \div 4$ **8** $m \div n$
    2 $4b \div 4b$ **6** $3f \div 5$ **9** $8p \div 2q$
    3 $6c \div 3$ **7** $8g \div 3$ **10** $r^2 \div r$
    4 $0 \div 4d$

4. **1** $a^2 \times a$ **5** $5f \times 4g$ **8** $4k \div 2k$
    2 $bc + cb$ **6** $3h - 2h$ **9** $5m \times n$
    3 $d + 3d$ **7** $0 \div 8j$ **10** $3p + 2q - 2p$
    4 $9e \div e$

Here are reminders of some other types of questions you have already met.

1   Making expressions

e.g. A minibus will hold 15 people.
(1) How many people will b buses hold ?
(2) How many buses must be booked to carry c people ?

For (1),   10 buses will hold 10 × 15 people
Similarly, b buses will hold $b \times 15$ people. This is written as $15b$.
For (2),   For 90 people, the number of buses needed is $90 \div 15$
Similarly, for c people, the number of buses needed is $c \div 15$.

This is written as $\dfrac{c}{15}$ or $\frac{1}{15}c$.

(If $\dfrac{c}{15}$ is not a whole number, the answer is the next whole number above.)

2   Substitution of numbers into expressions

e.g.   If $p = 4$, $q = 1$ and $r = 0$, find the values of the following:

$p^2 + q = 4^2 + 1 = 16 + 1 = 17$

$3pq = 3 \times 4 \times 1 = 12$

$\dfrac{p + q + r}{2} = \dfrac{4 + 1 + 0}{2} = \dfrac{5}{2} = 2\frac{1}{2}$ or 2.5

$2p + 4q - 5r = (2 \times 4) + (4 \times 1) - (5 \times 0) = 8 + 4 - 0 = 12$

3   Solving simple equations

e.g.   Solve the equation $9x + 5 = 13x - 23$

$$9x + 5 = 13x - 23$$

Subtract $9x$ from both sides

$$5 = 4x - 23$$

Add 23 to both sides

$$28 = 4x$$

Divide both sides by 4

$$7 = x$$

i.e. $x = 7$

To check the answer, substitute $x = 7$ into both sides of the equation separately.

LHS (left hand side) $= 9x + 5 = (9 \times 7) + 5 = 63 + 5 = 68$

RHS $= 13x - 23 = (13 \times 7) - 23 = 91 - 23 = 68$

The two sides are equal, both 68, so the equation checks and the solution $x = 7$ is correct.

Exercise 2.2

1.   Make expressions for the following:
   1   What is the cost in pence of x biros at b pence each ?
   2   If I spend x pence out of £c, how much have I left, in pence ?
   3   How many centimetres are there in d metres ?
   4   How many kilometres are there in d metres ?
   5   What number is 5 more than e ?
   6   If there are three consecutive numbers and the smallest one is x, what are the others ?
   7   If a square has sides f cm long, what is its perimeter ?
   8   If the perimeter of an equilateral triangle is g cm, how long is each side ?
   9   What is the total cost, in pence, of 5 books at h pence each and 6 books at $2h$ pence each ?
   10   From a piece of wood 1 metre long, a piece j cm long is sawn off and discarded. How long, in cm, is the remaining piece ?

2.   Find the values of the following when $a = 5$, $b = 3$, $c = 0$.

   1 $2a + 3b$ **5** $\dfrac{3a}{b}$ **8** b^3

   2 $4a - 3b + 2c$ **9** $\dfrac{5b}{3a}$

   3 ab **6** $\dfrac{a + b + c}{4}$

   4 $2ac$ **7** $2a^2$ **10** $a^2 - b^2 + c^2$

3.   Solve these equations.

1	$5x = 15$		**11**	$12 - 4x = 8$
2	$50 = 10x$		**12**	$\frac{2}{3}x + 9 = 19$
3	$\dfrac{x}{8} = 4$		**13**	$5x + 6 = 3x + 16$
			14	$4x - 5 = x + 7$
4	$\frac{1}{3}x = 12$		**15**	$5x - 15 = 2x + 6$
5	$3x + 8 = 26$		**16**	$6x + 4x = 65 - 3x$
6	$2x - 1 = 21$		**17**	$41 - 3x = 17 - x$
7	$35 = 12x - 13$		**18**	$4x = 81 - 5x$
8	$66 = 3x + 6$		**19**	$3x + 28 = 7x + 4$
9	$\frac{1}{2}x + 10 = 17$		**20**	$5x - 4 = 2x + 29$
10	$\dfrac{x}{5} - 6 = 3$			

Some equations may be more complicated. For these you need practice in collecting terms together, and in removing brackets.

Collecting terms together

Examples

1 Simplify $a + 3b - b - 3a$
Looking at the a's, $a - 3a = -2a$
Looking at the b's, $3b - b = 2b$
The simplest form is $-2a + 2b$, or this could be written as $2b - 2a$

2 Simplify $c - 2d + 3c + 2d$
Looking at the c's, $c + 3c = 4c$
Looking at the d's, $-2d + 2d = 0$
The simplest form is $4c$

3 Simplify $e - 1 + 2e - 3$
Looking at the e's, $e + 2e = 3e$
Looking at the numbers, $-1 - 3 = -4$
The simplest form is $3e - 4$

Removing brackets

Examples

$3(a + 2) = 3a + 6$
$5(2b - 1) = 10b - 5$
$7(c - 3d + 4) = 7c - 21d + 28$
$d(5e - 6) = 5de - 6d$
$4(fg + 5) = 4fg + 20$
$2h(h + 3) = 2h^2 + 6h$
$4(a - 3) + 2(a + 3) = 4a - 12 + 2a + 6 = 6a - 6$
$5(2b - 5) + 2(3b - 1) = 10b - 25 + 6b - 2 = 16b - 27$

If there is a minus sign immediately in front of a bracket, then when the bracket is removed all the signs from inside the bracket are changed, + to − and − to +.

Examples

$-5(a + 2b) = -5a - 10b$
$-(c - d) = -c + d$
$5(e - 2) - 4(e + 3) = 5e - 10 - 4e - 12 = e - 22$
$4(f - 3) - 2(f - 6) = 4f - 12 - 2f + 12 = 2f$
$h - (h + 7) = h - h - 7 = -7$

Equations involving terms using brackets

Example

Solve $3x - (x - 3) = 11 - 2(x + 1)$

Remove the brackets
$$3x - x + 3 = 11 - 2x - 2$$
Simplify
$$2x + 3 = 9 - 2x$$
Add $2x$ to both sides
$$4x + 3 = 9$$
Subtract 3 from both sides
$$4x = 6$$
Divide both sides by 4
$$x = 1\tfrac{1}{2}$$

To check the answer, substitute $x = 1\frac{1}{2}$ into both sides of the equation separately.

LHS $= 3x - (x - 3) = (3 \times 1\frac{1}{2}) - (1\frac{1}{2} - 3) = 4\frac{1}{2} - (-1\frac{1}{2}) = 4\frac{1}{2} + 1\frac{1}{2} = 6$
RHS $= 11 - 2(x + 1) = 11 - 2 \times (1\frac{1}{2} + 1) = 11 - (2 \times 2\frac{1}{2}) = 11 - 5 = 6$
Both sides are equal, both 6, so the equation checks and the solution $x = 1\frac{1}{2}$ is correct.

Notice that equations have solutions which are not necessarily whole numbers. Use fractions rather than decimals in cases where the fraction would not be an exact decimal.
e.g. If $x = 1\frac{1}{2}$, you could give the answer as $x = 1.5$, but if $x = 1\frac{2}{3}$, you should leave the answer as a fraction as you cannot express $\frac{2}{3}$ as an exact decimal. However, if the answer was wanted correct to 2 decimal places it would be 1.67.

Sometimes equations have solutions which are negative numbers.

Example

Solve $4(x - 3) = 2(x - 9)$

Remove the brackets
$$4x - 12 = 2x - 18$$
Subtract $2x$ from both sides
$$2x - 12 = -18$$
Add 12 to both sides
$$2x = -6$$
Divide both sides by 2
$$x = -3$$

To check the answer, substitute $x = -3$ into both sides of the equation separately.
LHS $= 4(x - 3) = 4 \times (-3 - 3) = 4 \times (-6) = -24$
RHS $= 2(x - 9) = 2 \times (-3 - 9) = 2 \times (-12) = -24$
Both sides are equal, both -24, so the equation checks and the solution $x = -3$ is correct.

Equations involving a fraction

First multiply both sides of the equation to remove the fraction.

Example

Solve $\dfrac{3x - 4}{7} = 5$

Multiply both sides by 7
$$3x - 4 = 35$$
Add 4 to both sides
$$3x = 39$$
Divide both sides by 3
$$x = 13$$

To check the answer, substitute $x = 13$ into the left hand side.

$$\text{LHS} = \frac{3x - 4}{7} = \frac{(3 \times 13) - 4}{7} = \frac{39 - 4}{7} = \frac{35}{7} = 5$$

Both sides are equal, both 5, so the equation checks and the solution $x = 13$ is correct.

Exercise 2.3

1. Simplify these expressions.

    1 $3a - b + 2a + b$ **6** $4j + 2j - k - 3j + k$
    2 $2c + 3d + 4c - d - 6c$ **7** $5m - 2n - m + n$
    3 $10 + 3e - 12 - e$ **8** $3 - p - p - p$
    4 $f + 3 + 2f - 1$ **9** $7r - 4r - 2r + s$
    5 $7g - h - 2g - 3h$ **10** $2t - 3 + t$

2. Remove the brackets from the following and simplify where possible.

    1 $2(6a + 1) - 3(1 + 4a)$ **6** $3(g - 2) + 4(g - 3)$
    2 $3(3b - 2) + 2(b + 7)$ **7** $5(h + 2) - (3h - 2)$
    3 $2c - 5d - (c - d)$ **8** $k(3k - 1) + 2(4k - 3)$
    4 $6e - (3e + f)$ **9** $m(m + 5) - 2(m - 4)$
    5 $3(2f - 1) - 2(3f + 1)$ **10** $(p + q - r) - (p - q + r)$

3.   Solve these equations.
    1 $3(4x - 2) = 2(2x + 9)$
    2 $2(5 - 2x) = 8 - 3x$
    3 $8(x - 1) + 3 = 4 - 2(x + 2)$
    4 $2(x + 18) = 5(x + 6) + 12$
    5 $6(x + 1) + 4(x + 2) = 3(5 - x) + 12$
    6 $4(3 - x) + 3(3x - 1) = 16$
    7 $3(3x - 2) + 45 = 15x + 5(2x - 5)$
    8 $3(4x - 11) = 5(2x - 4)$
    9 $5(1 - x) = 3(5 - x) - 2$
    10 $4(7 - x) = 15 + 5(2 + x)$

4.   Solve these equations.

    1 $\dfrac{2x - 1}{5} = 3$ **4** $\dfrac{3x - 5}{4} = 7$

    2 $\dfrac{3x + 8}{2} = 13$ **5** $\dfrac{x + 3}{5} = x$

    3 $\dfrac{4x + 5}{7} = 1$

Exercise 2.4   Applications and Activities

1.   A plumber charges a call-out
price of £10 for coming out
to mend a water pipe burst,
plus £8 per hour for the time
the repair takes. If the repair
takes t hours, find an
expression for the total
amount he charges.
If he charges £C, find a
formula for C in terms of t.

2. A minibus owner runs a weekly excursion to the seaside. Operating costs per trip are £60, and each passenger pays £9. The profit on a trip is 'amount paid by passengers − operating cost'.
What is an expression for the amount paid by *n* passengers ?
If the profit is £*P*, write down a formula for *P* in terms of *n*.

3. A stallholder sold soft toys, which were teddy bears and monkeys.
If he sold 150 toys altogether, of which *b* were teddy bears, how many, in terms of *b*, were monkeys ?
The teddy bears sold for £3 each and the monkeys for £2 each. Find an expression for the man's total takings, and simplify it. If the total takings were £364, write down an equation and solve it to find how many teddy bears were sold.

4. Using these diagrams, write down equations connecting the letters.

1

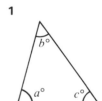

2

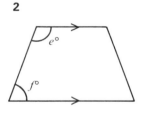

3

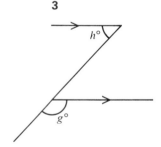

5. For an adventure park, an adult's ticket costs £2 more than a child's ticket. If an adult's ticket costs £*x*, find an expression for the total cost for 5 adults and 6 children, and simplify it.
If the total cost for these people was £43, write down an equation and solve it. Hence find the cost for an adult and for a child.

6. Alec, Bill and Charles together saved £180. Alec saved £20 less than Bill and Charles saved twice as much as Bill. How much did Bill save ?
(Begin by letting the amount Bill saved be £*x*.)

7. In a school, $\frac{1}{10}$ of the pupils were absent, and the remaining 234 pupils were present. How many pupils belonged to the school ?
(Begin by letting the total number of pupils be *x*.)

8. In a season, a football team played 42 games altogether, of which it only lost 8. If the number of matches the team drew was x, how many matches, in terms of x, did it win?

There were three points awarded for a win, one point for a draw and none for losing. How many points, in terms of x, did the team gain over the season ?

If, in fact, the team gained 94 points, write down an equation and solve it to find x.

How many matches did the team win, and how many were drawn ?

9. Two pieces of wood have lengths as shown.

In terms of x,

1   what is the total length of the two pieces,

2   how much longer is CD than AB ?

3   If CD is 11 m long, how long is AB ?

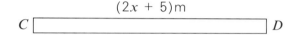

10. If the temperature is $F°$ Fahrenheit and $C°$ Celsius then F and C are connected by the formula $C = \dfrac{5}{9}(F - 32)$.

1   Find the temperature in Celsius degrees when it is 59°F.

2   If the temperature is 55°C, write down an equation and solve it to find the temperature in Fahrenheit degrees.

PUZZLES

7. Sort these out:
1   Oxton is north of Pexhill, while Queenham is west of Oxton and Ruffley is south of Queenham. Which place can be west of Pexhill ?
2   Alan is the father of Ben and the brother of Charles. What relation is Charles to Ben ?
3   Eric has more money than Frank or Colin but the same amount as George, who has less than Dave. Who has the most money ?
4   The Post Office is on the left of the newsagent's, and the Bank is on the left of the Post Office. Which is in the middle ?
5   Four men work for the same firm. Paul earns more than Richard or Thomas, while Richard earns more than Sam but not so much as Thomas. Who earns the least ?

8. James earns £4 an hour for working a 40-hour week. Any time which is worked over the 40 hours is paid at $1\frac{1}{2}$ times the hourly rate, except that any time worked on Sundays is paid at double the hourly rate. If in one week James worked 48 hours and was paid £220, how many hours had he worked on the Sunday ?

3 Thinking about decimals and

Decimals

Decimals are a very efficient way of writing tenths, hundredths, thousandths, etc. and with a modern calculator they are very easy to use in calculations.

The new five pence coin has diameter 18.0 mm and weight 3.25 g.

Using decimals

Try these questions, using the data shown.

1   A collection of 5 pence coins weighs 6.5 kg. How much are the coins worth ?

2   Viv Richards batted for 28 innings, but he was not out on 5 occasions, so in working out the average runs per innings this is counted as 23 completed innings. What was the total number of runs he scored altogether ? (This must be a whole number!)

3   How many kilocalories are there in an average helping of Alpen ?

Viv Richards, top scorer for Glamorgan in the Britannic Assurance County Championship in 1990, with an average of 61.96.

Nutritional Information	
(Nutrients per 100 g)	
Energy	
kilojoules	1537
kilocalories	366
Protein	12.0 g
Fat	5.0 g
Available	
carbohydrate	65.6 g
Dietary fibre	8.4 g

An average serving of
3 tablespoonfuls is
approximately 40 g

measurements

Measurements

We need standard measurements if we are to be able to trade fairly. If you go to buy a 1 kg bag of sugar you need to know that you will get 1 kg (or nearly so).

Old water pipes have to be replaced by new ones.

Measurements in Industry

The Thames Water Authority is responsible for 30 000 km of subterranean water mains, and supplies up to 5 000 000 000 litres of water per day to about 11 000 000 people, 7 000 000 of whom live and work in the London area. The daily average consumption per person is estimated at 160 litres.

A busy scene at Hull docks

Overseas trading

In order to buy and sell overseas a system of weights and measures that is recognised internationally is needed, and that is why the metric system, based on 10's, 100's, 1000's, etc. is so useful.

3 Decimals and Measurements

Decimals

In the number 21.748 (read as twenty-one point seven four eight)
the 7 is the figure in the 1st decimal place, and represents 7 tenths,
the 4 is the number in the 2nd decimal place, and represents 4 hundredths,
the 8 is the number in the 3rd decimal place, and represents 8 thousandths.

Here is the size of 7 tenths, compared to 1 unit.

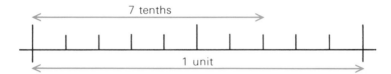

Here is the size of 4 hundredths, compared to 1 tenth.

Here is the size of 8 thousandths, compared to 1 hundredth.

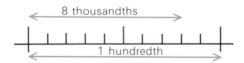

Here is the size of the decimal 0.748, compared to 1 unit.

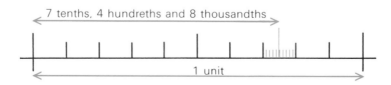

7 tenths is the same as 70 hundredths or 700 thousandths,

i.e. $\dfrac{7}{10} = \dfrac{70}{100} = \dfrac{700}{1000}$

4 hundredths is the same as 40 thousandths,

i.e. $\dfrac{4}{100} = \dfrac{40}{1000}$

So 0.748 is the same as $\dfrac{700}{1000} + \dfrac{40}{1000} + \dfrac{8}{1000} = \dfrac{748}{1000}$, 748 thousandths.

Similarly, 0.123 is the same as $\dfrac{123}{1000}$, 123 thousandths,

0.065 is the same as $\dfrac{65}{1000}$,

0.28 is the same as $\dfrac{28}{100}$ or $\dfrac{280}{1000}$.

Putting decimal numbers in order of size

Examples

1   To compare 0.7 and 0.23
    Since 0.7 is 7 tenths, and 0.23 is just bigger than 2 tenths, then the smaller number
    is 0.23
    You may find this easier to understand if you write 0.7 as 0.70 so that both
    numbers have the same number of decimal places.
    0.7 = 0.70 = 70 hundredths
    0.23 = 23 hundredths
    So 0.23 is the smaller number.

2   To compare 0.41, 0.119 and 0.28
    Looking at the tenths,
    0.41 is just over 4 tenths,
    0.119 is just over 1 tenth,
    0.28 is bigger than 2 tenths, but not as big as 3 tenths,
    In order of size, smallest first, they are 0.119, 0.28, 0.41.

    Or, you can write them all to 3 decimal places.
    0.41 = 0.410 = 410 thousandths,
    0.119 = 119 thousandths,
    0.28 = 0.280 = 280 thousandths.
    So in order of size, smallest first, they are 119 thousandths, 280 thousandths,
    410 thousandths,
    i.e. 0.119, 0.28, 0.41

3   To compare 0.56, 0.506, 0.566
They all have 5 tenths, so look at the hundredths.
0.56 and 0.566 both have 6 hundredths,
0.506 has no hundredths,
So 0.506 is the smallest.
Now comparing 0.56 and 0.566, where the tenths and hundredths are the same,
look at the thousandths.
0.56 has no thousandths,
0.566 has 6 thousandths,
so 0.56 is the smaller.
So in order of size, smallest first, the three numbers are 0.506, 0.56, 0.566

Or, if you write all the numbers with 3 decimal places,
0.56 = 0.560 = 560 thousandths,
0.506 = 506 thousandths,
0.566 = 566 thousandths.
In order of size, smallest first, they are 506 thousandths, 560 thousandths,
566 thousandths,
i.e.   0.506, 0.56, 0.566

Calculations with decimals

Here is a reminder of the methods.

Multiplying by 10, 100, 1000, . . .

To multiply by 10, 100, 1000, . . . , the numbers grow larger, so the figures move
upwards (to the left) 1, 2, 3, . . . places, assuming that the decimal point is fixed. Add
0's to fill any empty places between the figures and the decimal point.

Examples

$2.56 \times 10 = 25.6$
$3.5 \times 100 = 350$
$0.0041 \times 1000 = 4.1$

Dividing by 10, 100, 1000, . . .

The numbers become smaller, so the figures move downwards (to the right)
1, 2, 3, . . . places, assuming that the decimal point is fixed. Add 0's to fill any empty
places between the decimal point and the figures.

Examples

31.8 ÷ 10 = 3.18
23 ÷ 100 = 0.23
5.6 ÷ 1000 = 0.0056

Adding, subtracting. Multiplying and dividing by small whole numbers

Just keep the figures in their correct positions relative to the decimal point.

Examples

1 1.5 + 14.83

$$\begin{array}{r} 1.5 \\ + \ 14.83 \\ \hline 16.33 \end{array}$$

2 12.1 − 3.02

$$\begin{array}{r} 12.10 \\ - \ \ 3.02 \\ \hline 9.08 \end{array}$$

3 12.6 × 4

$$\begin{array}{r} 12.6 \\ \times \ \ \ 4 \\ \hline 50.4 \end{array}$$

4 27.6 ÷ 8

$$8\overline{)27.60} \atop \quad 3.45$$

Correcting a number up to a certain number of decimal places

Look at the figure to the right of the last figure you need. If this extra figure is 5 or more, add 1 to the final figure of your answer.

Examples

3.2976 = 3.3   to 1 decimal place
          = 3.30   to 2 decimal places

0.8692 = 0.9   to 1 decimal place
          = 0.87   to 2 decimal places

0.0827 = 0.1   to 1 decimal place
          = 0.08   to 2 decimal places

Exercise 3.1

1. State the value of the figure 7 in these numbers.
    1 273.1   **4** 52.571
    2 0.723   **5** 754 632
    3 5.0073

2. How many times larger is the 1st figure 3 than the 2nd one in these numbers ?
    1 273.36   **4** 300.3
    2 0.343   **5** 1.5353
    3 32.23

3. Say which is the smaller of these two numbers.
    1 0.06, 0.6   **4** 0.809, 0.79
    2 0.4, 0.33   **5** 0.91, 0.899
    3 0.01, 0.001

4. Write these numbers in order of increasing size.
    1 3.6, 3.505, 3.52   **4** 0.22, 0.222, 0.2
    2 0.048, 0.24, 1.208   **5** 0.035, 0.03, 0.005
    3 0.6, 0.67, 0.666

5. Use a piece of squared paper or graph
    paper to draw a square, 10 small squares
    each way.
    If the large square represents 1 unit, shade
    in squares to represent the decimal 0.37

    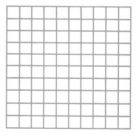

6. State the next two numbers in these sequences.
    1 400, 40, 4, 0.4, . . .
    2 0.01, 0.03, 0.05, 0.07, . . .
    3 0.0005, 0.005, 0.05, 0.5, . . .
    4 1.4, 1.3, 1.2, 1.1, . . .
    5 9.6, 4.8, 2.4, 1.2, . . .

7. Use the $\boxed{\sqrt{}}$ key on your calculator to find the square roots of these numbers, giving
    them correct to 2 decimal places.
    1 6   **4** 1.5
    2 200   **5** 11
    3 19

8. Try to do these questions without using your calculator.
    1 Two numbers add up to 5.2. One of them is 1.35. Find the other.
    2 The difference between two numbers is 7.89. The smaller number is 10.1. Find the other.
    3 The difference between two numbers is 5.07. The larger one is 9.8. Find the other.
    4 When a number is divided by 6 the answer is 3.84. What is the number ?
    5 When a number is multiplied by 5 the answer is 14.8. What is the number ?

9. **1** Express 3.14 and 2.8 correct to the nearest whole number, and find an estimated value for 3.14 × 2.8.
        Use your calculator to find the exact value and compare it with your estimate.
    2 Express 21.89 and 2.2 correct to the nearest whole number, and find an estimated value for 21.89 ÷ 2.2.
        Use your calculator to find the exact value, and compare it with your estimate.

10. Try to do this question without using your calculator.
    Write down any number between 1 and 10, add 3.2 and multiply the result by 6. Then subtract 12.03, divide by 3 and multiply by 10. Add 5.8, divide by 5 and subtract 5.94. Divide by the number you started with. What is your answer ?

Measurements

Here is a reminder of the tables.

The Metric System   **British Units**

Length

1000 mm = 1 m	12 inches = 1 foot
100 cm = 1 m	3 feet = 1 yard
1000 m = 1 km	1760 yards = 1 mile

The Metric System   British Units

Weight

```
1000 mg = 1 g
  100 cg = 1 g
 1000 g = 1 kg
1000 kg = 1 tonne
```

```
      16 ounces = 1 pound
      14 pounds = 1 stone
     112 pounds = 1 hundredweight
       8 stones = 1 hundredweight
    2240 pounds = 1 ton
20 hundredweights = 1 ton
```

Capacity

```
1000 ml = 1 ℓ
  100 cl = 1 ℓ
 1000 ℓ = 1 kl
```

```
8 pints = 1 gallon
```

Time

```
60 seconds = 1 minute
60 minutes = 1 hour
  24 hours = 1 day
    7 days = 1 week
  52 weeks = 1 year
  365 days = 1 year
  366 days = 1 leap year
 12 months = 1 year
```

Accuracy of measurements

There is a difference between counting, which is usually in whole numbers, but in any case goes up in jumps, and measurement, which goes up continuously.

We can never measure **exactly**, but with proper instruments we can get measurements as accurately as they are needed for any particular purpose.

When measuring a line in Geometry, it is sufficient to give the measurement to the nearest millimetre. The length of AB is 7.8 cm.

When measuring a piece of knitting for a pattern, it is probably sufficient to measure to the nearest centimetre.

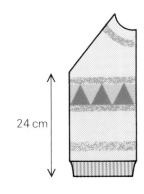

24 cm

In measuring a distance such as the length of a garden it is probably sufficient to measure to the nearest 10 cm, and in measuring larger distances the measurement would be taken to the nearest metre, tenth of a kilometre, or kilometre.
In British units the line would be measured in inches and tenths, the knitting to the nearest $\frac{1}{2}$ inch, the garden to the nearest foot and larger distances in yards or miles.

Similarly with weighing. 1 gram is such a small weight that it would only be used for scientific or medical purposes or when an expensive substance was being bought. In cookery it is sufficient to weigh to the nearest 25 g, and in shopping, goods which used to be packed in $\frac{1}{2}$ lb or 1 lb packets are now often packed in 250 g or 500 g packets. Larger items are weighed in kilograms, or to the nearest 10 kg or 100 kg, and very large objects are weighed in tonnes.

For capacity, medicines are given using a 5 ml spoonful, and in the kitchen liquids are measured in a litre jug with markings for every 50 ml. Larger quantities could be measured to the nearest 10 litres, 100 litres, etc.

You are familiar with measuring time. Hours and minutes are usually sufficient, but with a digital watch you can measure shorter intervals in seconds, and athletes will want to measure their times in tenths or hundredths of a second.

When you are doing calculations for practical purposes you will give answers to a sensible degree of accuracy.
'It will take me about 20 minutes to get there. I will spend about £10 on food. There are nearly 800 pupils in our school. The car was travelling at about 50 miles an hour.'

However, in giving the answer to a mathematical question in school, the teacher may wish to know that you can do an accurate calculation, so firstly you should give the accurate answer, or at least an answer corrected to 3 or 4 significant figures, and then if there are no further instructions in the question you should decide if that is a sensible answer, and amend it if necessary.

Examples

1   20 m of rope is divided equally into 7 lengths, to make skipping ropes for 7 children. How long is each skipping rope ?

20 m ÷ 7 = 2.85714 . . . m
Now it is no use measuring to less than a centimetre.
To the nearest cm, the length is 2.86 m.
With the practical difficulties of dividing and cutting the rope, it might be more sensible to give the answer as 2.85 m, to the nearest 5 cm.

2   A bag containing 5 kg of icing sugar was bought, and the contents shared out equally among 18 children, who were going to use it with other ingredients to make sweets. How much icing sugar did each child get ?

5000 g ÷ 18 = 277.777 . . . g
To the nearest gram, this is 278 g.
But for the children to decide what quantities of the other ingredients to use with the icing sugar, it would be sufficient for them to know that they each had 275 g, which is the answer to the nearest 25 g, or even 300 g, which is correct to the nearest 100 g.

Exercise 3.2

1.   How many
     1   cm in 5 m
     2   degrees in 2 right angles
     3   minutes in $2\frac{1}{2}$ hours
     4   mm in 3 m
     5   kg in 2 tonnes
     6   weeks in a year
     7   mm in $\frac{1}{2}$ cm
     8   seconds in $\frac{1}{2}$ minute
     9   m in 7 km
    10   ml in 2 cl
    11   mm in 7 cm
    12   g in 4 kg
    13   pence in £5
    14   cm in 6 m
    15   days in a year
    16   m in 4 km
    17   hours in 10 days
    18   mg in 2 g
    19   ml in 8 litres
    20   days in 2 weeks ?

2.   1   Write 1260 g in kg
     2   Write 5.9 cm in mm
     3   Write 30 cm in m
     4   Write 2.6 litres in ml
     5   Write 0.7 m in cm
     6   Write 0.75 kg in g
     7   Write 160 cl in litres
     8   Write 78 mm in cm
     9   Write 304 cm in m
    10   Write 2.1 kg in g

3.   Name a sensible metric unit for measuring or weighing in these cases.
  1   The height of a woman.
  2   The weight of a baby.
  3   The width of a street.
  4   The wool needed to knit a baby's coat.
  5   The petrol capacity of a car's tank.
  6   The distance between two towns.
  7   The weight of a loaded lorry.
  8   The amount of medicine in a dose.
  9   The weight of an envelope and contents, to find the cost of postage.
  10   The wood needed to make a shelf.

4.   These statements are to be used in everyday conversation. Re-write the numbers
        to a more sensible degree of accuracy.
  1   The height of the lamp post is 8.732 m.
  2   The sugar in a bowl weighs 271.32 g.
  3   The amount of water in a swimming pool is 416528 litres.
  4   The boundary of the cricket pitch is 372.915 m long.
  5   Michelle's age is 10 years 1 month 27 days 2 hours 45 minutes.
  6   The height of the tide yesterday was 5.516 m.
  7   Petrol costs 45 p per litre. This means that a gallon costs £2 and 4.57 pence.
  8   There is 2 litres of orangeade in the jug, so if I share it out among 6 of us
           we will each get 0.33333 litres.
  9   Dinner will be ready in 2 hours 16 minutes 20 seconds.
  10   Nellie the elephant weighs 5.4381 tonnes.

Exercise 3.3   Applications and Activities

1.   A tin of milk powder contains a plastic measuring spoon. The tin holds 2 litres
        of powder and the spoon holds 8.8 ml. How many spoonfuls can be obtained
        from the full tin ?

2.   An airline's luggage allowance for each
     passenger is 20 kg. One passenger
     weighed his luggage and it weighed 52 lb.
     How much was it overweight, in kg ?
     (1 lb = 453.6 g)

3.   A car's petrol tank holds 8.8 gallons. Now that petrol pumps measure in litres
     the driver needs to know how many litres this is. He finds in a reference book
     that 1 gallon = 4.546 litres, so how many litres will the tank hold ?

4.   To save up £112 for a school journey, Nirmal gets an evening job where he
     earns £1.65 each weekday evening. How many weekdays will he have to work
     to earn all the money ? How many weeks will this take ?

5.   An old knitting pattern requires
     12 oz of wool. Nowadays the wool
     is sold in 50 g balls. How many
     balls of wool should be bought ?
     (1 oz = 28.35 g)

6.   An electricity bill was made up of a fixed charge of £8.75 per quarter and a
     charge of 6.080 pence for each unit used.
     In a certain quarter, the meter reading was 56083 and the reading in the
     previous quarter had been 53557.
     1   How many units had been used in the present quarter ?
     2   What was the total bill ?

7.   Keith's pace is 70 cm long. He takes 55 paces to walk the length of the
     playground. Now Mr Ford takes 48 paces to walk from one end of the
     playground to the other. What is the length of his pace ?

8.   **School activities**

     1   Suppose you are planning to hold a concert in your school hall. You need
              to decide how many chairs you can fit in the hall, for the audience.
              Make measurements of the hall, and decide how much of the space is
              needed for the performers. Then measure the space needed for a few chairs
              arranged in rows, and decide how to arrange the seating. Say how many
              people you can fit in, in reasonable comfort and with reasonable views of
              the performance.

2   Suppose you are planning to hold an open day in your school and you expect to have lots of visitors coming by car. Decide how you can arrange your playground, or some other suitable area, as a car park. You want to fit as many cars as possible in, but there must be room for every car to be driven out at any time. Make suitable measurements and show how you will mark out the area. How many cars can you accommodate ?

9.   **Fibonacci sequence (3)**

(See pages 15 and 18)

   1, 1, 2, 3, 5, . . .

In this section you should investigate what happens when you divide each number of the sequence by the number before it.

i.e.   1 ÷ 1 =
       2 ÷ 1 =
       3 ÷ 2 =
       5 ÷ 3 =
       etc.

Give all results correct to 3 decimal places. Continue to about 15 terms. What do you notice ?

Now repeat this, dividing each number by the number following it.

i.e.   1 ÷ 1 =
       1 ÷ 2 =
       2 ÷ 3 =
       3 ÷ 5 =
       etc.

Compare the results of the two sections.

You may like to continue this investigation using alternate terms,

i.e.   2 ÷ 1 =   then   1 ÷ 2 =
       3 ÷ 1 =   1 ÷ 3 =
       5 ÷ 2 =   2 ÷ 5 =
       etc.   etc.

If you have a suitable computer program you can find many more terms of the sequence and you can work to more decimal places, and do a more thorough investigation.

4 Thinking about quadrilaterals

What is a quadrilateral ?

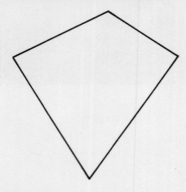

Why do you think that this word was chosen ? Look up the word in a dictionary to see how it was derived.

What other words do you know which begin with 'quad', and what are their meanings ?

Kinds of quadrilaterals

Draw some different-shaped quadrilaterals and find the mathematical names for these shapes.

Look at the pictures and name the kinds of quadrilaterals shown.

Look for quadrilaterals in the design of fabrics, wallpaper and floor coverings, and elsewhere.

What are the shapes that we see most often ?

Notice the quadrilaterals in this photograph. What sorts are they ?

What is the name of the quadrilateral shown by the brickwork pattern here ?

What is the name of the quadrilateral shown here ?

A table designed for easy stacking.
What is the name of its quadrilateral shape ?

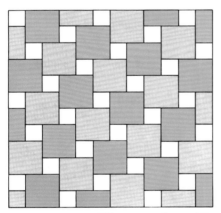

An attractive tiling pattern. What sort of quadrilateral is used ?

Another attractive pattern

Angles of a quadrilateral

What is the size of each angle in a rectangle or square ?
What is the sum of the angles of a rectangle or square ?
In an 'ordinary' quadrilateral, what do you think the sum of the angles will be ?
Draw an irregular quadrilateral, on paper, colour the angles and tear them off. Rearrange them so that they touch each other at their points. What do you notice ?

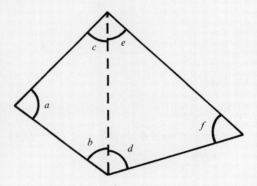

This quadrilateral has been divided into two triangles.
What is the sum of the angles $a + b + c$, and why ?
What is the sum of the angles $d + e + f$, and why ?
What is the sum of the angles $a + b + c + d + e + f$?
What is the sum of the angles of a quadrilateral ?

Special quadrilaterals

Can you discover extra facts about angles in other special quadrilaterals ?

4 Quadrilaterals

A **quadrilateral** is a figure with 4 sides.

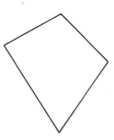

The sum of the angles of a quadrilateral is 360°.

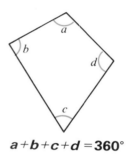

$$a+b+c+d = 360°$$

The perimeter of a quadrilateral is the sum of the lengths of its 4 sides.

Perimeter = $AB + BC + CD + DA$

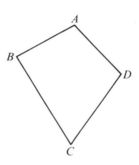

Names of some special quadrilaterals

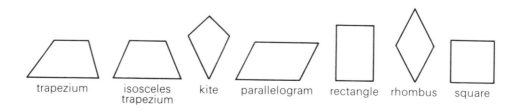

trapezium   isosceles trapezium   kite   parallelogram   rectangle   rhombus   square

Diagonals

A diagonal is a line which joins opposite points.

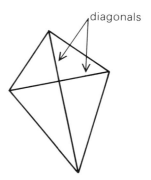

diagonals

You may need to use facts about angles and triangles.
The main facts are summarized here.

Angles at a point

These add up to 360°

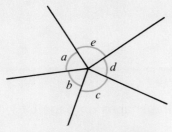

$a + b + c + d + e = 360°$

Adjacent angles

These add up to 180°

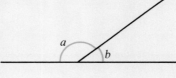

$a + b = 180°$

Vertically opposite angles

These are equal

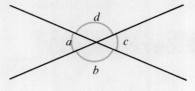

$a = c$
$b = d$

Corresponding angles
These are equal

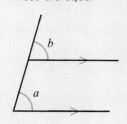

$a = b$

Alternate angles
These are equal

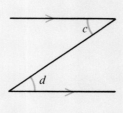

$c = d$

Interior angles
These add up to 180°

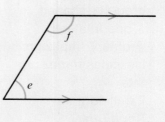

$e + f = 180°$

The sum of the angles of a triangle is 180°.

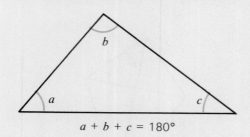

$a + b + c = 180°$

An exterior angle

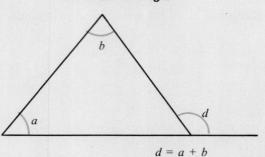

$d = a + b$

Angles in isosceles triangles

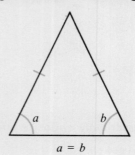

$a = b$

Angles in an equilateral triangle

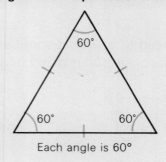

Each angle is 60°

Exercise 4.1

1. Sketch the figures named in this table. (You can copy the shapes on page 52.)
    1 Mark in any axes of symmetry with dotted lines.
    2 Mark clearly any points of symmetry.
    Then copy and complete the table.

Name	Number of axes of symmetry	Point of symmetry ? Yes/No
Irregular-shaped quadrilateral Ordinary trapezium Isosceles trapezium Kite Parallelogram Rhombus Rectangle Square		

3   For figures with axes of symmetry or points of symmetry, can you discover anything about lengths of sides or sizes of angles ? If so, for each one, label the points of the figure with letters *A*, *B*, *C*, *D* and list your discoveries.

2. **1**   Three angles of a quadrilateral are 60°, 65° and 113°. Find the size of the fourth angle.

2   Two angles of a quadrilateral are 74° and 116° and the other two angles are equal. What size are they ?

3   If all four angles of a quadrilateral are equal, what size are they ? What two sorts of quadrilateral could it be ?

3.   Calculate the sizes of the marked angles in these quadrilaterals.

1

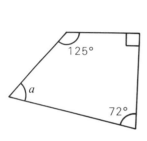

2

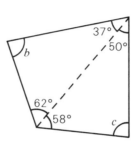

3

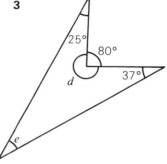

4.   In the diagrams, find the sizes of the marked angles.

1

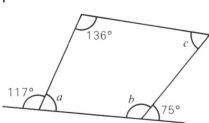

2

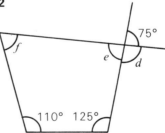

A Kite

This quadrilateral has no parallel sides, but two adjacent sides are equal and the other two adjacent sides are equal.

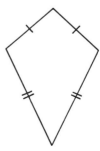

5. Estimate the sizes of the angles in this kite, in degrees. Check your estimates by measuring with your protractor. Find the sum of the 4 angles. Notice which angles are equal.

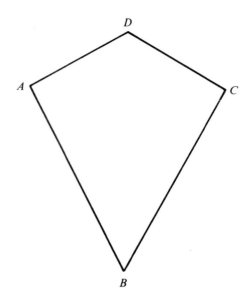

6. In this kite, *AC* is joined. What sort of triangles are triangles *ABC* and *ADC* ? If *BD* is joined, instead of *AC*, what do you notice about triangles *ADB* and *CDB* ?

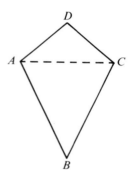

7. Construct this kite *ABCD*. Begin by drawing a line *AC*, 5.5 cm long. With centre *A* draw an arc, radius 5 cm, and with centre *C* draw an arc, radius 5 cm, to cut the first arc at *D*.
   With centre *A* draw an arc, radius 7 cm, on the other side of *AC*, and with centre *C* draw an arc, radius 7 cm, to cut the other arc at *B*.
   Join *AB, BC, CD, DA*.
   Measure ∠*A* (∠*DAB*) and ∠*C* (∠*DCB*). What do you notice ?
   Has a kite any axes of symmetry ? If so, draw them on a sketch diagram.

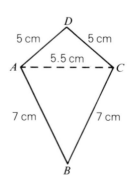

8. **An arrowhead** is a sort of kite. Draw
   this arrowhead and compare its properties
   with the usual type of kite.
   Start with a line $AC = 5.5$ cm. Continue
   as in question 7, making the arcs for **B**
   and **D** on the same side of AC.

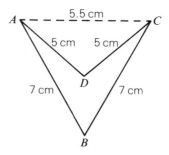

A Trapezium

This is a quadrilateral with one pair of parallel
sides.

9. In the diagram above, if $\angle A = 70°$,
   calculate the size of $\angle D$.
   If $\angle B = 54°$, calculate the size of $\angle C$.

10. Construct trapezium $ABCD$ accurately by
    drawing $AB = 8$ cm, $\angle A = 70°$,
    $\angle B = 54°$.
    Mark D making $AD = 4.8$ cm.
    Through D draw a line parallel to AB,
    meeting the line through B at C.
    Measure angles D and C to check the
    accuracy of your drawing.
    Is $AD = BC$?

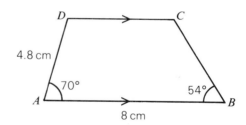

An Isosceles Trapezium

This is a special trapezium, with the two
non-parallel sides equal.

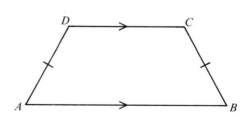

11. In the diagram above, if $\angle A = 66°$,
    calculate the size of $\angle D$.

12.   Construct this trapezium accurately, by
       drawing *AB* = 8 cm, ∠*A* = 66°, and
       AD = 5.2 cm.
       Through *D* draw a line parallel to *AB*.
       With centre *B* and radius 5.2 cm, draw an
       arc to cut the parallel line at *C*. (The arc
       cuts the line in two points. *C* is the one
       nearer *D*.) Join *BC*.
       Measure the angles *B, C, D*.
       Are there any axes of symmetry ? If so,
       draw them on your diagram.

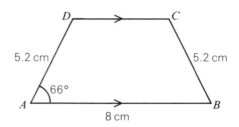

A Parallelogram

This is a quadrilateral with two pairs of sides
parallel.

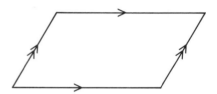

13.   Estimate the sizes of the angles in this parallelogram, in degrees.
       Check your estimates by measuring with your protractor.
       Find the sum of the 4 angles.
       Notice which angles are equal.
       Estimate, then measure, the lengths of the sides of the parallelogram.
       Notice which sides are equal.
       Find the perimeter of the parallelogram.

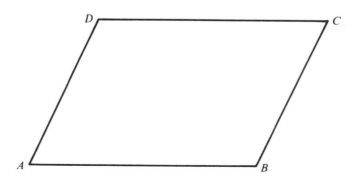

14. If $\angle A = 48°$, what are the sizes of angles B, C, D ?

Construct the parallelogram *ABCD*, beginning by making $AB = 9.2$ cm, $\angle A = 48°$, and $AD = 5.6$ cm.
Through *B* draw a line parallel to *AD*, and through *D* draw a line parallel to *AB*, letting these lines meet at *C*.
Measure the angles *B*, *C*, *D* to check the accuracy of your work.
Measure the lines *BC* and *DC*. What do you notice ?
Are there any axes of symmetry ? If so, draw them on your diagram.
Is there a point of symmetry ? If so, mark it on your diagram.

A Rhombus

This is a special parallelogram, with two adjacent sides equal.

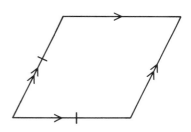

15. A rhombus can be called by a different name.
What is it ?

16. Repeat the work of question 14, but making $\angle A = 72°$ and $AB = AD = 6.8$ cm.

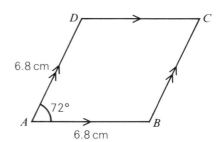

17. What sort of figure would a rhombus *ABCD* be, if $\angle A$ was a right angle ?

A Rectangle

This is a special parallelogram, with one angle a
right angle.

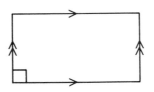

18.   A rectangle can be called by a different
       name. What is it ?

19.   Repeat the work of question 14, but
       making $\angle A = 90°$ and $AB = 9.2$ cm,
       $AD = 5.6$ cm.

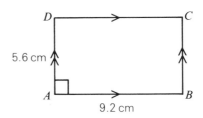

20.   What sort of figure would a rectangle
       ABCD be, if the sides *AB* and *AD* were
       equal ?

A Square

This is the very special parallelogram, which is
both a rectangle and a rhombus combined, i.e. it
has one angle a right angle and two adjacent
sides equal.

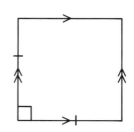

21.   Repeat the work of question 14, making
       $\angle A = 90°$ and $AB = AD = 6.7$ cm.
       You should discover that all its sides are
       equal and all its angles are equal (all 90°)
       and so it is called a **regular** figure.

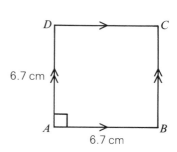

Here is a summary of the special quadrilaterals with their definitions and properties.

Special sorts of quadrilaterals

Trapezium

One pair of parallel sides

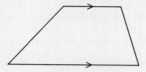

If the other 2 sides are equal it is an isosceles trapezium.

Kite

Two adjacent sides are equal and the other two adjacent sides are equal

Parallelogram

Opposite sides are parallel

Opposite sides are equal
Opposite angles are equal

Rectangle

It is a parallelogram with one angle a right angle

Opposite sides are parallel and equal
All angles are right angles

Rhombus

It is a parallelogram with one pair of adjacent sides equal

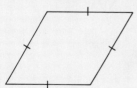

Opposite sides are parallel
All sides are equal
Opposite angles are equal

Square

It is a rectangle and a rhombus

Opposite sides are parallel
All sides are equal
All angles are right angles

Symmetry

An isosceles trapezium has one axis of symmetry.
A kite has one axis of symmetry. (It is a diagonal of the kite.)
A parallelogram has no axes of symmetry.
A rectangle has 2 axes of symmetry.
A rhombus has 2 axes of symmetry. (They are the diagonals of the rhombus.)
A square has 4 axes of symmetry. (Two of them are the diagonals of the square.)

The parallelogram, rectangle, rhombus and square have a point of symmetry at the point where the diagonals cross each other. They have rotational symmetry of order 2, except for the square, which has rotational symmetry of order 4.

Exercise 4.2

1. Calculate the sizes of the marked angles in these trapeziums.

    1 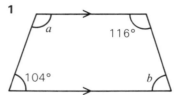 **2**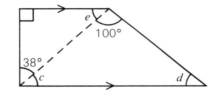

2. *ABCD* is a kite with *AB* = *BC* and
    AD = *DC* = diagonal *AC*. ∠*ABC* = 90°.
    Find the size of ∠*BAD*.

    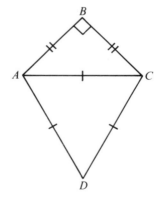

3. Find the sizes of the marked angles in these parallelograms.

    1 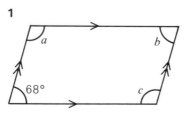 **2**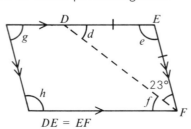

4. Find the sizes of the marked angles in this figure, which is a rhombus.

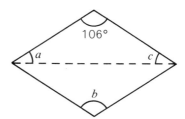

5. Find the sizes of the marked angles in this rectangle. $AB = BE$.

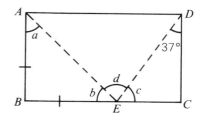

6. In the diagram, triangles ABC and AEF are equilateral. $ACDE$ is a square. What is the size of $\angle BAF$?

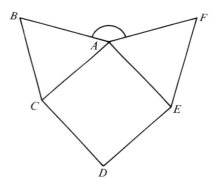

7. In the diagram, $ABCD$ is a square and $\triangle BEC$ is an isosceles triangle. Find the sizes of angles b, c, d.

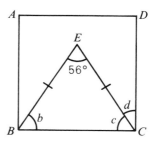

8. The outline of a quadrilateral is made by placing 4 rods together. Say which of these figures can be made in each case:- trapezium, kite, parallelogram, rectangle, rhombus, square.

    1 If the rods placed in order are 10 cm, 16 cm, 10 cm, 16 cm long, which two figures can be made ?

    2 If the same rods are placed in any order, what other figure can be made ?

    3 If the rods are 10 cm, 16 cm, 10 cm and 20 cm, which figure can be made ?

    4 If the rods are all 16 cm long, which two figures can be made ?

9. On graph paper, or squared paper, using a scale of 1 cm to 1 unit on both axes, draw axes for x and y from -8 to 8.

    1 Plot points A (2, 8), B (2, 6), C (8, 2), D (4, 8).
    Join AB, BC, CD, DA.
    What sort of quadrilateral is $ABCD$?

    2 Plot points E (-8, 2), F (-4, 4), G (-2, 8), H (-6, 6).
    Join EF, FG, GH, HE.
    What sort of quadrilateral is $EFGH$?

    3 Plot points J (-7, -1), K (-6, -5), L (0, -8), M (-1, -4).
    Join JK, KL, LM, MJ.
    What sort of quadrilateral is $JKLM$?

    4 Plot points N (-3, 0), P (-2, -2), Q (2, 0), R (1, 2).
    Join NP, PQ, QR, RN.
    What sort of quadrilateral is $NPQR$?

    5 Plot points S (3, 0), T (1, -5), U (6, -7).
    Join ST and TU.
    Find a point V such that $STUV$ is a square. Complete the square.
    What are the coordinates of V ?

10. Draw accurately the quadrilateral $PQRS$, using ruler, protractor and compasses.

    1 Measure the size of $\angle QRS$.

    2 Join PR and measure its length.

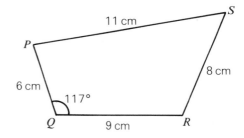

11. Draw accurately the parallelogram $PQRS$. Join PR.

    1 Measure $\angle RPQ$.

    2 Measure the length of PR.

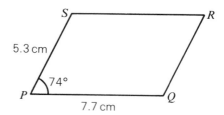

12. Construct the trapezium $PQRS$, using your set-square to draw the line SR. Measure the lengths of SR and QR.

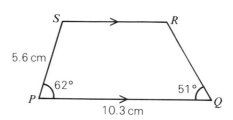

13.   Say which of these figures, trapezium, parallelogram, rectangle, rhombus, have these properties.
   1   Which figures have both pairs of opposite angles equal, although they are not right angles ?
   2   Which figure has only one pair of opposite sides parallel ?
   3   Which figure has all sides equal ?
   4   Which figure has all angles right angles ?
   5   Which figures have both pairs of opposite sides parallel, although the four sides are not all equal ?

14.   Sketch a rhombus, a rectangle and a square.
   What sort of triangles are these,
   1   △ABC, where $ABCD$ is a rhombus,
   2   △PQR, where $PQRS$ is a rectangle,
   3   △XYZ, where $WXYZ$ is a square ?

Exercise 4.3   Applications and Activities

1. $ABCD$ is a trapezium with AB parallel to DC and $AB = BC$.
   Calculate the sizes of the marked angles.

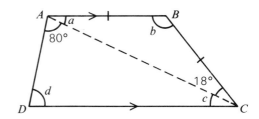

2. $ABCD$ is a parallelogram.
   1   Find the sizes of angles a and b.
   2   What sort of triangle is △AYX ?

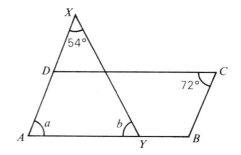

3. ABCD is a rectangle and ABX is an
    equilateral triangle.
    1   Find the sizes of a and b.
    2   Find the perimeters of the rectangle
           ABCD and the triangle ABX.

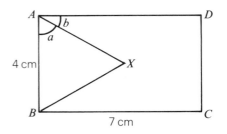

4. ABCD is a square and CDEF is a
    rhombus.
    1   Explain why AD = DE.
    2   Find the sizes of the angles a, b, c, d.

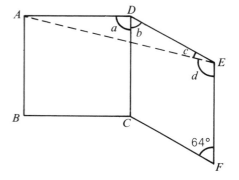

5. **1**   The angles of a quadrilateral are $2x°$, $3x°$, $4x°$ and $6x°$. Write down an
           equation and solve it to find the value of x. Find the sizes of the angles.
    2   If the angles of a quadrilateral are $x°$, $2x°$, $4x°$ and $y°$, write down a formula
           for y in terms of x.

Investigating the diagonals

6. Construct a quadrilateral ABCD by
    drawing this figure and joining AB, BC,
    CD, DA.
    Measure AB, to the nearest mm.
    Measure ∠ABC.
    What sort of quadrilateral is ABCD ?

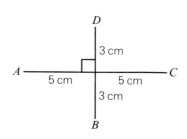

7.   Construct the parallelogram *ABCD*.

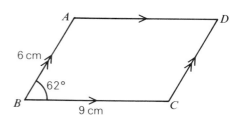

Draw the diagonals of the parallelogram and let them meet at *X*.
1   Measure *AC* and *BD*. Are the diagonals equal ?
2   Measure *AX* and *CX*, *BX* and *DX*. Do the diagonals bisect each other (cut each other in half) ?
3   Measure ∠*BXC*. Do the diagonals intersect each other at right angles ?

These facts about diagonals are true for any parallelogram. (Keep the results to use in question 11.)

8.   Repeat question 7 with a rectangle *ABCD*.
     Make ∠*B* = 90° instead of 62°.
     The facts about diagonals are true for any rectangle.

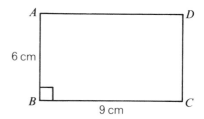

9.   Repeat question 7 for a rhombus *ABCD*.
     Make *BC* = 6 cm instead of 9 cm.
     The facts about diagonals are true for any rhombus.

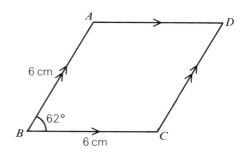

10. Repeat question 7 for a square *ABCD*.
     In addition,
     4   Measure the size of ∠*DBC*.
     The facts about diagonals are true for any square.

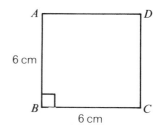

11.   Use your results from questions 7 to 10 for this question. Of the figures
parallelogram, rectangle, rhombus and square,
   1   which have diagonals which bisect each other,
   2   which have diagonals which cut each other at right angles,
   3   which have diagonals which are equal ?

Write your results in a table, putting 'yes' or 'no' in the columns.

	Diagonals bisect each other	Diagonals cut each other at right angles	Diagonals are equal
Parallelogram Rectangle Rhombus Square			

Here is a summary of the properties of diagonals.

Isosceles trapezium

Diagonals are equal (but do not bisect each other).

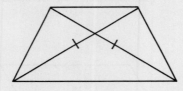

Kite

One diagonal is a line of symmetry. It bisects the other diagonal at right angles.

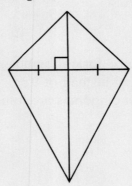

Parallelogram

Diagonals bisect each other.

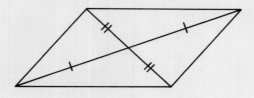

Rectangle

Diagonals bisect each other. Diagonals are equal.

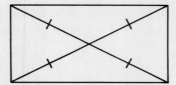

Rhombus

Diagonals bisect each other at right angles.
They also bisect the angles of the rhombus.

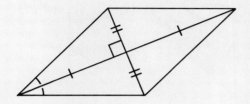

Square

Diagonals bisect each other at right angles.
Diagonals are equal.
Diagonals make angles of 45° with the sides of the square.

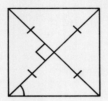

12. Find the marked angles in these figures.

1

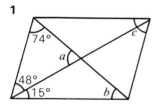

a parallelogram

2

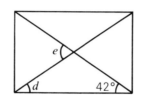

a rectangle

3

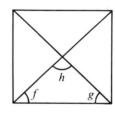

a square

13. The diagonals *AC* and *BD* of a parallelogram *ABCD* are 10 cm and 8 cm long respectively, and intersect at *E* at an angle of 50°. Construct the parallelogram, beginning by drawing the diagonal *AEC*.
Estimate and then measure the lengths of *AB* and *AD* and the size of ∠*DAB*.

14. Sketch a parallelogram, a rhombus, a rectangle and a square, and their diagonals.
Are they all symmetrical about the point where the diagonals cross ?
If so, what is the order of rotational symmetry for each one ?

PUZZLE

9. An encyclopaedia, with six hundred leaves per volume, is arranged on a book-shelf. A grub, lying on page one of the first volume, eats its way right through the books until it reaches the last page of volume five. How many leaves has it eaten through ?

5 Thinking about fractions and

Fractions

The first number that you learnt about, which was not a whole number, was probably one-half.
'Give me half of your apple.'
'You can play out for half-an-hour.'
'The players have a rest at half-time.'
After that, you would understand about quarters.

½ a pound of tuppenny rice
½ a pound of treacle
That's the way the money goes
Pop goes the weasel.

Other fractions

The other fractions, such as thirds, fifths, eighths, etc. are not used so often, although if you belong to a family with three children, you are used to sharing and getting one-third each, and if you have milk at school it could be $\frac{1}{3}$ pint.
The difficulty with $\frac{1}{3}$ and $\frac{2}{3}$ is that they cannot be written as exact decimals.
We cannot divide £1 exactly into thirds.

Bonbons
46p
a quarter

How many ounces in a quarter (of a lb) ?

Using fractions

Some calculations are easier to do in your head using fractions rather than decimals.
e.g. To find $\frac{1}{4}$ of £6 = £6 ÷ 4 = £1.50
It is easier to work it out that way than to work out 0.25 × £6.
So fractions are still useful, although decimals are easier to use with a calculator.

What time is it ?

percentages

Which notice is easier to understand ?

Essential equipment in many households

What is **your** spending priority ?

Percentages

These are being used more and more in the age of calculators and computers, so it is useful to know such things as that '20% off' means one-fifth off, that inflation at 8% means that goods which previously cost £100 could now cost £108, and that a pay-rise of 6% means that you can calculate your new salary by multiplying the present salary by 1.06.

Using percentages

When two or more sets of figures have to be compared, it is useful to have them expressed in percentages.

Percentage ownership per household

	1979	1987
car	57	64
central heating	55	73
washing machine	74	83
freezer	40	74
television	97	98
telephone	67	83

Spending priorities of young people (aged 15 to 24)

	Male %	Female %
clothes	57	79
records, tapes, music	40	27
going out, drinking	23	18
save towards holiday, special purchase	16	25
something for car or motorbike	20	6
cosmetic, haircare products	1	15
books	8	7
sport	12	2
other hobbies	11	3

Comment on these figures.

5 Fractions and Percentages

Fractions

Fractions are numbers such as $\frac{1}{4}$ (one-quarter), $\frac{1}{3}$ (one-third), $\frac{2}{5}$ (two-fifths), $\frac{5}{9}$ (five-ninths).

The number underneath is called the **denominator**. It tells us how many smaller equal parts the whole unit is divided into.

The number on top is called the **numerator**. It tells us how many of the smaller parts are counted.

e.g. A square is divided into 9 equal parts, and 5 of the parts are shaded.
The shaded region is $\frac{5}{9}$ of the whole square, (and the unshaded region is $\frac{4}{9}$ of the whole square).

Converting fractions to decimals

1. Simple fractions, with denominators which are factors of 10 or 100

e.g. $\frac{1}{2} = \frac{5}{10} = 0.5$

$\frac{1}{4} = \frac{25}{100} = 0.25$

$\frac{2}{5} = \frac{4}{10} = 0.4$

$\frac{3}{20} = \frac{15}{100} = 0.15$

$\frac{1}{25} = \frac{4}{100} = 0.04$

2. Using your calculator

If the denominators are powers of 2, i.e. 2, 4, 8, 16, . . . , or powers of 5, i.e. 5, 25, 125, . . . , or combinations of these such as 20, 40, 50, . . . , then there will be an exact decimal.

e.g. $\frac{3}{8} = 3 \div 8 = 0.375$

$\frac{7}{16} = 7 \div 16 = 0.4375$

$\frac{9}{125} = 9 \div 125 = 0.072$

3. Fractions with other denominators

These will not give exact decimals so, since you are unlikely to need several decimal places, you must give the decimal correct to 2 or 3 decimal places, as needed.

e.g. $\frac{1}{3}$ = 1 ÷ 3   = 0.3333 . . .   = 0.33 to 2 decimal places
                                              = 0.333 to 3 decimal places

   $\frac{1}{6}$ = 1 ÷ 6   = 0.1666 . . .   = 0.17 to 2 decimal places
                                              = 0.167 to 3 decimal places

   $\frac{5}{7}$ = 5 ÷ 7   = 0.7142 . . .   = 0.71 to 2 decimal places
                                              = 0.714 to 3 decimal places

   $\frac{27}{31}$ = 27 ÷ 31 = 0.8709 . . .   = 0.87 to 2 decimal places
                                              = 0.871 to 3 decimal places

Multiplication with fractions

If the fractions make exact decimals then you can turn them into decimals to work out the multiplication.

e.g. $5\frac{3}{4}$ × 8   = 5.75 × 8 = 46

   $1\frac{3}{4} \times 2\frac{2}{5}$ = 1.75 × 2.4 = 4.2 (This is $4\frac{1}{5}$ if you want the answer as a fraction.)

If the fractions do not turn into exact decimals then you will have to use different methods for multiplying fractions.

Multiplying a fraction by a whole number

e.g. $\frac{5}{6} \times 4 = \frac{20}{6} = \frac{10}{3} = 3\frac{1}{3}$
You can cancel by 2 before multiplying, dividing both numerator and denominator by 2.

$$\frac{5}{\overset{}{\underset{3}{6}}} \times \overset{2}{\cancel{4}} = \frac{10}{3} = 3\frac{1}{3}$$

Multiplying a mixed number by a whole number

Method 1 Turn the mixed number into an improper fraction.

e.g. $3\frac{2}{3} \times 5 = \frac{11}{3} \times 5 = \frac{55}{3} = 18\frac{1}{3}$

If you need the answer as a decimal, work out 11 × 5 ÷ 3, getting 18.33, to 2 decimal places.

Method 2 Multiply the whole number part and the fraction part separately and add the results together.

e.g. $3\frac{2}{3} \times 5 = (3 \times 5) + (\frac{2}{3} \times 5)$ $\frac{2}{3} \times 5 = \frac{10}{3} = 3\frac{1}{3}$
           $= 15 + 3\frac{1}{3}$
           $= 18\frac{1}{3}$

If you need the answer as a decimal, multiply 3 by 5 first, put the result in the memory, then work $2 \times 5 \div 3$ and add the memory to the answer, getting 18.33 to 2 decimal places.

To multiply two mixed numbers

Turn both numbers into improper fractions.

e.g. $3\frac{1}{9} \times 3\frac{3}{4} = \dfrac{\overset{7}{\cancel{28}}}{\underset{3}{\cancel{9}}} \times \dfrac{\overset{5}{\cancel{15}}}{\underset{1}{\cancel{4}}} = \frac{35}{3} = 11\frac{2}{3}$ (cancelling by 4 and by 3)

If you need the answer in decimal form you can use your calculator at the stage $28 \times 15 \div 9 \div 4$, getting 11.67, to 2 decimal places.

Whenever you use your calculator, do all the multiplication before the division. This may give a more accurate answer if the division is not exact.

Fractional changes

Examples

1   Decrease 22 by $\frac{1}{3}$ of itself.

This leaves $\frac{2}{3}$ of 22 $= \frac{2}{3} \times 22 = \frac{44}{3} = 14\frac{2}{3}$, or 14.67 to 2 decimal places.

Alternatively, you could find $\frac{1}{3}$ of 22 ($=7\frac{1}{3}$) and subtract this from 22, getting $14\frac{2}{3}$.

2   Increase 27 by $\frac{3}{5}$ of itself.

This makes $1\frac{3}{5}$ of 27 $= \frac{8}{5} \times 27 = \frac{216}{5} = 43\frac{1}{5}$ or 43.2

Since $\frac{3}{5}$ is 0.6 you could find 1.6×27 instead.

Alternatively, you could find $\frac{3}{5}$ of 27 or 0.6×27 ($=16.2$) and add this to 27, getting $43\frac{1}{5}$ or 43.2

Exercise 5.1

1. Copy and complete this table. Try to learn some of the decimal equivalents of simple fractions.

Fraction	Decimal
$\frac{1}{2}$	0.5
$\frac{1}{4}$	
$\frac{3}{4}$	
$\frac{1}{5}$	
$\frac{2}{5}$	
$\frac{3}{5}$	

Fraction	Decimal
$\frac{4}{5}$	
$\frac{1}{8}$	
$\frac{3}{8}$	
$\frac{5}{8}$	
$\frac{7}{8}$	

2. Use your calculator to find the exact decimals corresponding to these fractions.

1 $\frac{3}{50}$ 6 $\frac{7}{80}$

2 $\frac{5}{16}$ 7 $\frac{9}{250}$

3 $\frac{1}{125}$ 8 $\frac{19}{20}$

4 $\frac{9}{32}$ 9 $\frac{49}{50}$

5 $\frac{3}{25}$ 10 $\frac{33}{40}$

3. Use your calculator to find the decimals corresponding to these fractions, correct to 3 decimal places.

1 $\frac{4}{9}$ 6 $\frac{4}{7}$

2 $\frac{5}{6}$ 7 $\frac{9}{11}$

3 $\frac{1}{11}$ 8 $\frac{1}{17}$

4 $\frac{2}{7}$ 9 $\frac{1}{6}$

5 $\frac{5}{13}$ 10 $\frac{8}{9}$

4. In these questions, turn the fractions to decimals and use your calculator to work out the answers, in decimal form.

1 $\frac{3}{4} \times 5$ 6 $4\frac{1}{2} \times 3\frac{3}{4}$

2 $3 \times \frac{9}{10}$ 7 $2\frac{3}{5} \times 1\frac{1}{10}$

3 $4\frac{1}{2} \times 3$ 8 $4\frac{4}{5} \times 2\frac{1}{4}$

4 $3 \times 1\frac{3}{5}$ 9 $8\frac{1}{4} \times 1\frac{7}{10}$

5 $1\frac{3}{4} \times 2\frac{2}{5}$ 10 $2\frac{1}{4} \times 2\frac{1}{4}$

5. Work out these multiplication questions, giving exact answers.

    1 $\frac{3}{14} \times 2$ **6** $3\frac{1}{3} \times 2$

    2 $\frac{5}{6} \times 4$ **7** $1\frac{2}{7} \times 3$

    3 $\frac{2}{3} \times 5$ **8** $6 \times 1\frac{1}{3}$

    4 $\frac{9}{10} \times 9$ **9** $8 \times 2\frac{5}{6}$

    5 $2\frac{2}{3} \times 5$ **10** $3 \times 3\frac{1}{9}$

6. Turn these numbers into improper fractions and work out the questions, giving exact answers.

    1 $1\frac{1}{2} \times 2\frac{1}{3}$ **6** $2\frac{1}{7} \times 1\frac{2}{5}$

    2 $6\frac{1}{9} \times 1\frac{7}{11}$ **7** $5\frac{1}{6} \times 4\frac{1}{2}$

    3 $2\frac{6}{7} \times 6\frac{1}{8}$ **8** $3\frac{1}{3} \times 3\frac{1}{3}$

    4 $4\frac{1}{2} \times 3\frac{2}{3}$ **9** $1\frac{1}{2} \times 1\frac{2}{3}$

    5 $4\frac{4}{5} \times 5\frac{5}{6}$ **10** $10\frac{2}{3} \times 6\frac{1}{4}$

7. Find the values of the following:

    1   24 increased by $\frac{3}{4}$ of itself

    2   40 decreased by $\frac{2}{5}$ of itself

    3   90 increased by $\frac{1}{3}$ of itself

    4   66 decreased by $\frac{2}{3}$ of itself

    5   70 decreased by $\frac{3}{10}$ of itself

    6   30 increased by $1\frac{1}{2}$ times itself

    7   45 increased by $\frac{1}{4}$ of itself

    8   18 decreased by $\frac{1}{5}$ of itself

    9   32 decreased by $\frac{3}{10}$ of itself

    10 56 increased by $\frac{1}{3}$ of itself, correct to 2 decimal places.

Percentages

The symbol % stands for 'per cent', which means 'out of 100'.
So, 7% means 7 out of 100.
As a fraction this is $\frac{7}{100}$
As a decimal it is 0.07

Fractions into percentages

1. **Fractions which have denominators which are factors of 100**, such as 2, 4, 5, 10, . . . can be turned into fractions with denominator 100 and then simply written as percentages.

   e.g. $\frac{1}{2} = \frac{50}{100} = 50\%$ Multiply numerator and denominator by 50, to change denominator 2 into 100

   $\frac{4}{5} = \frac{80}{100} = 80\%$ Multiply numerator and denominator by 20, to change denominator 5 into 100

   $\frac{13}{20} = \frac{65}{100} = 65\%$

2. **Other fractions**
   Multiply by 100 and write the % sign.

   e.g. $\frac{3}{8} = \frac{3}{8} \times 100\% = \frac{300}{8}\% = 37\frac{1}{2}\%$ or 37.5%

   $\frac{1}{3} = \frac{1}{3} \times 100\% = \frac{100}{3}\% = 33\frac{1}{3}\%$, or 33.3% to 1 decimal place

   $\frac{5}{7} = \frac{5}{7} \times 100\% = \frac{500}{7}\% = 71\frac{3}{7}\%$, or 71.4% to 1 decimal place

To change a percentage into a fraction

e.g. $23\% = \frac{23}{100}$

   $14\% = \frac{14}{100} = \frac{7}{50}$

   $23\frac{1}{3}\% = \frac{23\frac{1}{3}}{100} = \frac{70}{300}$ multiplying both numerator and denominator by 3 to change $23\frac{1}{3}$ into a whole number

   $= \frac{7}{30}$ dividing both numerator and denominator by 10

It is useful to learn the percentages corresponding to simple fractions or decimals.

Fraction	Decimal	Percentage
$\frac{3}{4}$	0.75	75%
$\frac{1}{2}$	0.5	50%
$\frac{1}{4}$	0.25	25%
$\frac{1}{5}$	0.2	20%
$\frac{1}{10}$	0.1	10%
$\frac{1}{100}$	0.01	1%

Also, $33\frac{1}{3}\%$ is equivalent to the fraction $\frac{1}{3}$,

and $66\frac{2}{3}\%$ is equivalent to the fraction $\frac{2}{3}$.

To find a percentage of a sum of money or a quantity

Examples

1   Find 28% of £19

28% as a decimal is 0.28 so find £(0.28 × 19) = £5.32

2   Find 12% of 2 litres

12% is 0.12 so find 0.12 × 2 litres = 0.24 litres = 240 ml

3   Find $21\frac{1}{2}$% of 2 metres

$21\frac{1}{2}$% is 0.215 so find 0.215 × 2 m = 0.43 m = 43 cm

To increase or decrease by a percentage

Examples

1   Increase £19 by 28%

Either find 28% of £19 (as above) and add it to £19, making £24.32

Or, the original amount is 100%
   the increase is 28%
   the new amount is 128%
   so find 128% of £19 = £(1.28 × 19) = £24.32

2   Decrease 2 litres by 12%

Either find 12% of 2 litres (as above) and subtract it from 2 litres, making 1.76 litres.

Or, the original amount is 100%
   the decrease is 12%
   the new amount is 88%
   so find 88% of 2 litres = 0.88 × 2 litres = 1.76 litres

To express one quantity as a percentage of another

Example

What percentage is 43 cm of 2 m ?

First find what fraction 43 cm is of 2 m, then change this fraction to a percentage.

$$\frac{43\,cm}{2\,m} = \frac{43\,cm}{200\,cm} = \frac{43}{200}$$

Change to a percentage by multiplying by 100 and writing the % sign.

$$\frac{43}{2\cancel{00}} \times 1\cancel{00}\% = \frac{43}{2}\% = 21\tfrac{1}{2}\% \text{ or } 21.5\%$$

Exercise 5.2

1. Express these percentages as fractions in their simplest forms.
   1 70%   **4** $17\tfrac{1}{2}\%$
   2 25%   **5** $13\tfrac{1}{3}\%$
   3 85%

2. Express these percentages as decimals.
   1 62%   **4** $11\tfrac{1}{2}\%$
   2 35%   **5** 99%
   3 $16\tfrac{3}{4}\%$

3. Change these fractions to percentages.
   1 $\frac{3}{5}$ **4** $\frac{2}{3}$
   2 $\frac{7}{8}$ **5** $\frac{1}{6}$
   3 $\frac{3}{20}$

4. Find the values of
   1 15% of £30   **4** $2\tfrac{1}{2}\%$ of 8 ℓ
   2 90% of 5 m   **5** 18% of 5 hours
   3 24% of 2 kg

5. **1** Increase 2.5 kg by 8%
   2 Increase 66 cm by 65%
   3 Decrease 2750 units by 10%
   4 Increase £240 by $12\tfrac{1}{2}\%$
   5 Decrease 450 mg by $33\tfrac{1}{3}\%$

6.   Find what percentage the 1st quantity is of the 2nd.

1	£2.40, £5.00	**6**	1.5 cm, 2.4 cm
2	125 g, 2 kg	**7**	1.5 ℓ, 4.0 ℓ
3	48 min, 1 h	**8**	£3, £600
4	£26, £80	**9**	77 cm, 66 cm
5	£135, £90	**10**	£224, £700

Exercise 5.3   Applications and Activities

1.   A kilogram is approximately $2\frac{1}{5}$ lb. What is
this number in decimal form ?
What does a bag containing 5 kg of
fertilizer weigh in lbs ?

2.   A litre is approximately $1\frac{3}{4}$ pints. What is
this number in decimal form ? A container
holds 5 ℓ. Is this greater or less than a
gallon, and by how much ?

3.   A bicycle wheel moves through a distance of approximately $3\frac{1}{7}$ times its diameter
in one revolution. If its diameter is 56 cm, what is this distance ? After 500
revolutions how far has the bicycle travelled ?

4.   Eighteen-carat gold contains $\frac{18}{24}$ of its
weight in pure gold. The rest is an alloy.
How much pure gold is there in an
18-carat ring weighing 10 g ?

5.   When she retired, Mrs Green's annual salary was £18 500. Since she had
worked for the firm for 30 years, she is now paid an annual pension of $\frac{30}{80}$ of this
salary.
    1   What is $\frac{30}{80}$ as a fraction in its simplest form ?
    2   What is Mrs Green's annual pension ?

6.   Copy and complete this number pattern up to the line beginning $10\frac{1}{2}^2$.

$$\frac{1}{2}^2 = (0 \times 1) + \frac{1}{4} = \quad\frac{1}{4}$$
$$1\frac{1}{2}^2 = (1 \times 2) + \frac{1}{4} = 2\frac{1}{4}$$
$$2\frac{1}{2}^2 = (2 \times 3) + \frac{1}{4} = 6\frac{1}{4}$$

Use the pattern to find the value of $20\frac{1}{2}^2$.

7. By turning these fractions into decimals (correct to 3 decimal places if they are not exact) or otherwise, write them in order of size, smallest first.

$\frac{3}{10}$, $\frac{2}{5}$, $\frac{1}{3}$, $\frac{2}{7}$, $\frac{3}{8}$

8. To make time for an extra concert rehearsal, all lessons on one day are reduced by $\frac{1}{8}$ of their times. How long will a lesson last, if it is usually 40 minutes long ?

9. In a club, three-fifths of the members are Junior members. If there are 42 Junior members, how many members are there altogether ?

10. Miss Andrews, Mr Barker and Mrs Currie own shares in a business. Miss Andrews owns $\frac{2}{5}$ of it, Mr Barker owns $\frac{2}{7}$ of it and Mrs Currie owns the rest. One year the total profits were £2450 and they divided these in proportion to their shares. How much money did they each get ?

11. An estate agent charges a fee of £250 plus 2% of the price that the house is sold for. If he arranges the sale of a house for £85 000, how much will he earn ?

12. Salim's test marks are 36 out of 45. What is this as a percentage ? His friend Rafiq's percentage mark was 60%. What was Rafiq's original mark out of 45 ?

13. Mrs Kelly bought 500 souvenirs for £1.80 each. Of these, 20 were damaged and she could not sell them, but she sold the rest and made an over-all profit of $33\frac{1}{3}$%. At what price did she sell each one for ?

14. A trader was selling oranges at 15p each. To increase trade he decided to sell them at 5 for 69p. By what percentage has he reduced his price ?

15. Mr Scott bought some wood for £5, from which he made 8 pairs of book-ends. He sold the book-ends for £2 per pair. What was his percentage profit ?

16. A car insurance premium is £225 but there is a deduction of 40% for 'no claim discount'. How much is deducted, and how much remains to be paid ?

17. Sauce was normally sold in bottles containing 567 g of the sauce.

  1 What is 20% of 567 g ?

  2 As you can see, this bottle contains 681 g. Is the manufacturer correct in advertising it as containing 20% extra ?

18. A restaurant bill for £35 became £39.20 after a service charge was added. What was the percentage rate of the service charge ?

19. A television set costs a total of £405 if bought on a credit sale agreement. The same set costs £360 if bought for cash.

    1 If the credit sale agreement is for an initial payment of £55 followed by 20 equal monthly payments, how much would be paid each month ?

    2 Find the extra cost involved in buying by credit sale, as a percentage of the cash price.

    3 During a sale the cash price of all goods is reduced by 5%. How much is deducted from the cash price of the television set ?

20. **Addition and subtraction of fractions**

Here are the methods for addition and subtraction of fractions, which you may need to use in future work.

It is easy to add or subtract fractions if they have the same denominator.

e.g. $\frac{2}{9} + \frac{3}{9} = \frac{5}{9}$ (**Two** ninths plus **three** ninths equals **five** ninths)

$\frac{7}{8} - \frac{3}{8} = \frac{4}{8} = \frac{1}{2}$

If the fractions have different denominators, change them into fractions with the same denominator.

e.g. $\frac{5}{6} + \frac{3}{4}$

Change $\frac{5}{6}$ and $\frac{3}{4}$ into fractions with denominator 12, because 12 is the smallest number into which 6 and 4 both divide. $\frac{5}{6} = \frac{10}{12}$ and $\frac{3}{4} = \frac{9}{12}$.

$\frac{5}{6} + \frac{3}{4} = \frac{10}{12} + \frac{9}{12} = \frac{19}{12} = 1\frac{7}{12}$

$\frac{5}{6} - \frac{7}{12} = \frac{10}{12} - \frac{7}{12} = \frac{3}{12} = \frac{1}{4}$

If there are mixed numbers do the whole numbers and the fraction parts separately.

e.g. $3\frac{5}{6} + 2\frac{3}{4} = 5\frac{10}{12} + \frac{9}{12} = 5\frac{19}{12} = 6\frac{7}{12}$

$3\frac{5}{6} - 1\frac{7}{12} = 2\frac{10}{12} - \frac{7}{12} = 2\frac{3}{12} = 2\frac{1}{4}$

Sometimes in subtraction we have to use 1 from the whole number and change it into a fraction.

e.g. $1 - \frac{4}{9} = \frac{9}{9} - \frac{4}{9} = \frac{5}{9}$

$7\frac{5}{8} - 3\frac{3}{4} = 4\frac{5}{8} - \frac{6}{8} = 3 + \frac{8}{8} + \frac{5}{8} - \frac{6}{8} = 1\frac{7}{8}$

(since we cannot take 6 from 5, 1 was changed into $\frac{8}{8}$)

Practise addition and subtraction by doing these questions.

1 $\frac{1}{2} + \frac{1}{3} + \frac{1}{4}$ **6** $2\frac{1}{2} - 1\frac{5}{12}$

2 $3\frac{1}{5} + 1\frac{3}{4}$ **7** $1\frac{1}{2} + 1\frac{3}{10}$

3 $3\frac{5}{6} - 2\frac{1}{3}$ **8** $2\frac{2}{3} - 1\frac{3}{4}$

4 $3\frac{1}{2} + 2\frac{2}{3}$ **9** $3\frac{1}{10} - 1\frac{3}{5}$

5 $4\frac{1}{2} - \frac{7}{8}$ **10** $2\frac{5}{12} + 1\frac{1}{3}$

21. **A number pattern**

Copy and complete this pattern to the line beginning with $\frac{1}{9}$.

$\frac{1}{1} + \frac{1}{2} = \frac{2+1}{2 \times 1} = \frac{3}{2}$

$\frac{1}{2} + \frac{1}{3} = \frac{3+2}{3 \times 2} = \frac{5}{6}$

$\frac{1}{3} + \frac{1}{4} = \frac{4+3}{4 \times 3} = \frac{7}{12}$

. . .

Make a similar pattern for $\frac{1}{1} - \frac{1}{2}, \frac{1}{2} - \frac{1}{3}$, etc.

Use the rules of the patterns to find $\frac{1}{24} + \frac{1}{25}$ and $\frac{1}{24} - \frac{1}{25}$.

22. **Division of fractions**

Work out the answers to these pairs of questions. The fractions in the first column can be turned into decimals and you can use your calculator to divide.

$19 \div \frac{1}{2}$ 19×2

$24 \div \frac{1}{5}$ 24×5

$14 \div \frac{4}{5}$ $14 \times \frac{5}{4}$

$39 \div \frac{13}{10}$ $39 \times \frac{10}{13}$

$49 \div \frac{7}{4}$ $49 \times \frac{4}{7}$

What do you notice about the pairs of questions and their answers ?

This gives us a method for dividing by fractions, which we can use in cases where the fraction is not an exact decimal.

Turn all mixed numbers into improper fractions, then,

to divide by $\frac{1}{3}$, multiply by 3,

to divide by $\frac{2}{3}$, multiply by $\frac{3}{2}$,

to divide by $\frac{5}{3}$, multiply by $\frac{3}{5}$,

and similarly for other fractions.

This method can also be used for dividing by a whole number.

e.g. to divide by 2, multiply by $\frac{1}{2}$,

  to divide by 5, multiply by $\frac{1}{5}$, and so on.

Examples

1 $1\frac{19}{45} \div 3\frac{5}{9} = \frac{64}{45} \div \frac{32}{9} = \frac{\overset{2}{\cancel{64}}}{\underset{5}{\cancel{45}}} \times \frac{\overset{1}{\cancel{9}}}{\underset{1}{\cancel{32}}} = \frac{2}{5}$ (cancelling by 9 and by 32)

2 $3\frac{3}{7} \div 4 = \frac{\overset{6}{\cancel{24}}}{7} \times \frac{1}{\underset{1}{\cancel{4}}} = \frac{6}{7}$

Practise division by doing these questions.

1	$\frac{4}{9} \div \frac{8}{15}$	**6**	$\frac{5}{6} \div 1\frac{1}{9}$
2	$\frac{7}{8} \div \frac{5}{6}$	**7**	$5\frac{5}{8} \div 3$
3	$1\frac{1}{6} \div \frac{3}{10}$	**8**	$2\frac{3}{4} \div 4\frac{1}{8}$
4	$\frac{2}{3} \div \frac{8}{9}$	**9**	$1\frac{1}{8} \div 11\frac{1}{4}$
5	$1\frac{1}{4} \div \frac{5}{12}$	**10**	$8\frac{3}{4} \div 4\frac{2}{3}$

23. **Fractions as decimals**
Use your calculator to find the fractions $\frac{1}{2}, \frac{1}{3}, \frac{1}{4}, \frac{1}{5}, \ldots$ to $\frac{1}{20}$, expressed as decimals.
Write down the results in a list, giving them correct to 1 less decimal place than is shown on your calculator if the answer is a long list of figures.
Some fractions have exact decimal equivalents.
Obviously $\frac{1}{10}$ does, since 0.1 is another way of writing $\frac{1}{10}$

$\frac{1}{20}$ is half of this, so it is 0.05

$\frac{1}{5}$ is $\frac{2}{10}$, so it is 0.2

Look at the fractions $\frac{1}{2}, \frac{1}{4}, \frac{1}{8}, \frac{1}{16}$. They all have exact decimal equivalents. See how they match each other.

Now look at $\frac{1}{3}$ and $\frac{1}{9}$. They do not have exact decimal equivalents, and the sequence of figures is endless. Decimals which repeat endlessly in a pattern are called recurring decimals.

$\frac{1}{3} = 0.3333\ldots$ and this can be written as $0.\dot{3}$ (with a dot on top of the 3)

How would you write the decimal for $\frac{1}{9}$?

The other multiples of 3 are also recurring decimals, e.g. $\frac{1}{12} = 0.08333\ldots$

The other numbers in the list are also recurring decimals with their own patterns.

$\frac{1}{11} = 0.090909\ldots$ which can be written as $0.\dot{0}\dot{9}$ with dots on the 0 and the 9 to show that they both recur.

Find the decimals of $\frac{2}{11}, \frac{3}{11}, \frac{4}{11}, \ldots \frac{10}{11}$ also. Write these down in a list and comment about them.

$\frac{1}{7} = 0.142857142857\ldots$ which can be written as $0.\dot{1}4285\dot{7}$. The dots at the beginning and end of the six figures show that they all recur.

Investigate $\frac{2}{7}, \frac{3}{7}, \ldots \frac{6}{7}$ also. Look for any patterns in these results.

Finally, you can do a similar investigation for $\frac{1}{13}, \frac{2}{13}$, etc. You will need to use a calculator which gives more than 6 decimal places if you are to discover the repeating patterns. Also, do not rely on the final figure on the calculator, which may have been rounded up.

24. **VAT.   Value Added Tax**

This tax is added to the cost of many things you buy. In most shops the price marked includes the tax so you do not have to calculate it.

Occasionally, however, the prices are given without VAT and it has to be added to the bill.

The present rate of this tax is 15% so the final price is 115% of the original price. To find the final price, multiply the original price by 1.15.

Examples

1   A builder says he will charge £500 for doing a job. To this, VAT at 15% is added. What is the total cost ?

  The total cost is £500 × 1.15 = £575

If a price includes VAT, to find the original price divide by 1.15

2   A video camera costs £750. How much of this cost is tax ?

  The original price was £750 ÷ 1.15 = £652.17 (working to the nearest penny)

  The VAT is £750 − £652.17 = £97.83

Answer these questions.

Note   The rate of tax might be changed. If it has, work out the examples and the questions using the up-to-date rate.

1   Mr Williams buys some DIY materials marked at £76.   VAT at 15% is added to that price. What is the total cost, including the tax ?

2   Mrs Gill employed a firm to do some repairs and the bill, including VAT at 15%, came to £322. How much of this was the price for the work, and how much was the tax ?

3   Sharon thinks she is too young to pay taxes, but she gets £3.00 pocket money each week, plus £1.60 from her grandparents, and she usually spends this on sweets, and the occasional record. How much of her weekly money is she actually paying out for VAT ? How much will this come to in a year (52 weeks) ?

Some things are exempt from VAT, or zero-rated, which means that no tax is payable. Find out and list some of these.

25.   **Simple Interest**
If you invest money, this money earns money which is called Interest. e.g. If you invested money in a Bank or Building Society which was paying interest at 12% (per year), then for every £100 invested you get £12 interest every year.

Example

If £600 is invested at 8% per annum for 4 years, what is the Simple Interest ?
Every £100 invested gains £8 interest per year.   ('per annum' means 'per year')
So £600 invested gains £48 interest per year.
£600 invested for 4 years gains £48 × 4 = £192.
The Simple Interest is £192.

This can also be worked out using the formula

$$I = \frac{PRT}{100}$$ where I is the Simple Interest

P is the Principal, (the money invested)
R is the rate per cent (per annum)
T is the time (in years)

In this example, P = £600, R = 8, T = 4

$$I = \frac{PRT}{100} = £\frac{600 \times 8 \times 4}{100} = £192$$

(This is called **Simple Interest** because it assumes that you are paid the interest each year but it is not put into the account so the money invested stays the same. If you leave the interest in the account then the money invested increases, and so does the interest for the following year, and the total interest for a number of years is called **Compound Interest**.)

Work out the Simple Interest on these amounts:

1   £200 invested for 4 years at 9%
2   £1200 invested for 3 years at 11%
3   £575 invested for 2 years at 12%

See if you can find the up-to-date rates of interest offered by Banks and Building Societies in your district.

PUZZLES

10. Here are some more numbers from a popular quiz. Can you supply the missing words, whose initial letters are given ?

5 C on the OGF
12 S of the Z
24 BB in a P
88 K on a P
100 Y in a C
101 D
112 P in a H
147 is the MB in S
200 P for PG in M
212 DF, the T at which WB

11. Start from ★, going horizontally or vertically (not diagonally), and spell out the names of eight four-sided figures.

P	E	S	Q	R	E	L	A	T	E
A	Z	M	U	A	Q	I	L	A	R
R	I	U	E	A	U	R	R	E	C
T	M	A	H	D	A	D	L	G	T
O	G	R	W	O	T	I	E	N	A
L	E	L	L	R	E	K	R	H	O
★P	A	R	A	R	A	S	U	B	M

6 Thinking about collecting information

Asking questions

Have you or your parents ever been stopped in the street, to be asked for your opinion about some topical subject ? Perhaps a researcher has called at your house to ask questions.

Political surveys

If there is a General Election, the main parties try to find out beforehand how people intend to vote. They do this by taking a survey. They can use this information to decide whether they are likely to win, or not, and they can plan the rest of their campaign accordingly. In particular, they can target their resources to the marginal seats which they might win, giving less time to those constituencies where they are sure to win, or those that they can't possibly win.

Of course, the results of the survey might be misleading, leading to surprises when the actual votes are counted.

The Houses of Parliament

Market research

Television and radio advertising, and advertising in newspapers and magazines, and on hoardings, is big business nowadays. Every manufacturer wants to sell his product, and needs to get his message across to the customers. But advertising costs money, and the manufacturers need to know whether the advertising is effective. So they do 'market research', paying people to find out from the public just how effective the advertising is.

What makes a good advertisement ?

Questionnaire

I am doing a survey to discover what pupils eat and drink for breakfast.
Would you please help me by answering the following questions?

Age .... years .... months

Place a tick in the box (boxes) which apply to you.

Q1. Gender   Male ☐₁   Female ☐₂

Q2. Do you eat:
Cornflakes ☐₁   Weetabix ☐₅
Rice Krispies ☐₂   muesli ☐₆
porridge ☐₃   bacon ☐₇
eggs ☐₄   toast ☐₈
others (please state)................................ ₉

Q3. Do you drink:
orange juice ☐₁   apple juice ☐₄
grapefruit juice ☐₂   milk ☐₅
tea ☐₃   coffee ☐₆
others (please state)............................. ₇

What did **you** have for breakfast today ?

The census counts . . .

● the number of people in each area

● the numbers of men and women and whether they are single, married, widowed or divorced

● how many children there are, how many teenagers, people in their twenties, thirties, forties . . . retired people and so on.

A family group 100 years ago

Local opinion

There may be local surveys so that the Council can gather opinions about what the public think about such things as shopping facilities, transport services, provision of schools, etc.

Surveys and questionnaires

Ask your family and friends if they have ever taken part in a survey, and what it was for. Make a list of the replies. Include whether the survey was carried out in the street, at home, or elsewhere, and whether there was a questionnaire to be filled in.

The Census

The main Government survey is called a **Census**, and this is held every 10 years. The latest one is due to be held in April, 1991, so by the time you read this it should have been held, and you can find out about it. What sort of questions were asked, and what use will the Government make of the information ?
The individual details will not be made public for 100 years.

Family history

The results of the 1891 Census will be made available in 1991, so if you are researching your family history and know where your ancestors lived (in Britain) 100 years ago, you may be able to find out more about them.

6 Collecting Information

Statistics includes
1   the collection of data,
2   the display of the data, in the form of a table or a diagram,
3   the study of the data, often in order to make decisions for the future.

Statistical Diagrams

A line-graph (time-series graph)

These graphs always have time on the horizontal axis and the quantity which is being recorded on the vertical axis.

They are useful to show if there is any **trend**, that is a gradual increase or decrease as time goes on, or if there are any patterns such as seasonal patterns, and they also show any irregular variations.

Example

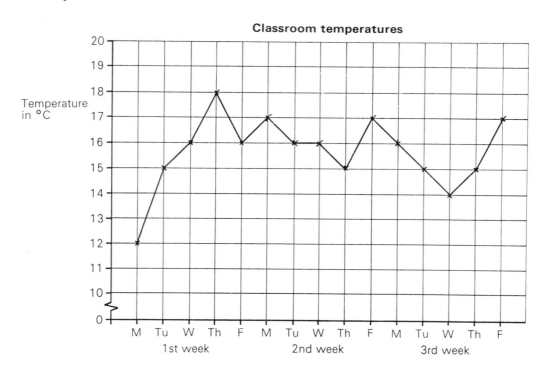

On which day was it very cold in the classroom ? Give a possible reason for this. The points are joined from one to the next by straight lines, because this shows increases and decreases more easily, but in this graph the lines have no other meaning. We cannot use the graph to find temperatures at in-between times, because that would be meaningless.

Here is a reminder of other types of diagrams.

Pictogram showing how office workers get to work

Car	16	𝕏𝕏𝕏𝕏𝕏 𝕏𝕏𝕏𝕏𝕏 𝕏𝕏𝕏𝕏𝕏 𝕏
Motorbike	4	𝕏𝕏𝕏𝕏
Bus	6	𝕏𝕏𝕏𝕏𝕏 𝕏
Walk	12	𝕏𝕏𝕏𝕏𝕏 𝕏𝕏𝕏𝕏𝕏 𝕏𝕏

Bar chart showing how office workers get to work

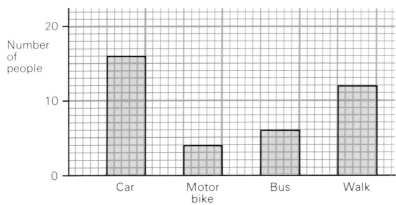

Pie chart to show the composition of eggs

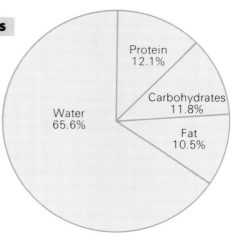

Bar-line graph to show the distribution of sizes of households

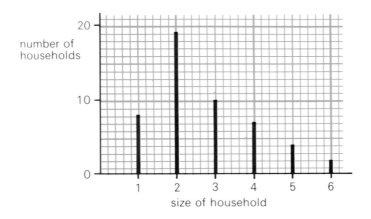

Histogram to show the distribution of weights of 100 young men

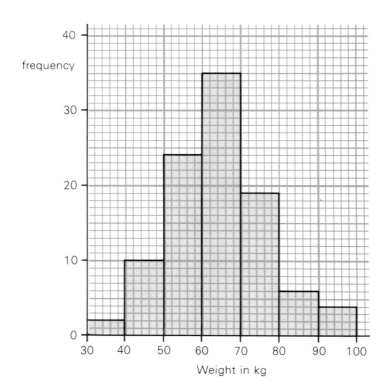

Mean and range of a set of data

Examples

1st week	20
2nd week	19
3rd week	24
4th week	22
5th week	20
6th week	23
7th week	20
8th week	28
9th week	24
10th week	20

1   This list shows the number of people attending a weekly meeting, for the first 10 weeks.
What is the average attendance ?

The usual average is found by adding up the numbers. This gives a total of 220, over 10 weeks.
So the average attendance is 220 ÷ 10, which is 22.

This kind of average is called the **arithmetic mean**, or simply the **mean**.

The symbol we use for the mean is x with a bar on top, $\bar{x}$, called x-bar.

$$\bar{x} = \frac{\text{sum of the items}}{\text{number of items}} = \frac{S}{n}$$

In the example, $\bar{x} = \dfrac{S}{n} = \dfrac{220}{10} = 22$

There are other kinds of average used in Statistics, but at present we will just use the mean.

Now although there were, on average, 22 people attending each week, the lowest attendance was 19 and the highest was 28.
The difference between these is called the **range**.

$$\text{Range} = \text{highest value} - \text{lowest value}$$
$$= 28 - 19 = 9$$

2   Here are the weights of 8 boys, in kg.
53, 49, 41, 55, 46, 57, 52, 51.

Mean weight $\bar{x} = \dfrac{S}{n} = \dfrac{404}{8}\,\text{kg} = 50.5\,\text{kg}$

Range of weights $= (57 - 41)\,\text{kg} = 16\,\text{kg}$

Exercise 6.1

1. Find the mean and range in the following cases.
    1 The numbers of matches in a sample of 12 boxes were:
        36 35 38 41 43 39 33 41 39 37 35 42
    2 The temperatures in a city each day of a summer week were (in °C):
        21 22 24 23 19 20 18
    3 The weights, in kg, of 10 children are:
        57 52 65 54 68 60 53 51 61 48
    4 The weekly wages for 8 workers were
        £109, £133, £141, £126, £119, £138, £150, £124.
    5 The ages of 6 girls are 12y 5m, 13y 0m, 14y 0m, 12y 8m, 12y 3m, 13y 2m.

2. The U.K. population figures are given in this table. (Figures to the nearest million.)

Year	1901	1911	1921	1931	1941	1951	1961	1971	1981
Population (in millions)	38	42	44	46	48	51	53	56	56

Draw a line-graph to represent the data.
Comment on the trend shown.

3. The sales of gas to domestic users (not industry) over 3 years are shown in this table. The figures are in 100 000 000 therms.

1st year				2nd year				3rd year			
Quarters											
1	2	3	4	1	2	3	4	1	2	3	4
20	10	7	17	23	11	6	18	24	11	7	19

Draw a line-graph to represent the data.
Comment on the seasonal variations.

Statistical Investigations

Here are some examples of statistical investigations and the purpose of each.

1   To see how much pocket money children of various ages get, and what they spend it on.
Suppliers of sweets, snacks, soft drinks, magazines, etc. find this information useful. It should also be useful if you are running a school tuck-shop.

2   To ask for pupils' opinions about school dinners, to see whether they are satisfactory or not.
This information might be useful to the school authorities and of benefit to the pupils. The quality of the meals is largely determined by the price charged and by certain local rules, but it may be possible to make changes which lead to improvement.

3   If you want to persuade the Council that a pedestrian crossing is needed on a road in your area, you should get some data about the amount of traffic using the road (preferably at different times of day) and the numbers of pedestrians at different times of day (possibly grouped into children, adults and elderly people).

4   A small shopkeeper will keep a record of the sales of different items, to see if sales are rising, steady or falling. He must also take account of seasonal variations. Some things sell better in summer, or warm weather, and many things sell well at Christmas.

To carry out a statistical investigation

1.   Decide what you are trying to find out. This is the **aim** of the investigation, and you should write it down as a heading.

2.   Decide how you are going to collect the information. Sometimes you will make your own observations, such as counting cars in a traffic survey. Sometimes you will ask other people questions, and sometimes you can find the data in newspapers or reference books.

3. If you are making your own observations, decide what you are going to observe. Design an 'observation sheet' on which to record your data. This could be in the form of a tally table.

e.g.

To record traffic Time _ _ _ _ to _ _ _ _		
	Towards town	From town
Cars	II	⊬⊬⊬
Buses	II	
Vans	IIII	I
Lorries	I	
etc.		

Afterwards you can make a summary of the results.

4. If you are going to ask people questions, decide who you are going to ask. If it is a survey of your class you may want to ask everyone in the class, but if it is a school matter you will probably want to ask just a sample of pupils. You will have to decide how many people to have in your sample, and how to select them. The sample should be a random sample, chosen fairly, so that each person has an equal chance of being selected. It should be a large enough sample to represent fairly the different categories or views of all the people involved. For example, in a survey about views on school uniform (in a mixed school) the sample should include all age-groups and both girls and boys.

5. **Questionnaires**

If you are going to ask people questions you must decide what you are going to ask them. You want to ask everyone the same questions, so write them down in a list which is called a **questionnaire**. You can either give people the questionnaire to fill in themselves or you can ask the questions and write down the answers.

1   Decide exactly what information you want and how you are planning to use the answers.

2   Keep the questionnaire as short as possible, and keep the questions short, clear and precise.

3   Avoid questions which people may not be willing to answer because they are embarrassing or offensive.

4   Try to ask questions which can be answered by 'yes', 'no' or categories such as

strongly agree	agree	don't know/ no opinion	disagree	strongly disagree

where you can put a tick in one of the boxes.

If you want a numerical answer, you can also include different boxes to be ticked.
e.g. How much sleep did you have last night ?

less than 6 hours	between 6 and 8 hours	between 8 and 10 hours	between 10 and 12 hours	over 12 hours

It is a good idea to try out your questionnaire on a few people first to see if it is clear enough and likely to give you the data you need, or whether it needs improving. This is called a **Pilot survey**.

5   You will get biased answers if you phrase your questions in the wrong way.
e.g. 'Most sensible people would say that teenagers should be allowed to choose their own clothes. Do you agree ?'
To disagree here would imply that you were not sensible! A fairer way to ask the question would be
'Do you think that teenagers should be allowed to choose their own clothes ?'

Yes	
No	
Don't know	

6. When you have collected all the data, you can make a summary of it, using lists or tables. You should then study it. It is often clearer if you draw statistical diagrams. You may want to do some calculations, such as finding means (averages) and ranges of the data.

7.   You should study your results and write down any conclusions you can make
      from them.

Note   Choose your investigation carefully and check with your teacher and your
parents before you go ahead. You should not approach strangers unless your teacher is
supervising you. If you are doing an observation on a busy road then do be careful to
keep well away from the road. Out-of-doors it is sensible to be with friends, not alone.
In school hours your teacher should be in charge of you. Out of school hours your
parents should know where you are and what you are doing.

Exercise 6.2

1.   Here is a table to show the staff employed by a firm.

Employees on 1st January each year

	Men	Women	Total
1988			
1989			
1990			

Copy and fill in the table, using this information.
On 1 Jan 1988 the company had 500 employees of which 320 were male.
During the year, 80 employees left, 60 of these being men, but there were 60 new
employees of which 48 were men.
During 1989, 40 men and 20 women left, and the only new employees were 8
men and 12 women.
Calculate the percentage decrease in the total number of employees from 1 Jan
88 to 1 Jan 90.

2. A firm sold two models of a product, standard and de-luxe, and they made them
    in three colours, red, green and blue.
    A salesman took the orders shown below.
    R (red), G (green), B (blue), S (standard), D (de-luxe).

    GS   BS   BS   RS   GD   RS   BS   RD   RD   GD   RS   RS

    RD   BS   GD   GD   BS   GS   RD   BS   RS   RD   RS   RD

    RD   BS   BD   RS   RD   RD   GD   RD   BD   RS   RS   BD

    RS   GS   BS   RD   RS   RD   GD   RS   GD   GS   GS   RD

    BD   GD   RS   RD   RD   RS   BD   BD   BD   RD   BS   RS

    Design a table for him to use to record the orders by tally marks, and fill it in.
    Make another table showing the number of orders for each item, and also
    showing the totals for standard models and de-luxe models, and the totals for red,
    green and blue models, with a final total of all the orders.

3. The owners of a local newspaper, *News
    Extra*, wish to obtain information on any
    improvements that could be made to
    increase the sales of the paper. They
    decide to send out a questionnaire, asking
    the following questions:
    1   What is your name ?
    2   Do you like *News Extra* ?
    3   What feature of *News Extra* do you
            read first ?
    4   Do you read a morning newspaper ?
    5   Do you like sport ?
    6   What kind of work do you do ?
    7   What is your income group ?

    Are these questions suitable ? Where necessary, replace them by more useful
    ones.

4. Your Council would like to build a sports centre, library and restaurant all on one
    site in your district. The Council needs to know whether these facilities would be
    used by local people, and how often. They also want to know how much car
    parking space would be necessary.
    Design a questionnaire which could be sent to each household in the district, to
    get the information.
    Fill in the answers for your own family.

Exercise 6.3   Applications and Activities

Here are some ideas for statistical investigations. You may decide on different ones which are topical or more relevant to your school or area. For instance, if at your school it is planned to change the school uniform then you could gather opinions by designing a questionnaire, collecting replies to it and analysing the results.

1.   You may decide to find out how you and your friends spend your time on an average weekday, and on Saturdays and Sundays.
      Design a questionnaire for obtaining the information.
      Design a table to record the times spent sleeping, eating, at school, on homework, watching TV, etc.
      Summarize the information.
      Analyse the data by drawing diagrams, and finding average times.
      Comment on the data. Do you think the times are satisfactory ? Is there any way you can improve your lifestyles ?

2.   You decide to find out how you and your friends spend (or save) your pocket money. (Your friends must be willing to do this with you.)
      Design a questionnaire for obtaining the information. You will have to record this for about 4 weeks.
      Summarize the information.
      Find the average amounts per week for each person.
      Analyse the data by drawing diagrams.
      You will have to decide how to cope with the fact that you do not all have equal pocket money. Perhaps you might work out the percentages spent on each item.
      Complete the investigation and comment on the data. Are you satisfied with how you spend your money, or could you make better use of it ?

3.   Make a survey of the TV viewing habits and preferences of children of your age.
      1   Decide on some aim or aims for the survey.
      2   Design a questionnaire to give you the required information. (Do not have too many questions, have a maximum of 10.)
      3   Decide how many children you want in your sample, and explain how you will choose them.
      4   Carry out the survey and analyse the results. Show them by diagrams and averages.
      5   Comment on the results of the survey.
      You could do a similar survey with adults, and compare their replies with those of the children.

4.   Are there more goals scored in the Scottish Divisions than in the English/Welsh Divisions of the top football leagues ?
      Carry out an investigation, using the results in the newspaper over a few weeks. Comment on the results.
      Think of other investigations you can do, also using the football results.

5.   **The Average Person in your class**
      If there are girls and boys in your class, find separate averages so that you have 'the average girl' and 'the average boy'.
      This is just a bit of fun! We often hear the media talk about the average family which has 2.2 children, so you can see what your average member is like.
      Organise the collection of data in a suitable way, so that each person is collecting one set of statistics and everybody's own statistics are included.
      For certain things the mean can be worked out, e.g. height, weight, number of brothers, number of sisters, size of shoes, length of handspan, length of hair, time of bedtime, amount of pocket money, number of pets. As well as working out the mean and range you can make a frequency distribution of the data and show it on a histogram or vertical bar chart.
      You can also collect data of favourite sport, colour, food, subject at school; ways of travelling to school, type of house or flat, colour of hair, etc. You cannot find the averages of these but you can show the results on bar charts or pie charts.
      Make a poster with a drawing of the average person and attach labels giving details of height, weight, etc. Put the histograms and charts on the poster.

PUZZLES

12.   Copy and complete this magic square. All rows and columns add up to 34, and so do the four corners, the four centre squares and the main diagonals. When complete all numbers from 1 to 16 are used.

13			2
	1		
	15		
		5	16

13.   All the trains from our station go to Kirton. From Kirton, some go on to Ashley, others, to Dunster and then on to Elmridge; others, again, to Haymills and on to Lenham. The fare is £8 to Ashley, Elmridge or Lenham; elsewhere it is only £5.
      Elizabeth is in a hurry. She has bought a £5 ticket. The first train to come was going to Elmridge, but Elizabeth did not get in.
      What was Elizabeth's destination ?

Miscellaneous Section A

Aural Practice

Often in life you will need to do quick calculations without using pencil and paper or calculator. Sometimes you will **see** the numbers written down, and sometimes you will just **hear** the questions. These aural exercises will give you some practice in **listening** to questions.

These aural exercises, A1 and A2, should be read to you, probably by your teacher or a friend, and you should write down the answers only, doing any working out in your head. You should do the 15 questions within 10 minutes.

Exercise A1

1. What are the next two numbers in the sequence 100, 94, 88, 82, 76, . . . ?

2. What is the cost of 500 oranges at 12 pence each ?

3. Write down an approximate value for the product of 39 and 41.

4. 6 angles meet at a point. How big are they if they are all equal ?

5. In the number 5.842, what is the value of the digit 4 ?

6. 5 people share equally a bill for £26. How much does each one pay ?

7. Simplify the expression $6a \times 5b$

8. How many cakes, each using 250 g of flour, can be made from a 3 kg bag of flour ?

9. In 3 tests a girl got 15, 12 and 6 marks. What was her average mark ?

10. I think of a number, multiply it by 4 and subtract 7. The answer is 93. What was the number I thought of ?

11. Three angles of a quadrilateral are each 100°. What is the size of the fourth angle ?

12. If bus fares are increased by 10%, what is the new fare when the old fare was 70 pence ?

13. A bus leaves town at 12.35 pm. The journey to the village takes 45 minutes. At what time should the bus arrive there ?

14. What is the value of $10^2 - 5^2$?

15. The cost of a fairground ride for an adult is 80 pence and children pay half-price. How much would it cost for a mother and her 3 children to go on the ride ?

Exercise A2

1. Write in figures, four million and fourteen.

2. Find the value of x if $x + 18 = 4x$.

3. A sale is advertised as '$\frac{1}{4}$ off all prices'. What percentage is taken off each price ?

4. Write down an estimated whole number answer to the question 8.9 × 2.1.

5. If the temperature is $-5°$ Celsius and rises in the morning by 9 degrees, what is the new temperature ?

6. Write down the next 2 terms in the sequence beginning with 3, 5, 9; where the rule is 'Double the last number and subtract 1'.

7. What is the name for a quadrilateral with just one pair of sides parallel ?

8. Write down an expression for the number of centimetres in d metres.

9. 2 angles in a triangle are 40° and 45°. How big is the 3rd angle ?

10. What is the cost of 5 pairs of socks at 99 pence per pair ?

11. Which is the bigger number, 0.18 or 0.081 ?

12. If today's date is 24th September, what will the date be on the same day next week ?

13. A field is 128 m long. What is this length correct to 2 significant figures ?

14. What is three-fifths as a decimal ?

15. A car travels 140 miles on 4 gallons of petrol. How many miles per gallon is this ?

Exercise A3   Revision

1.   Find the value of 409^2
     1   by using long multiplication,
     2   by using the formula $409^2 = 400^2 + 9^2 + (2 \times 9 \times 400)$,
     3   by using your calculator.

2.   In the diagram, **PQR** is an isosceles triangle with **PQ** = **PR** and ∠**PQR** = 72°.
     PQST and **PRUV** are squares.
     Find the size of angle **TPV**.

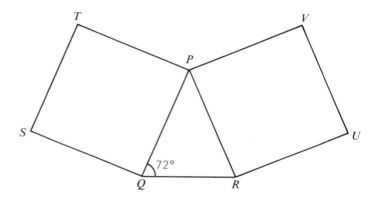

3.   What is 50 m as a fraction of $2\frac{1}{2}$ km ?

4.   For what value of x is the expression $9x - 11$ equal to the value of the
     expression $7x - 8$?

5.   Mr Kirkham's car will run for about 8 miles on 1 litre of petrol, and petrol costs
     45p per litre. What is the approximate cost for a journey of 160 miles ?

6.   Sketch these figures and mark in any axes of symmetry. Say how many axes of
     symmetry each figure has.
     1   Right-angled isosceles triangle,
     2   equilateral triangle,
     3   parallelogram,
     4   rhombus,
     5   square.

7.   If $f = \dfrac{v^2 - u^2}{2s}$, find the value of f when $v = 30$, $u = 24$ and $s = 18$.

8.   A man who owes £8800 says that he can only pay 65p for each £1 he owes.
     How much will he pay altogether ?

9. In the diagram, $AB = AC$ and $BC = CD$.
    Find the sizes of
    1 $\angle ABC$
    2 $\angle BCD$
    3 $\angle DBC$
    4 $\angle ABD$.

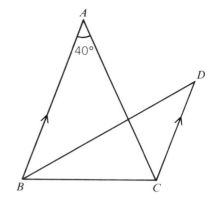

10. Mrs Knight's annual salary was £15 000 until she was given a pay rise of 6%. What was her new salary ?
    At the end of the next year she heard that the firm was going to increase all wages by 4%. What would her new salary be then ?

11. The temperature readings taken at noon each day during a winter week in a town are shown in the table.
    1 How much did the temperature rise between Sunday and Monday ?
    2 What was the average daily noon temperature for the week ?

Sun	$-5°C$
Mon	$2°C$
Tues	$-5°C$
Wed	$0°C$
Thur	$3°C$
Fri	$2°C$
Sat	$-4°C$

12. Assuming that 1 m = 39.3708 inches, express 1 km in yards, correct to the nearest yard. (1 yard = 36 inches)

13. An old recipe for making jam says that you should use $\frac{3}{4}$ lb of sugar for every 1 lb of fruit.
    How much sugar would you need if you had bought 10 lb of fruit ?

14. Find an expression for the total cost of x packets of sweets at 15 pence per packet and 10 packets of sweets at x pence per packet,
    1 in pence,
    2 in £'s.

15.   One number in each of these sequences is incorrect. Copy the sequences,
      replacing the wrong number by the correct number.
      1   100, 92, 84, 76, 66, 60.
      2   1, 3, 6, 9, 15, 21, 28.
      3   1, 4, 9, 15, 25, 36.
      4 $1, 4\frac{1}{2}, 9, 13\frac{1}{2}, 18, 22\frac{1}{2}$.
      5   1, 6, 27, 64, 125, 216.

16.   A greengrocer buys tomatoes at 72p per
      lb, and sells some of them at 90p per lb.
      What percentage profit does he make on
      these ?
      Some of the tomatoes are not top quality
      and he sells these at 60p per lb.
      What percentage loss does he make on
      these ?

17.   The weight of 1 ml of water is 1 g. What is the weight, in kg, of 5 litres of
      water ?

18.   The table shows the average daily hours of sunshine over the month for the 12
      months of a year, at a weather station.
      Plot the data on a line-graph, and comment on it.

Jan	Feb	Mar	Apl	May	Jun	Jly	Aug	Sep	Oct	Nov	Dec
1.6	1.7	3.6	5.4	5.6	8.5	8.3	8.3	3.6	2.2	2.1	1.9

19.   Peter said 'I am three times as old as my brother, but in 6 years time I will only
      be twice as old as him'.
      If Peter's brother's age **now** is x years, how old is Peter, in terms of x ?
      How old will they each be, in 6 years time ?
      Write down an equation and solve it to find their ages now.

20.   Construct this quadrilateral, beginning by
      drawing AB, $\angle A$ and AD. Use compasses
      to find point C. Join AC, and measure it,
      to the nearest mm.

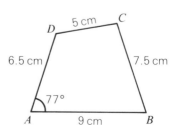

Exercise A4   Activities

1. **Sums and differences, products and squares**

    Choose any two numbers. Let the larger one be x and the smaller one be y.
    Make a table like this.

x	y	$x + y$	$x - y$	xy	$(x + y)^2$	$(x - y)^2$	$(x + y)^2 - (x - y)^2$
20	13	33	7	260	1089	49	1040
5	2	7	3	10	49	9	40

    Column (6) is column (3) squared,
    column (7) is column (4) squared,
    column (8) is column (6)—column (7).

    Repeat with other pairs of numbers.

    Can you find any connection between column (8) and one of the other
    columns ?

2. **A booklet about measuring and weighing**

    Make a booklet suitable for teaching a younger child about metric measures and
    weights.
    Use 3 or 4 pieces of plain A4 paper, folded in half and stitched or stapled
    together to make a booklet of A5 size.
    Design an attractive title page.
    Then use the next few pages to explain about length, with simple explanations
    of millimetres, centimetres, metres and kilometres, and examples of some
    lengths. Illustrate these with pictures.
    Continue with weights, and then capacity.
    You can include suitable questions, or puzzles, and cartoon-type drawings.
    If you do this as a class activity you could have a display of your booklets.
    You may like to make a photocopy of your booklet to keep for yourself, and
    then give the original to a younger brother, sister or friend.

3. **Inside a quadrilateral**

    Draw neatly a quadrilateral $ABCD$ of irregular shape. Find the mid-points of the
    sides, labelling these in order, P, Q, R, S. Join PQ, QR, RS, SP.

    What can you discover about the quadrilateral $PQRS$?

    Repeat, beginning with other quadrilaterals of different sizes and shapes, and see
    if your discoveries apply in every case.

4.   **Seven**

Seven seems such a special number that you may like to collect facts about it and present them in a booklet or on a poster.
See what you can find out from reference books and write about them.

Here are some ideas which you can give more details about.

7 days in a week,
7 colours of the rainbow,
7 wonders of the world,
7th son of a 7th son,
7 dwarfs,
7 virtues,
7 deadly sins,
the seven seas,
7 league boots,
7 bodies in alchemy,
7 champions of Christendom,
7 Bibles,
7 letters for the notes in music.
'As I was going to St Ives,
I met a man with seven wives,
. . .'

Muddy Waters

On the 7th hour,
On the 7th day,
On the 7th month,
The 7 doctors say,
He was born for good
luck.

(From a blues song by Muddy Waters)

. **pattern with 7 stars**

What is the probability of getting the sum of 7 when you throw two dice ? How does this compare with the probabilities of other scores ?

As in question 23 on page 85 you can investigate the decimal equivalents for $\frac{1}{7}$, $\frac{2}{7}$, etc.
When you divide 1.0000000 by 7, what are the remainders at each stage ? Write these down and add the 1st and 4th, 2nd and 5th, and 3rd and 6th of these numbers.

Find the words for number 7 in different languages and compare them. In Greek it is *hepta*, in Latin *septem*, and in Anglo-Saxon it was *seofan*.
(Why is September so called, when it is the ninth month ?)
What other words, linked with 7, do you know, beginning with 'sept' or 'hept' ?

5. **Planning for Christmas**

(If you and your family do not celebrate Christmas, there is probably another festival time at which you gather together and give gifts to each other, so make your plans for that.)

When you were a small child, you probably thought of Christmas as a time when Santa Claus came mysterious'y in the night and left presents for you.

Perhaps this year, as you are a little older, you can think of Christmas as a time of goodwill, and plan how you can do your share of giving, to make others happy. If you are truly penniless, you can still make others happy by giving some of your time and effort in other ways.

Do you plan to send any Christmas cards ? If so, to whom ? How many ? Work out the cost of the cards and the stamps. (No, you can't expect your mother to buy the cards that you will send!) You can reduce the cost of postage by delivering some cards by hand, and you can send attractive home-made cards instead of buying them.

Do you plan to give any presents ? Make a list of your family and friends to whom you would like to give presents, and beside each name write down a suggestion for a gift and the approximate amount you will spend. Add up the costs to get a total.

In your plans, remember to include any elderly relatives or neighbours who may be lonely at Christmas and who would be so happy to get a card or a small gift from you. You may also want to give something to your Church or to charities who collect specially at that time.

Now, do you have enough money ? Can you save enough by Christmas ? Decide how much of your pocket money you will have to save each week between now and then.

If the sum you need is too much, you will have to alter your plans. Perhaps you can make some gifts instead of buying them. Perhaps you can do some jobs at home to earn some money.

Whatever you do, make your plans in good time, and have an enjoyable Christmas.

6.   **Stars for Christmas decorations**

These do-it-yourself stars can be made
from thin cardboard and do not need
glueing. They can be pulled apart for
storage.

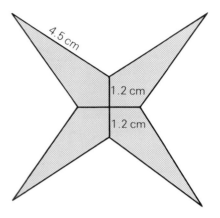

Make a pattern on tracing paper. The cross in the centre is 2.4 cm wide and long.
Draw that first. Then use compasses radius 4.5 cm to find the 4 outer points. You
can vary the measurements if you want to make larger stars.

Copy the pattern onto cardboard by putting the cardboard underneath the pattern
and pricking through the main points using your compasses. (Put something
underneath to protect the desk.) Then join these points. You need 2 whole pieces
A and B and 2 part pieces for C and D.

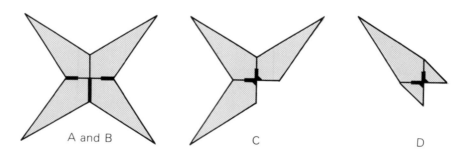

Cut out the 4 pieces.
Make slots as shown. The small ones go exactly halfway. Slots should be wide
enough to fit the thickness of the cardboard between them. Cut off small points
on C and D as shown, to make assembly easier.
Fit the large slot of A into the large slot of B. Fit the 2 slots of C into 1 slot of A
and 1 slot of B. Fit the 2 slots of D into the other slots of A and B.

Make the stars in different colours or paint them. You can spray glitter on them.
Hang them up using cotton thread.

7. **Moebius bands**

These are long strips of paper glued
together at the ends to form a loop.
The paper used in cash machines (till rolls)
is quite suitable to use, or you can get a
large sheet of paper, such as wrapping
paper, and cut it into strips about 5 cm
wide. You can join two or more strips
together if you need a larger loop.
By making one or more twists in the paper
before you join the loop you get different
kinds of bands.

Carry out each investigation on bands with no twists, 1 twist, 2 twists, 3 twists
and 4 twists.

1 Has the band a one-sided or a two-sided surface ? Draw a line with crayon
down the centre of the strip. Does the line go along both sides of the band
before you get back to the beginning ? If so, it has a one-sided surface.

2 How many edges has the band ? Draw along one edge and continue until
you get back to the beginning. Has the other edge been marked as well ? If
so the band has only one edge.

3 Predict what will happen when you cut a band lengthways down a centre
line. Will it fall into two loops or stay as one loop ? If there are two loops,
are they interlocked ? What about the lengths of the loops compared with the
original ? What about their width ? How many twists have they ? How many
surfaces and edges have they ?

4 Check your answers to **3** by doing the investigation.

5 Predict what will happen when you cut a strip lengthways along a line which
is $\frac{1}{3}$ of the width across, repeating the questions of **3**.

6 Check your answers by doing the investigation.

7 Make a summary of your results in a table, and comment on them. Is there a
general pattern in them ?

8 Moebius was a mathematician who lived in the 19th century. Look in
reference books and see what you can find out about him.

Perhaps you can make a poster about Moebius bands.

8. **Make a guess-the-number game to puzzle your friends**

You need 6 pieces of cardboard 8 cm square. On one piece you will write on both sides.

Mark the pieces like this. Write YES and NO on the cards, as shown.

The shaded parts are 4 cm long and the width, in cm, is marked.

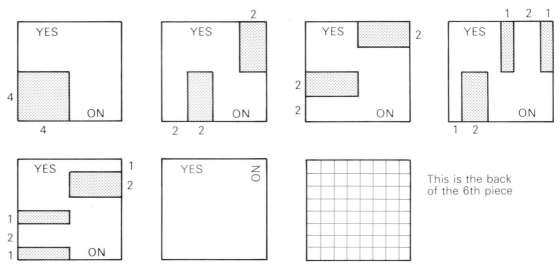

This is the back of the 6th piece

Cut out the shaded parts on the first five squares.

In the small squares on the back of the sixth card, write numbers from 1 to 64, choosing places to put them at random, but those in the quarters shown here as B and C write sideways, the same way up as B and C are shown here.

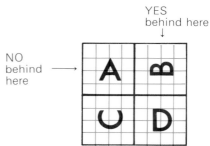

Put card 1 down with YES at the top. Put card 6 on top of it with YES at the top. Turn both cards over together and make a list of all the numbers you can see (through the cut-out part of card 1).

Then put card 1 down with YES at the top and put card 6 on top of it with NO at the top. Turn both cards over together and add to your list all the numbers you can see now.

Sort out these numbers in order of size and write them down neatly on card 1, below YES.

Repeat in turn for cards 2 to 5, each with card 6.

For card 6, write down all the numbers in quarters A and D. These are the ones the same way up as YES on the other side. After sorting them, write them down below YES.

Your game is now complete.

Ask your friend to choose a number between 1 and 64 but not to tell you what it is.

Show him/her card 1 and ask if the number is listed on it. If YES, put YES at the top, if not, turn the card round and put NO at the top. Repeat with cards 2 to 5, piling them neatly on top of card 1. Finally repeat with card 6. Note that for NO on this card you only turn the card sideways, not upside down.

Pick the pile up with the back of the cards facing you, not your friend, and as you straighten them together, just glance at the back and you will see just one number showing.

If you have done this correctly, this will be the chosen number.

Put the pile of cards down (face upwards) and appear to be thinking about the number, then announce what it is.

9. **Using the computer**

If you have the use of a computer at home or at school, then you can use it in your mathematical activities.

Maybe you can write your own programs, or maybe you will use commercially-produced spreadsheet programs, database programs and other mathematical programs.

If possible, use a printer to keep a record of the work you do with the computer.

1   We have already suggested using a computer to help with investigations into the Fibonacci sequence. You can also produce many other sequences and patterns and investigate their properties. Recurring decimals of fractions such as $\frac{1}{17}$ and $\frac{1}{19}$ can be investigated.

2   The data from statistical investigations can be stored using a computer database program or spreadsheet program. It can be sorted, counted and studied. Averages and ranges can be calculated, and data can be represented graphically. You could also design a questionnaire to be shown on a computer. Those answering it would enter their answers simply by pressing suitable keys. The computer could be programmed to count each type of answer and list the results.

3   Quadrilaterals of various kinds can be drawn and their properties studied. You can make a series of small changes in lengths or angles of a figure drawn on the screen, and notice the effect on the original figure. For instance, you can turn a parallelogram into a rhombus by making the longer sides grow gradually smaller, and notice the changes in the angles between the diagonals.

7 Thinking about ratio

Dividing money

When money is shared out, it is not necessarily shared out in equal amounts. One person could get more than another, for various reasons. For instance, if two people do a piece of work, and one works for 7 hours and the other for 4 hours, then the price for doing the job could be split between them in the ratio 7 : 4. This means that the first person gets $\frac{7}{11}$ of the total and the other one gets $\frac{4}{11}$.

Mixing quantities
Concrete

There is a similar idea when mixing quantities. For instance, cement, sand and gravel have to be mixed to make concrete, but not in equal amounts. One type of concrete uses these materials in the ratio 1 : 2 : 4 by volume. This means mixing 1 bucketful of cement with 2 bucketfuls of sand and 4 bucketfuls of gravel, but different ratios are needed for other strengths of concrete, depending on what it has to be used for.

Liquids

Liquids are diluted by mixing them with water, again in a certain ratio, e.g. to dilute condensed milk to the strength of fresh milk it should be mixed with water in the ratio 2 : 3.

Coins are made at the Royal Mint, Llantrisant, South Wales.

Metals

Metals are mixed in certain ratios to make alloys.

For 1 penny and 2 pence coins, copper, zinc and tin are mixed in the ratio 194 : 5 : 1.

For 50 pence, 10 pence and 5 pence coins, copper and nickel are mixed in the ratio 3 : 1, but for the 20 pence coins the ratio is 21 : 4.

The £1 coin uses copper, nickel and zinc in the ratio 140 : 11 : 49.

Photographs, maps and plans

When photographs are enlarged, every length on the photo is increased in the same ratio, otherwise the enlargement would not be similar to the original. The same idea applies to drawings. In maps and plans every length on the actual area or solid object is reduced in the same ratio.

The scale used for Ordnance Survey maps is 1 : 50 000 so 1 cm on the map represents 50 000 cm (which is 500 m) on the actual ground.

7 Ratio

The fraction $\frac{5}{6}$ can be written as a **ratio** in the form 5 : 6.
(This is read as 5 to 6.)

Ratio is a useful way of comparing two (or more) quantities.

e.g. If the ratio of weight of object A : weight of object B = 4 : 5,
then A weighs $\frac{4}{5}$ as much as B,

B weighs $1\frac{1}{4}$ times as much as A, (since $\frac{5}{4} = 1\frac{1}{4}$)

or, in decimals,
A's weight = B's weight × 0.8 (since $\frac{4}{5} = 0.8$)

B's weight = A's weight × 1.25 (since $\frac{5}{4} = 1.25$)

or, in percentages,
A's weight is 80% of B's weight (since $\frac{4}{5} = 80\%$)

B's weight is 125% of A's weight (since $\frac{5}{4} = 125\%$)

Ratios have no units, they are just numbers.

If weight of object A : weight of object B = 4 : 5, then
if we know B's weight in grams, we can find A's weight in grams,
if we know B's weight in lb, we can find A's weight in lb, and so on.

In each case we use the ratio 4 : 5 so we multiply B's weight by $\frac{4}{5}$, 0.8 or 80%.

Examples

1 Express 50 cm : $1\frac{1}{4}$ m as a ratio in its simplest form.

First, find this ratio as a fraction in its simplest form, and then re-write the answer in ratio form.

$$\frac{50 \text{ cm}}{1\frac{1}{4} \text{ m}} = \frac{50 \text{ cm}}{125 \text{ cm}} = \frac{50}{125} = \frac{2}{5}$$

The ratio is 2 : 5
This means that 50 cm is $\frac{2}{5}$ of $1\frac{1}{4}$ m.

It also means that $1\frac{1}{4}$ m is $2\frac{1}{2}$ times 50 cm (since $\frac{5}{2}$ is $2\frac{1}{2}$).

2 What is the ratio length : breadth in this rectangle ?

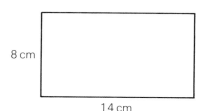

8 cm

14 cm

$$\frac{\text{Length}}{\text{Breadth}} = \frac{14 \text{ cm}}{8 \text{ cm}} = \frac{14}{8} = \frac{7}{4}$$

Ratio, length : breadth = 7 : 4
This means that the length is $1\frac{3}{4}$ times as long as the breadth (since $\frac{7}{4} = 1\frac{3}{4}$).

It also means that the breadth is $\frac{4}{7}$ of the length.

3 A pygmy shrew weighs 3 g, an elephant weighs 9 tonnes. What is the ratio of their weights ?

$$\frac{\text{Weight of shrew}}{\text{Weight of elephant}} = \frac{3 \text{ g}}{9 \text{ tonnes}} = \frac{3 \text{ g}}{9\,000\,000 \text{ g}} = \frac{1}{3\,000\,000}$$

Ratio, weight of shrew : weight of elephant = 1 : 3 000 000
This means that the weight of the shrew is a three-millionth of the weight of the elephant.
It also means that the elephant weighs three million times as much as the shrew.

4 Divide £36 in the ratio 3 : 5.

3 : 5 gives 8 parts
1 part is $\dfrac{£36}{8}$ = £4.50
The shares are 3 × £4.50 and 5 × £4.50, i.e. £13.50 and £22.50.

5 The weights of two sizes of model airplane are in the ratio 1 : 8.
If the smaller model weighs 200 g, what is the weight of the larger one ?

The larger one weighs 8 times as much as the smaller one, this is
8 × 200 g = 1600 g = 1.6 kg.

6 Increase 60 kg in the ratio 7 : 3.

The new weight is $\frac{7}{3}$ of 60 kg
$\frac{1}{3}$ of 60 kg = 20 kg
$\frac{7}{3}$ of 60 kg = 7 × 20 kg = 140 kg
The new weight is 140 kg.

7   Decrease £100 in the ratio 5 : 8.

The new amount is $\frac{5}{8}$ of £100
$\frac{1}{8}$ of £100 = £12.50
$\frac{5}{8}$ of £100 = 5 × £12.50 = £62.50
The new amount is £62.50.

There can be more than two quantities expressed as a ratio. In this case you cannot write them as a fraction.

8   What is the ratio of the amounts £2, £2.50, £3.75, in its simplest form ?

Working in pence, the amounts are 200p, 250p, 375p.
The ratio is 200 : 250 : 375
To get the ratio in its simplest form, divide all three numbers by 25.
The ratio is 8 : 10 : 15.

9   The angles of a quadrilateral are in the ratio 1 : 3 : 7 : 9. Find their sizes.

1 : 3 : 7 : 9 gives 20 parts
The sum of the angles is 360°
1 part is $\frac{360°}{20}$ = 18°
The angles are 1 × 18°, 3 × 18°, 7 × 18° and 9 × 18°, i.e. 18°, 54°, 126° and 162°.
(If the angles are listed in order, what sort of quadrilateral is it ?)

Exercise 7.1

1.   Express as ratios in their simplest forms
   1   36 cm : 81 cm   **4**   2.4 kg : 3.6 kg
   2   £1.05 : 75p   **5**   2 litres : 500 ml
   3   20 minutes : 2 hours

2.   **1**   Divide 84p in the ratio 2 : 5
   2   Divide £1.64 in the ratio 1 : 3
   3   Divide £280 in the ratio 5 : 3
   4   Divide £1.32 in the ratio 7 : 4
   5   Divide £6 in the ratio 5 : 7

3.   **1**   Increase £330 in the ratio 4 : 3
   2   Increase £23 in the ratio 3 : 1
   3   Increase £60 in the ratio 8 : 5
   4   Increase £250 in the ratio 11 : 10
   5   Increase £12 in the ratio 9 : 2

4. **1**   Decrease 150 cm in the ratio 3 : 5
    2   Decrease 18 kg in the ratio 5 : 9
    3   Decrease $3\frac{1}{2}$ hours in the ratio 4 : 7
    4   Decrease 1 gallon in the ratio 5 : 8
    5   Decrease £2.60 in the ratio 1 : 10

5. Express as ratios in their simplest forms
    1   75p : £1.20 : £1.80
    2   132 cm : 165 cm : 220 cm
    3   45 min : 1 hr 30 min : 2 hr 15 min
    4   45° : 63° : 72°
    5   1.5 kg : 2.7 kg : 3.3 kg

6. **1**   Divide £270 in the ratio 2 : 3 : 4
    2   Divide 5.5 m in the ratio 1 : 4 : 6
    3   Divide 2 litres in the ratio 2 : 3 : 5
    4   Divide 4 kg in the ratio 5 : 7 : 8
    5   Divide £1.25 in the ratio 6 : 9 : 10

7. The edges of two model statues are 6 cm and 7.5 cm. Find the ratio of the edges, in its simplest form.

8. The sides of a triangle are in the ratio 3 : 5 : 7. The longest side is 21 cm. What are the lengths of the other sides ? What is the length of the perimeter of the triangle ?

9. A line AB of length 8 cm is divided at P
    so that $AP : PB$ = 3 : 7.
    Find the length of AP.

10. On a map of scale 1 : 500 000 the distance between two towns is 11 cm. Find the actual distance in km.

11. A sum of money was divided into two parts in the ratio 5 : 2. The larger share was £10.50. What was the total amount of money ?

12. A map scale is shown as '1 cm represents 2 km'. What is the scale shown in ratio form ?

13. The scale of a map is 1 : 25 000. How far apart on the map are two villages which are actually 12 km from each other ?

14. What is the ratio of 9 inches : 2 feet, in its simplest form ?

15. Express as a fraction in its simplest form the ratio 210 g : 2.8 kg.

16. If $AX : XB$ = 5 : 7 and AX = 3.5 cm,
    what is the length of AB ?

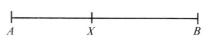

17.   Three children whose ages are 7, 8 and 10 years divided £75 in proportion to their ages. What did they each receive ?

18.   The angles of a triangle are in the ratio 3 : 4 : 5. Find their sizes.

Exercise 7.2   Applications and Activities

1.   To make gunmetal, copper, tin and zinc are used in the ratio 43 : 5 : 2. What quantities of tin and zinc are used with 86 kg of copper ?

2.   A shortbread recipe uses flour, butter, sugar and nuts in the ratio, by weight, of 9 : 6 : 3 : 2. How much of each ingredient is used in making 1 kg of the mixture ?

3.   A concrete mixture is made by mixing cement, sand and gravel, by volume, in the ratio 1 : 2 : 4. If 2 m³ of gravel is used, how much cement and sand must be added ?

4.   A group of men invested money in a business and shared the profits in the same ratio as their investments. One man invested £3000 and received £750 from the profits. What did another man invest if he received £1250 from the profits ?

5.   In a class of 28 children the ratio of number of boys to number of girls is 3 : 4. Find how many boys and how many girls there are in the class. After 1 girl leaves, what is the new ratio boys : girls, in its lowest terms ?

6.   In a particular examination, the marks are divided in the ratio 4 : 1 between the written examination and the practical work. If the total exam mark is 100%, what percentage mark is given for the practical work ?

7.   Orange squash is diluted by mixing 1 part of squash with 4 parts of water. What is this, expressed as a ratio ?
How much diluted squash can be made from a 2 litre bottle of squash ?
A glass holds 160 ml of liquid. How much (undiluted) squash should be supplied, to provide 100 drinks ?

8. A school collected £240 for charity. It was decided to divide the money among 3 charities, A, B and C, according to the votes received for each. The votes were as follows:- for A 120, for B 200, for C 160.
    Express the votes for A, B and C as a ratio in its simplest form.
    Find how much money was sent to each charity.

9. Two painters charge £175 for painting a building. Bob works for 11 hours and Derek works for 14 hours. They split the money in the same ratio as the number of hours they have worked. How much extra does Derek earn than Bob ?

10. Two sizes of packets of soap powder contain 2.4 kg and 3.0 kg. Express these amounts as a ratio in its simplest form. If the smaller packet costs £2.80, what would be the equivalent cost for the larger packet ?

PUZZLES

14. Swinging their tomahawks, the Big Indian and the Little Indian came striding down the road.
    The Little Indian was the son of the Big Indian.
    Yet the Big Indian was not the father of the Little Indian.

    Can you explain how this is ?

15. **A sliding block puzzle**

    Make 9 pieces, using plywood, or cardboard. The six rectangles measure 4 cm by 2 cm, one square has sides of 4 cm and the other two pieces are squares of side 2 cm.
    Make a rectangular base to put them on. This should be just slightly larger than 10 cm by 8 cm. Arrange the 9 pieces on the base as shown in the diagram.
    By sliding the pieces into empty spaces, and keeping them inside the rectangle, you should move the large square to the bottom left-hand corner of the rectangle.

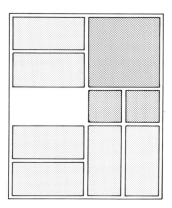

8 Thinking about polygons

What is a polygon ?

After giving special study to 3-sided figures (triangles) and 4-sided figures (quadrilaterals), we deal with all the other figures with straight sides together and call them polygons.

What is the meaning of the word polygon ?

What other words begin with the letters 'poly', for a similar reason ?

What are the special names given to polygons with 5, 6, 7, 8 and 10 sides ?

Convex and re-entrant polygons

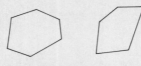

convex polygons

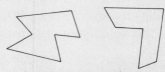

re-entrant polygons

How would you explain the difference between convex and re-entrant polygons ?

Regular polygons

What is special about a regular polygon ?

What is the order of rotational symmetry of a regular polygon with n sides ?

Exterior angles of a convex polygon

Chalk a polygon on the floor. Start at a point of the polygon facing along one side and walk along the sides of the polygon in turn. At each point notice that you turn through the size of the exterior angle to get in the right direction to go along the next side. When you get back to the starting point end by facing in the original direction.

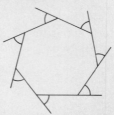

exterior angles

What is the total angle through which you have turned ?

What is the sum of the exterior angles of the polygon ?

Does the answer depend on how many sides the polygon has ?

Polygons split into triangles

5-sided   6-sided   7-sided   8-sided

What is the expression for the sum of the angles of the triangles which would be formed if the polygon had *n* sides ?

How can this method help you to find the sum of the angles of a polygon ?

What is an expression for the sum of the angles of a polygon with *n* sides ?

A natural example of regular hexagons

The old 3d coin had 12 edges. The 50p and 20p coins are 'curved regular heptagons'.

What sort of polygons are used in this design ?

8 Polygons

A **polygon** is a figure with straight sides.

Number of sides	Name
3	triangle
4	quadrilateral
5	pentagon
6	hexagon
7	heptagon
8	octagon

pentagon

hexagon

octagon

Regular Polygons

A regular polygon has all sides equal and all angles equal.

Number of sides	Name
3	equilateral triangle
4	square
5	regular pentagon
6	regular hexagon
7	regular heptagon
8	regular octagon

Regular polygons

pentagon

hexagon

heptagon

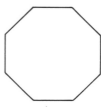

octagon

Sum of the angles in a polygon

Split the polygon into triangles as shown. The sum of the angles in each triangle is 180°. The number of triangles is 2 less than the number of sides of the polygon.

Pentagon

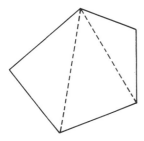

Hexagon

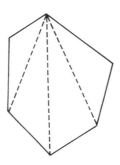

Heptagon

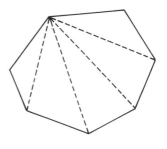

3 triangles
Sum of angles
in a pentagon
= 3 × 180°
= 540°

4 triangles
Sum of angles
in a hexagon
= 4 × 180°
= 720°

5 triangles
Sum of angles
in a heptagon
= 5 × 180°
= 900°

Copy and complete this pattern of results:

Name of polygon	Number of sides	Number of triangles made	Sum of angles in polygon
Pentagon	5	3	3 × 180° = 540°
Hexagon	6	4	4 × 180° = 720°
Heptagon	7	5	5 × 180° = 900°
Octagon	8	.	.
Nonagon	9	.	.
Decagon	10	.	.

Can you find a general formula for the sum s of the angles in a polygon with n sides ?

Size of each angle in a regular polygon

Copy and complete this table of results, using the previous table for the sum of the angles.

Name of regular polygon	Number of sides	Sum of angles of polygon	Each angle
Equilateral triangle	3	180°	180° ÷ 3 = 60°
Square	4	360°	360° ÷ 4 = 90°
Regular pentagon	5	540°	540° ÷ 5 = 108°
Regular hexagon			
Regular heptagon			
Regular octagon			
Regular nonagon			
Regular decagon			

If you have found a general formula for the sum of the angles of a polygon with n sides, use it to find a formula for the size of each angle in a regular polygon with n sides.

An alternative method to find the size of each angle in a regular polygon.

Exterior angles of a convex polygon are the angles formed when each side is produced (extended) in order.

The sum of the exterior angles is 360°.

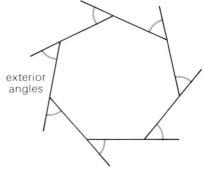

exterior angles

To find the size of an exterior angle in a **regular** polygon, divide 360° by 'number of sides'.

At each vertex,
    interior angle + exterior angle = 180°
so interior angle = 180° − exterior angle.

interior angle

exterior angle

Examples

1 Find the angles of a regular octagon.

Sum of the exterior angles = 360°
Each exterior angle = 360° ÷ 8 = 45°
Each interior angle = 180° − 45° = 135°

2 Find the angles of a regular 24-sided polygon.

Sum of the exterior angles = 360°
Each exterior angle = 360° ÷ 24 = 15°
Each interior angle = 180° − 15° = 165°

3 A regular polygon has interior angles of 160°. How many sides has it ?

Each exterior angle = 180° − 160° = 20°
Sum of exterior angles = 360°
Number of exterior angles = 360 ÷ 20 = 18
The polygon has 18 sides.

Exercise 8.1

1.

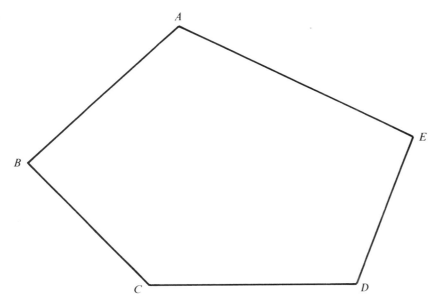

1 Measure the angles of this pentagon and find their sum.
2 Measure the sides of the pentagon, to the nearest mm, and find the perimeter.

2. Copy these polygons on tracing paper and draw on your figures any lines of symmetry.

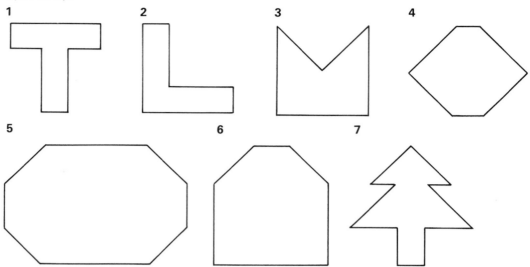

3. What is the name of the shape
    ABCDEFGH ?
    Put your ruler along *AD*.
    What is the name of the shape *ABCD* ?
    What is the name of the shape *ADEFGH* ?

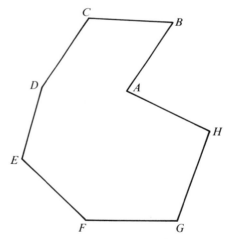

4. Using tracing paper, draw an equilateral triangle and a square, and copy the four regular polygons from page 124.
    On your figures mark any lines or points of symmetry.
    Copy and complete this table.

name of figure	number of axes of symmetry	Has it a point of symmetry ?	order of rotational symmetry
equilateral triangle square			
. . .			

    Is there a pattern in your answers?

5. **1** What is the sum of the angles of a pentagon ? Four of the angles of a pentagon are 72°, 112°, 126° and 144°. Find the size of the fifth angle.

2 What is the sum of the angles of a hexagon ? Five of the angles of a hexagon are 104°, 101°, 118°, 122° and 125°. Find the size of the sixth angle.

3 What is the sum of the angles of an octagon ? Five of the angles of an octagon are each 120°, two other angles are 155° and 160°. Find the size of the remaining angle.

4 Three of the angles of a pentagon are 110°, 120° and 130°. The other two angles are equal. Find their size.

5 Four of the angles of a hexagon are each 115°. One other angle is 90°. Find the size of the remaining angle.

6. **1** A regular polygon has 10 sides. What is the size of an exterior angle, and of an interior angle ?

2 A regular polygon has 45 sides. What is the size of an interior angle ?

3 A regular polygon has exterior angles of 30°. How many sides has it ?

4 A regular polygon has interior angles of 135°. What is the size of each exterior angle, and how many sides has the polygon ?

5 A regular polygon has interior angles of 162°. How many sides has it ?

7. **1** What is the sum of the exterior angles of a hexagon ?
Five of the exterior angles of a hexagon are 45°, 55°, 60°, 65° and 85°. Find the size of the sixth exterior angle.

2 Nine of the ten angles of a decagon are each 150°. What are the sizes of their exterior angles ? Find the size of the tenth exterior angle and hence find the size of the tenth interior angle.

3 Two sides of a regular pentagon are produced (extended) to meet at a point *P*.
Find the size of the exterior angle *a*.
Find the size of ∠ *P*.

4 If one of the exterior angles of an octagon is 80° and all the other exterior angles are equal, what is the size of one of them ?

5 If two of the exterior angles of a hexagon are each 80° and the other four exterior angles are equal, what is the size of one of them ?

8. *ABCDE* is a regular pentagon.
1 Find the size of angle *b*.
2 What kind of triangle is Δ*ABC* ?
3 Find the sizes of angles *a* and *c*.
4 Explain how you know that *AC* and *ED* are parallel.

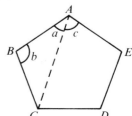

9.   Here are 2 flow charts for finding the size of each interior angle of a regular polygon.

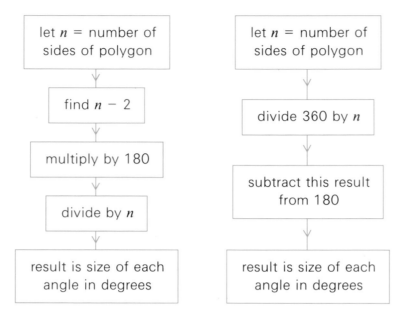

Use each flow chart to find the size of an interior angle in

1   a regular pentagon,   **2**   a regular 30-sided polygon.

10.   *ABCDEF* is a regular hexagon, *O* is the point of symmetry, and *AD*, *BE*, *CF* are axes of symmetry.

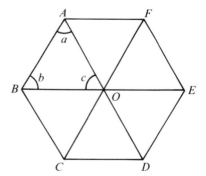

1   What is the size of an interior angle of the hexagon ?

2   Find the sizes of angles *a*, *b*, *c*.

3   What sort of triangle is Δ*AOB* ?

4   What sort of quadrilateral is *ABCO* ?

5   What sort of quadrilateral is *ABCD* ?

Geometric patterns

We see many examples of patterns in our daily lives.

Look for symmetry in buildings, and in natural objects such as flowers, trees, birds and animals.

Notice the patterns on wallpaper, fabric, flooring and brickwork.

Tessellations

Tessellations are patterns covering an area, made by using congruent shapes. ('Congruent' means 'exactly alike'.)

Here are some tessellations using rectangles.

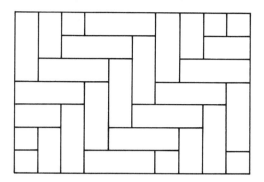 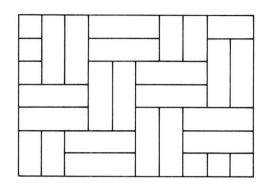

Here are some more examples using other figures.

triangles covering a surface   hexagons   rhombuses

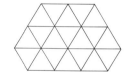   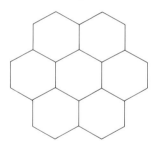   

If we take triangles or other shapes out of 2 sides of a square

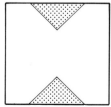

and add them to the other 2 sides

the shapes will still fit together, and make a more interesting pattern.

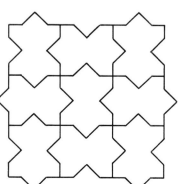

Tessellations can also be made using some combinations of regular polygons.
The sum of the angles at each point must be 360°, for the pieces to fit together.

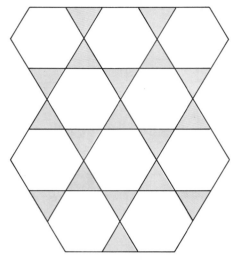

triangles and hexagons

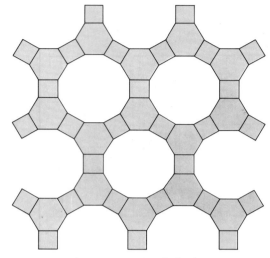

squares, hexagons and dodecagons

The possibilities are endless.
Make up your own designs, using tessellations.

Exercise 8.2   Applications and Activities

1.   Sketch this regular hexagon and join
     points as necessary.
     What sort of quadrilaterals are
     1   *ABCF*,   **2**   *BCEF* ?
     What sort of triangles are
     3   △*ABC*,   **4**   △*ACD*,   **5**   △*ACE* ?

2.   *ABCDEFGH* is a regular octagon, whose
     point of symmetry is *O*.
     1   What is the size of ∠*AOB* ?
     2   What is the size of ∠*ABC* ?
     3   If *AC*, *CE*, *EG* and *GA* are joined,
           what sort of quadrilateral is formed ?

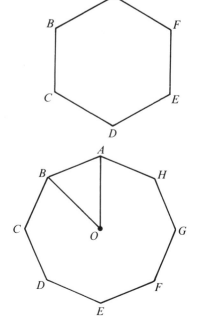

3. *ABCD* is a square and *ABPQR* is a
   regular pentagon.
   1   What kind of triangle is Δ*RAD* ?
   2   Find the size of ∠ *RAD*.
   3   Find the size of ∠ *DRA*.

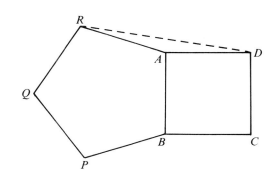

4. The diagram shows part of a regular
   polygon. If it has 9 sides, find the size of
   angle *a*.

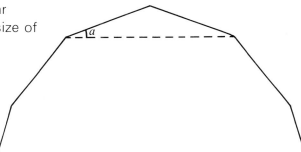

5. Write down an equation involving *x* from
   this irregular hexagon and solve it to find
   the value of *x*.
   Give the numerical values for the sizes of
   the angles *A*, *B*, *C* and *D*.

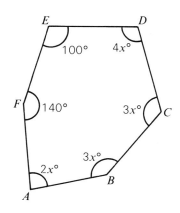

6. Write down an equation involving *x* from
   this irregular pentagon and solve it to
   find the value of *x*.
   Give the numerical values for the sizes of
   each **interior** angle of the pentagon.

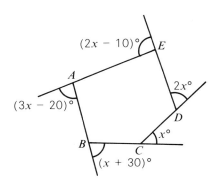

7. **An alternative method for finding the sum of the angles in a polygon**
    Choose a point inside the polygon and
    join every vertex to this point.
    e.g. For this octagon.
    There are 8 sides, so there are 8 triangles.
    Sum of the angles of the polygon
    = sum of all the angles in the triangles
       − sum of angles at the centre point
    = 8 × 180° − 360°
    = 1440° − 360°
    = 1080°

    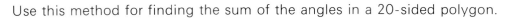

    Use this method for finding the sum of the angles in a 20-sided polygon.

    Can you use it to find a general formula for the sum s of the angles in a polygon
    with n sides ?

8. Here is part of a floor pattern made with
    two kinds of tiles.
    1   How many sides have the large
            polygons ?
    2   At point A, what is the size of the
            angle in the equilateral triangle ?
    3   At point A, what is the size of the
            angle in each regular polygon ?

    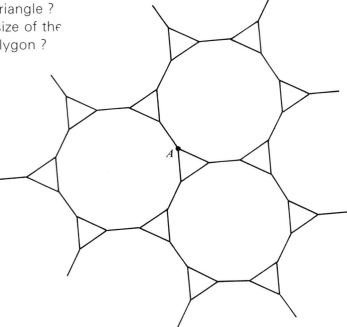

9. Draw on squared paper and cut out several pieces of each of these shapes.
    Draw outlines on squared paper to show how each shape can be used to
    tessellate an area.

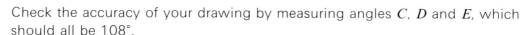

10. **To construct a regular pentagon *ABCDE***

    Method 1

    Draw *AB* = 6 cm, make angles of 108° for
    ∠ *BAE* and ∠ *ABC*.
    Mark off 6 cm on these lines for points *E*
    and *C*.
    To find *D*, with compasses centre *C*,
    draw an arc of radius 6 cm, with centre *E*
    draw an arc of radius 6 cm, to meet the
    first arc at *D*.
    Join *CD* and *ED*.

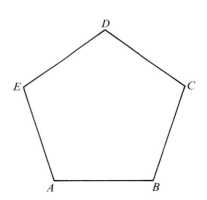

    Check the accuracy of your drawing by measuring angles *C*, *D* and *E*, which
    should all be 108°.
    Measure the distance from *A* to *D*. (You can also measure the other 4 diagonal
    lengths of the pentagon, which should all be equal.)

    Method 2

    Starting at a point *O*, draw 5 lines *OA*,
    OB, *OC*, *OD* and *OE*, each 5 cm long,
    with an angle of 72° between each one
    and the next.
    Join *AB*, *BC*, *CD*, *DE*, *EA* and measure
    these lines (which should be equal in
    length).

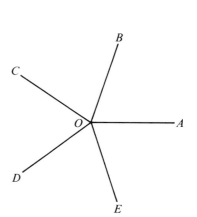

11. **To construct a regular hexagon *ABCDEF***

You can use methods similar to those given for a pentagon.

For method 1, the interior angles are each 120°.

For method 2, the angles between the lines are 60°.

Here is a method using compasses.
With compasses mark a centre *O* and
draw a circle, radius 6 cm.
Take 1 point on the circumference to be *A*.
With compasses, radius 6 cm, centre *A*,
mark off an arc to cut the circumference
at *B*.
Repeat with centre *B* to get point *C*.
Continue this method to get points *D*, *E*
and *F*.
As a check, *FA* = 6 cm.
Join the sides *AB*, *BC*, *CD*, *DE*, *EF* and
FA.

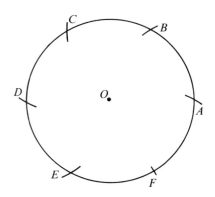

12. Draw a regular hexagon with side 4 cm on thick card. Cut it out. By drawing
round the outside, make several more hexagons. Also make some equilateral
triangles and some squares of side 4 cm.
Draw sketches of these tessellated areas.
   1   Use equilateral triangles and regular hexagons, so that 1 hexagon and 4
         triangles meet at every point.
   2   Use equilateral triangles, regular hexagons and squares. How many of each
         meet at every point ?
   3   Use equilateral triangles and squares.

13. **Paper knots making regular polygons**
   Use strips of paper which keep the same width. Practise with narrow strips first.
   Tie an ordinary knot to get a pentagon.
   Tie a reef knot in two strips of paper to get a hexagon.

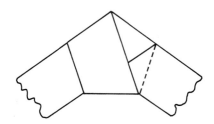
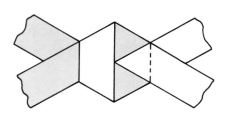

14. **To construct a regular octagon from a square**

Draw a square *ABCD* of side 6 cm and
find its centre *E* by joining its diagonals.
Using compasses, centre *A*, with radius
the same length as *AE*, make 2 arcs
cutting *AB* at *Q* and *AD* at *V*.
With centre *B* and the same radius, find
points *P* and *S*.
With centre *C*, find points *R* and *U*.
With centre *D*, find points *T* and *W*.
Join *QR, ST, UV, WP*.
Then *PQRSTUVW* is a regular octagon,
with sides of length 2.5 cm.
(If you want the octagon to have edges
of a certain length, begin with a square
with edges 2.4 times that length.)

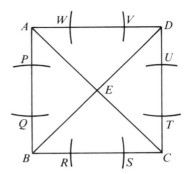

15. Make a regular octagon as shown in question 14, copy it onto cardboard, cut it
out, and by drawing round the outside make several more octagons. Also make
several squares with edges of the same size as those of the octagon.
Arrange the octagons and squares to make a tessellated area and show your
design on a sketch.

PUZZLES

16. In this division sum, every letter stands for a different figure from
0 to 9.
Find which figure each letter represents.
Replace these figures by the corresponding letters to make a statement.
740 748 24894 0 962

```
       P L A N
L O )T O K E N
      U P
      ‾‾‾‾
      C K
      C L
      ‾‾‾‾
      P E N
      P E N
      ‾‾‾‾‾
```

17. A bag contains 360 nuts. They are divided amongst 9 boys. A takes a certain number, B
takes 3 more than A, C takes 3 more than B, and so on with the others. When they have
all taken their nuts, the bag is empty.
How many nuts did each of the boys take ?

18. **1** What is the fewest number of cuts that would be needed to cut a loaf of bread into
eight parts ?
2 What is the fewest number of cuts that would be needed to cut a length of string into
eight pieces ?

9 Thinking about probability

Probability (or chance)

This is one branch of mathematics that we learn about instinctively from an early age. All life consists of making judgements as to what is likely to happen as a result of our actions.

You could go to the cinema.

Making choices

Suppose there are three likely things for you to do tonight.
1   Go to the cinema,
2   go swimming,
3   stay in and watch television.
You can make an estimate of the probability of making each choice.

Mutually exclusive events

If the probability of going to the cinema is 0.5 (because it depends on whether or not your mother can take you), and the probability of going swimming is 0.3 (because you will only go there if you don't go to the cinema, and only then if your friend calls for you), then this leaves the third alternative, that you will stay in and watch television.
The three choices are **mutually exclusive** events, because if one of them happens, the others cannot happen.

You could go swimming

Certainty

If these are the **only** possible choices then it is **certain** that one or other of them must happen, so what is the sum of the three probabilities ? In this case, what is the probability of staying in and watching television ?

Exceptions

Explain why these events are not mutually exclusive:
1   I will have chips for tea today,
2   I will have beefburgers and beans for tea today.

You could stay in and watch television.

Calculating the probability

Suppose that in a packet of sweets there is a picture card of a series. You are collecting the series, there are 10 cards altogether, and you have now got 9 of them, so you only want one more card, which is number 5. Assuming that the cards have been put into the packets in random order, what is the probability that you will get the card in the next packet that you buy ?

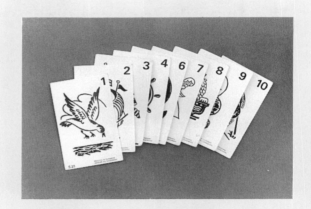

Independent events

At the shop, there is a special offer whereby you can buy two packets of sweets wrapped together at a lower price than two separate packets, so you decide to buy the double pack. If the cards in these two packets are still put in at random, then the picture card in the second packet does not depend on which card is in the first packet.
This is an example of **independent events**.

What is the probability that you will get the card you want in at least one of the two packets ?
What is the probability that both packets will contain number 5 cards ?

Finding the answers

You can work out the probabilities by drawing a table.
(See page 145 for an example of a table.)

How many equally likely outcomes are there in the table ?
How many of them are successful outcomes ?
What is the probability of a successful outcome ?

Extending the idea

In actual fact, there could be more than 10 cards in the series, so the table would be much larger, but the idea is the same.
What would the probabilities be if there were 50 cards in the series ?

9 Probability

The formula for probability

Probability of a successful outcome $= \dfrac{s}{n}$

where n is the total number of equally likely outcomes, and s is the number of successful outcomes.

When tossing a coin and looking at the outcomes, there are two possibilities, heads or tails.
(We will ignore the other remote possibilities of the coin landing and staying on its edge, or of disappearing down a hole.)
What is the probability of the coin showing heads ?
What is the probability of the coin showing tails ?
What is the sum of these probabilities ?
What does a probability of 1 mean ? How does this fit in with your previous answers ?

When throwing a die and looking at the outcomes of the number on top, there are 6 possibilities, the numbers 1 to 6.
If it is a fair die, what is the probability of each number occurring ?
What is the sum of these probabilities ?

There are 13 discs in a bag. 5 are red, 4 blue, 3 green and 1 yellow. One is taken out without looking.
What is the probability that it is red ?
What is the probability that it is blue ?
What is the probability that it is green ?
What is the probability that it is yellow ?
What is the sum of these probabilities ?
What is the probability that the disc drawn out is not red ?
What is P(red) + P(not red) ? (P(red) means the probability of a red disc.)

There are 200 components in a batch. It is expected that, on average, 5% of all components are defective. (This means that they are unsatisfactory.)
What percentage of components are expected to be satisfactory ?
How many components in this batch are expected to be defective ?
How many components in this batch are expected to be satisfactory ?
If a component is taken from the batch at random,
what is the probability that it is defective ?
What is the probability that it is satisfactory ?
What is the sum of these probabilities ?

Mutually exclusive events

When there are two or more outcomes of an event and at each time only one of these outcomes can happen (because if one outcome happens, this prevents any of the other outcomes happening), then the outcomes are called **mutually exclusive events**.

For instance, a coin shows a head **or** a tail. (Either one or other must show.)
A die shows one of the numbers from 1 to 6.
If there are red, blue, green and yellow discs in a bag and one is drawn out, it must be either red **or** blue **or** green **or** yellow.
A component is either defective **or** satisfactory.

The sum of all possible mutually exclusive events is 1.

This also means that

The probability of an event happening = 1 − the probability of the event not happening.

Exercise 9.1

1. When this spinner is spun, it is equally likely to come to rest on any of its five edges, and the number on that edge is the score.
    1 What is the probability of getting a score of 5,
    2 what is the probability of not getting a score of 5 ?

2.   16 discs, numbered from 1 to 16, are placed in a bag, and one is drawn out at
      random without looking at it.
      What is the probability of getting a disc with
      1   a 2-figure number,
      2   a 1-figure number,
      3   a square number,
      4   a number which is not a square number ?

3.   Kate can go home from work by train, by bus or by taxi. The probability that she
      will go home by train is 0.5, and by bus 0.4. What is the probability that she
      will go home by taxi ?

4.   A large batch of white hyacinth bulbs has been accidently mixed with some
      yellow hyacinth bulbs, so that the probability of picking a yellow hyacinth bulb
      is $\frac{4}{7}$.
      What is the probability of picking a white hyacinth bulb ?

5.   By long experience, Sarwar has decided that the probability that the traffic light
      at the crossroads shows green when he gets to it is $\frac{5}{6}$.
      What is the probability that it is not green ?

6.   From a pack of 52 cards the 7 of hearts was taken out. If a card is drawn at
      random from the remaining pack,
      1   what is the probability that it is a 7,
      2   what is the probability that it is not a 7,
      3   what is the probability that it is a heart,
      4   what is the probability that it is not a heart ?

7.   In a certain country, the probability that a baby will be a boy is 0.52.
      What is the probability that a baby will be a girl ?

8.   It is forecast that the probability that United will win the match next Saturday is
      0.7 and that they will draw it is 0.2.
      What is the probability that they will lose it ?

9.   Three boys Karl, Colin and Christopher are entered for a race as the only three
      runners. Their trainer says that the probability of Karl winning is $\frac{1}{7}$ and the
      probability of Colin winning is $\frac{2}{7}$.
      What is the probability of
      1   Karl not winning,
      2   Colin not winning,
      3   Christopher winning ?

10.   A darts player aiming at treble 20 hits his
      target 4 times out of 20, in the long run.
      On his next throw, what is the probability
      that he will hit the treble ?
      What is the probability that he will miss
      the treble ?

11.   Julie buys some raffle tickets. The probability of her winning the prize is 0.003.
      What is the probability of her not winning ?

12.   It is estimated that the chance of winning a certain Bingo game is $\frac{1}{100\,000}$.
      What is the chance of not winning ?

Independent Events

When a coin is tossed twice in succession, or two coins are tossed, the second result
does not depend on whether the first result was heads or tails.
When a die is tossed twice in succession, or two dice are tossed, the second result
does not depend on the number shown by the first result.
If there are coloured beads in a bag, and one is picked out and its colour noted, and
then it is replaced and the beads mixed up, the colour of the next bead picked out
does not depend on the colour of the first one.

Such events, where the outcome of the second event does not depend on the outcome
of the first event, are called **independent events**.

We can show the combined outcomes of both events in a list, a table or a tree
diagram.

Examples

1   If a coin is tossed, the probability of a head is $\frac{1}{2}$, and the probability of a tail is $\frac{1}{2}$.
If two coins are tossed, the 4 outcomes are shown in this table and in this list.

Table

		1st coin	
		H	T
2nd H		HH	TH
coin T		HT	TT

List

HH
HT
TH
TT

In this case, all 4 outcomes are equally likely outcomes.

The probability of getting two heads is $\dfrac{s}{n} = \frac{1}{4}$

(s is the number of successful outcomes = 1 (HH)
n is the total number of equally likely outcomes = 4)

Here are the outcomes shown on a diagram which is called a **tree-diagram**.

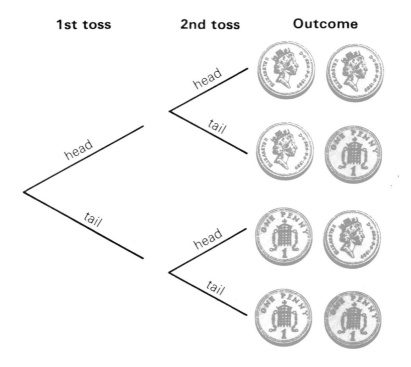

2   The outcomes when two dice are thrown.

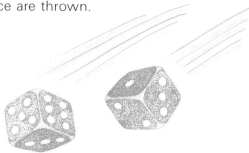

Since there are 36 outcomes, a list or a tree-diagram is not as suitable as a table.

Table

		1st die					
		1	2	3	4	5	6
	1	1,1	2,1	3,1	4,1	5,1	6,1
2nd	2	1,2	2,2	3,2	4,2	5,2	6,2
die	3	1,3	2,3	3,3	4,3	5,3	6,3
	4	1,4	2,4	3,4	4,4	5,4	6,4
	5	1,5	2,5	3,5	4,5	5,5	6,5
	6	1,6	2,6	3,6	4,6	5,6	6,6

Make a similar table, but instead of showing the outcomes as 1,1; 1,2; etc. show the **total** scores 2, 3, etc.

The 36 results are equally likely.

By counting, and using the formula Probability $= \dfrac{s}{n}$, find the probabilities of each of the scores from 2 to 12.

Set the results down in a table like this, keeping each fraction with a denominator of 36.

Total score	Probability
2	$\frac{1}{36}$
3	$\frac{2}{36}$
etc.	

What is the sum of the probabilities ?
How can you use this sum to check your results ?

3 Emily often walks to school but she sometimes goes by bus. Occasionally she is taken by car. The same things happen when she comes home from school, she either walks, comes by bus or comes in a friend's car. This is regardless of which way she travelled to school in the morning.

These are the combined outcomes of how she goes to school and returns from school on the same day, shown in a table and a tree-diagram.
W = walk, B = by bus, C = car.

		Going		
		W	B	C
Coming home	W	WW	BW	CW
	B	WB	BB	CB
	C	WC	BC	CC

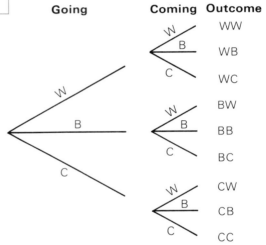

(These are not equally likely outcomes so until we have more information we cannot calculate the probability of each of them.)

Exercise 9.2

1. On the way to work Miss Desai passes through two sets of road works, controlled by traffic lights which just show red or green. The colour showing on the second set of lights is not linked in any way to that showing on the first set. Show in a table, and in a tree diagram, the combined outcomes of whether she can stop or go at these road works.
   (Since we do not know whether these are equally likely outcomes we cannot calculate the probability of each of them.)

2. In a fairground game a pointer is spun,
    with the outcomes win (W) or lose (L).
    Show in a table the combined outcomes
    when it is spun twice.
    If the result of a spin is equally likely to be
    win or lose, what are the probabilities of
    1 winning both times in 2 spins,
    2 losing both times in 2 spins,
    3 winning just once out of 2 spins ?

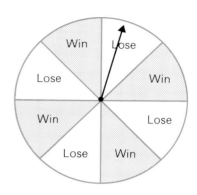

3. Anna, Beverley and Carole are the only competitors in a 100 m race and also in
    the high jump. The result of the high jump will not be affected by their
    performances in the race.
    Show, in a table or tree-diagram, the combined outcomes of winners in the race
    followed by the high jump.
    (Since these may not be equally likely outcomes we cannot calculate the
    probability of each of them.)

4. In a bag there are some red discs, some blue ones and some yellow ones.
    A disc is drawn out and its colour noted, and then it is replaced and the discs
    mixed up. Then a second disc is drawn out and its colour noted.
    Show in a table the combined outcomes of colours.
    If there are equal numbers of discs of each colour then the outcomes in your table
    are equally likely. In this case, find the probabilities that, when two discs are
    drawn as stated above,
    1 both discs are red,
    2 both discs are the same colour,
    3 at least one disc is blue.

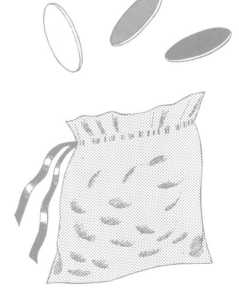

5. There are 4 choices of 1st course at a canteen, beefburgers and beans, sausages and mash, ham salad, or fish and chips, and there are 3 choices of sweet course, apple pie, trifle, or cheese and biscuits.
    Show in a table the combined choices of a 2-course meal.
    (Since some choices may be more popular than others we cannot calculate the probability of each of them being chosen.)

6. In a game, a die is thrown first, showing a number from 1 to 6, and then a card is picked at random from 5 cards numbered from 1 to 5.
    Show in a table the combined outcomes of numbers.
    How many equally likely outcomes are there ?
    Use the table to find the probabilities that
    1   the numbers on the die and the card are both 4,
    2   the numbers on the die and the card are both the same,
    3   the number on the die is a 5 or a 6 and the number on the card is 4 or 5,
    4   the sum of the numbers on the die and the card is 6.

Exercise 9.3   Applications and Activities

1. To start a game of snakes and ladders, Noreen must throw a six. On her first turn,
    1   what is the probability of her getting a six,
    2   what is the probability of her not getting a six ?

2. A retailer received a batch of 100 calculators, of which 5 were faulty.
    If he tests one of the calculators, chosen at random,
    1   what is the probability that it is a faulty one,
    2   what is the probability that it is in working order ?
    If it is faulty, he rejects the batch and returns them all to the manufacturer.
    If it is not faulty, he tests another one.
    3   What is the probability that this one is faulty ?
    4   What is the probability that this one is in working order ?

3. Simon was told that the probability of being injured at work during the year was only 0.005.
    What is the probability that he will not be injured ?
    Can Simon do anything to lessen the possibility of being injured ?

4. There are 5 cards numbered from 1 to 5. One card is selected at random and then replaced and the cards mixed up. Then a second card is selected.
    Show in a table the outcomes of the sums of the numbers on the two cards.
    How many equally likely outcomes are there ?

		1st card				
		1	2	3	4	5
	1	2	3	.	.	.
	2					
2nd	3					
card	4					
	5					

    Set down the results in a table like this, keeping all fractions with the same denominator.
    What is the sum of the probabilities ?

Total score	Probability
2	.
3	.
.	
.	

    If you choose 1 card, what is the probability of getting the number 1 ?
    If you choose 2 cards as above, what is the probability of getting the number 1 twice in succession ?
    Can you suggest a rule for calculating the combined probabilities of independent events if you know the separate probabilities ?

5. Oliver has to do a multiple-choice contest. There are 10 questions but he is sure of the answers to 8 of them. For question 9 he has 4 choices A, B, C and D; and for question 10 he knows that the answer is not D, so he has 3 choices A, B and C.
    Make a table showing the combined guesses for questions 9 and 10.
    As he is going to guess at random, each combination of choice is equally likely.
    If the correct answers are:- question 9, A and question 10, C; what is the probability of
    1   Oliver getting both answers correct,
    2   Oliver getting both answers wrong,
    3   Oliver getting just one of the two answers correct ?

6. This question concerns throwing 2 dice. You should use the results of example 2, page 145.

    1 What is the probability of getting a six on both dice ?

    2 What is the most likely total score using both dice ? What is the probability of getting this score ?

    3 What is the probability of scoring the same number on both dice ?

    4 What is the probability of scoring different numbers on the two dice ?

    5 If the 2 dice were thrown 180 times altogether, then the theoretical frequency of each total score is found by multiplying the probability by 180. Find the theoretical frequency of each score.

    Do this by cancelling by 36.

    e.g.   the theoretical probability of a score of 2 is $\dfrac{1}{\cancel{36}_{1}} \times \cancel{180}^{5} = 5$

    Draw a vertical bar chart or histogram showing these theoretical frequencies.

    6 Throw 2 dice 180 times (or use the results of previous throws) and make a tally table of the total scores.

    Draw a vertical bar chart or histogram showing these actual frequencies and compare it with the previous diagram, and comment about them.

    7 Can you name any games in which you use a die, and some games where you play with two dice ?

7. Look at example 1, page 144, where two coins are tossed.
    Draw a tree-diagram to show the outcomes when 3 coins are tossed.

    1 How many equally likely outcomes are there ?

    What is the probability of getting

    2 3 heads,

    3 2 heads and 1 tail,

    4 1 head and 2 tails,

    5 3 tails,

    6 at least one head ?

    7 If the 3 coins were tossed 80 times altogether, what are the theoretical frequencies of 0 tails, 1 tail, 2 tails, 3 tails ?

    Draw a vertical bar chart or histogram showing the theoretical frequencies.

    8 Toss 3 coins 80 times (or use the results of previous tosses in three's) and make a tally table of the number of tails.

    Draw a vertical bar chart or histogram showing these actual frequencies and compare it with the previous diagram, and comment about them.

    You may like to extend your investigations to what happens if 4, or more, coins are tossed.

8.   Nine samples of a meat product and one sample of an artificially-produced food are set out for members of the public to taste and choose the odd-one-out.
     1   If a person guesses at random, what is the probability of being right ?
     2   What is the probability of being wrong ?
     3   If 100 people are involved in the testing, how many would you expect to guess correctly, if they guess at random ?

PUZZLES

19. A man left $\frac{1}{4}$ of his money to his eldest son, $\frac{1}{4}$ of the remainder to the next son, and so on, the final remainder going to his only daughter. He left £128 000 and the daughter received £40 500. How many sons had he ?

20. **1**   What is the largest number you can write using the Roman numerals C, D, I, L, M, V, X, once each ?
     2   What is the smallest number you can write using the same Roman numerals, once each ?

21. Marie, Patricia, Eleanor and Joan are sisters. They have four different occupations. One of them (not Patricia) is a teacher of music, one of them (not Eleanor) is a nurse, one is a computer programmer and the remaining sister is a television presenter.
     The other day I was discussing music with the computer programmer. 'My sister who is a nurse is a very good pianist,' she said. 'She is much better than Patricia, and Patricia can play better than Marie.'
     Who is the music teacher ?

22. On a certain island there are 500 inhabitants. 4% of them are wearing one ear-ring. Of the other 96%, half are wearing two ear-rings, half are wearing none. How many ear-rings altogether are being worn ?

23.

'There is treasure in the 500th box,' said the quiz-master, but that is counting backwards and forwards like this:-

```
      1   2   3   4   5
    9   8   7   6
      10  11  12  13
              14
```

You have 30 seconds in which to open the right box.'
Is there a quick way to tell which box to open ? Which is it ?

10 Thinking about functions and

Functions

Here are examples of two sets, x and y, of numbers shown in a mapping diagram, and there is some connection between them.

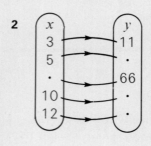 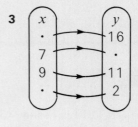

In **1**, what is the rule which connects y to x ? Find the missing numbers.

In **2**, the rule is 'To get the value of y, square x and add 2'. Find the missing numbers.

In **3**, the rule is '$y = 20 - x$'. Find the missing numbers.

Rule **3** is expressed as an equation. Express the rules for **1** and **2** as equations.

Coordinates

The functions can be represented by plotting points on a graph. If the functions are defined for all values of x, not just whole numbers, the points can be joined by either a straight line or a smooth curve.

Here are sketch graphs of the functions above for positive values of x. (Scales on the graphs are not shown.)

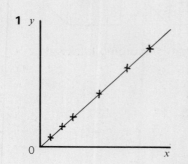 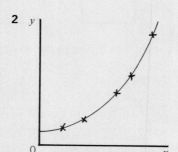 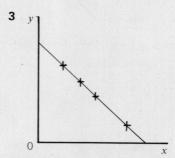

coordinates

René Descartes, 1596–1650

Descartes

Our system of coordinates is called Cartesian Coordinates, named after René Descartes, a Frenchman who lived from 1596 to 1650, and who was the son of a wealthy landowner. He was a delicate child so he was encouraged to lie in bed as late as he pleased in the mornings. He therefore stayed in bed whenever he wished to think. His method for representing algebraic functions on graphs gave a new method for studying curves, and linked algebra and geometry.

Curves and their equations

Some functions can produce interesting curves.

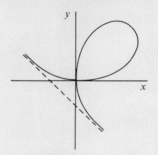

The folium of Descartes
$$x^3 + y^3 = 3axy$$

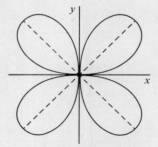

A rose of Grandi
$$(x^2 + y^2)^3 = 4a^2 x^2 y^2$$

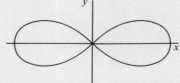

The lemniscate of Bernoulli
$$(x^2 + y^2)^2 = a^2 (x^2 - y^2)$$

10 Functions and Coordinates

Functions

If there is an equation connecting y with x, such as $y = 3x + 5$, then y is said to be a **function** of x.

For each value of x there is only one value of y.

e.g. $y = 3x + 5$

When $x = 1$, $y = (3 \times 1) + 5 = 8$

When $x = 2$, $y = (3 \times 2) + 5 = 11$

When $x = 3$, $y = (3 \times 3) + 5 = 14$

When $x = 4$, $y = (3 \times 4) + 5 = 17$

and so on.

The other way of expressing this function is

$x \rightarrow 3x + 5$

This is read as 'x is mapped into $3x + 5$'.

A function can be represented by a mapping diagram.

e.g.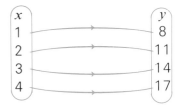

It can be represented by a table.

x	1	2	3	4
y	8	11	14	17

It can be represented by pairs of numbers.

(1, 8), (2, 11), (3, 14), (4, 17).

Each pair is written in a bracket with the first number the value of x and the second number the corresponding value of y.

Exercise 10.1

1. For each of these functions, and for $x = 1, 2, 3, 4, 5$, represent the function by
   (1) a mapping diagram,
   (2) a table,
   (3) pairs of numbers.

   1 $y = 3x$ or $x \rightarrow 3x$
   2 $y = 5x - 4$ or $x \rightarrow 5x - 4$
   3 $y = x^2$ or $x \rightarrow x^2$
   4 $y = 2x + 2$ or $x \rightarrow 2x + 2$
   5 $y = 10 - x$ or $x \rightarrow 10 - x$

2. Look at each table of values. Notice the pattern formed by the y-values as x increases. Find the connection between the x-values and the corresponding y-values. Write this down as an equation in the form $y =$ 'expression involving x'.

   1

x	0	1	2	3	4
y	0	4	8	12	16

   4

x	10	20	30	40
y	50	100	150	200

   2

x	1	2	3	4	5
y	4	7	10	13	16

   5

x	0	1	2	3	4
y	0	1	8	27	64

   3

x	0	1	2	3	4
y	20	18	16	14	12

3. Make a table of values for $x = 0, 1, 2, 3, 4$ for these functions.

   1 $y = 5x + 2$ **4** $y = \frac{1}{2}x$
   2 $y = 2x + 10$ **5** $y = 2x^2$
   3 $y = 12 - 3x$

4. Find the equations in the form y = 'expression involving x' for these functions
    given as pairs of numbers.
    1 (0, 9) (1, 8) (2, 7) (3, 6) (4, 5)
    2 (1, 5) (2, 7) (3, 9) (4, 11)
    3 (1, 1) (2, 4) (3, 9) (4, 16) (5, 25)
    4 (1, 0) (2, 3) (3, 8) (4, 15) (5, 24)
    5 (1, 12) (2, 6) (3, 4) (4, 3) (5, 2.4) (6, 2)

5. Find the missing numbers in these mapping diagrams, which represent simple
    functions. Then give the equations of the functions.

1 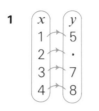 **2** 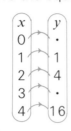 **3** 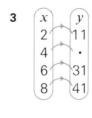 **4** 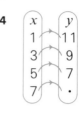 **5**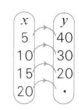

Representing functions by graphs

Example

Draw the graph of the function $y = 2x + 3$ for values of x from 0 to 5.

First find the values of y when x = 0, 1, 2, 3, 4, 5.
When $x = 0$, $y = (2 \times 0) + 3 = 0 + 3 = 3$
When $x = 1$, $y = (2 \times 1) + 3 = 2 + 3 = 5$
etc.
Represent these results in a table:

x	0	1	2	3	4	5
y	3	5	7	9	11	13

or represent them by pairs of numbers (0, 3), (1, 5), (2, 7), etc.
These pairs of numbers are the coordinates of the points which we will plot on the
graph.
On the graph, the x-axis should go from 0 to 5. Choose a suitable scale, e.g. 2 cm
to represent 1 unit.
The y-axis goes from 0 to 13. Choose a suitable scale for this axis,
e.g. 1 cm to 1 unit.

Draw the axes, label them, and plot the points (0, 3), (1, 5), etc.

Do your points lie on a straight line ?

(They should do, so if they do not, check to see where you have gone wrong.)

Draw the line, using a ruler.

Label the line $y = 2x + 3$.

This is the graph of the function $y = 2x + 3$ (for values of x from 0 to 5).

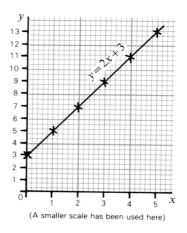

(A smaller scale has been used here)

Up to now we have chosen positive whole numbers or 0 for values of x, but the function can exist for other values of x.

e.g. The function $y = 3x + 5$

When $x = \frac{1}{2}$, $y = (3 \times \frac{1}{2}) + 5 = 1\frac{1}{2} + 5 = 6\frac{1}{2}$

When $x = 9.9$, $y = (3 \times 9.9) + 5 = 29.7 + 5 = 34.7$

When $x = 4\frac{2}{3}$, $y = (3 \times 4\frac{2}{3}) + 5 = 14 + 5 = 19$

and so on, for any values of x.

We could also include negative values of x.

When $x = -1$, $y = (3 \times (-1)) + 5 = -3 + 5 = 2$

When $x = -2$, $y = (3 \times (-2)) + 5 = -6 + 5 = -1$

When $x = -3$, $y = (3 \times (-3)) + 5 = -9 + 5 = -4$

When $x = -4$, $y = (3 \times (-4)) + 5 = -12 + 5 = -7$

When $x = -5.2$, $y = (3 \times (-5.2)) + 5 = -15.6 + 5 = -10.6$

and so on.

To draw the graph of the function $y = 3x + 5$, for values of x from -4 to 4.

We have already found the values of y when $x = -4, -3, -2, -1$, (see above) and when $x = 1, 2, 3, 4$, (page 154)

When $x = 0$, $y = (3 \times 0) + 5 = 5$

We can represent all these results in a table.

x	-4	-3	-2	-1	0	1	2	3	4
y	-7	-4	-1	2	5	8	11	14	17

On the graph the x-axis should go from -4 to 4. A suitable scale would be 2 cm to 1 unit.

The y-axis will go from -7 to 17. A suitable
scale would be 1 cm to 2 units.
The x-axis will be 4 cm from the bottom of the
page.
The y-axis will be 8 cm from the left side of the
page.
Draw the axes, label them, and plot the points
$(-4, -7)$, $(-3, -4)$, $(-2, -1)$, $(-1, 2)$, $(0, 5)$,
$(1, 8)$, $(2, 11)$, $(3, 14)$, $(4, 17)$.
Do your points lie on a straight line ? They should
do.
Draw the line, using a ruler.
Label the line $y = 3x + 5$.
This is the graph of the function
$y = 3x + 5$ (for values of x from -4 to 4).

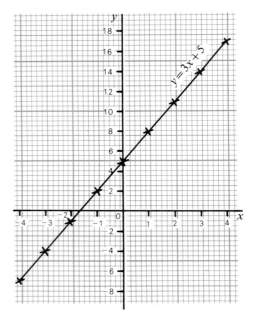

Equations of lines parallel to the axes on graphs

On the line AB, the x-coordinates of all points
is 3, and the equation of the line is $x = 3$.
Similarly, the equation of the y-axis is $x = 0$.

On the line CD, the y-coordinates of all points
is -2, and the equation of this line is $y = -2$.
Similarly, the equation of the x-axis is $y = 0$.
AB and CD cross at the point $(3, -2)$.

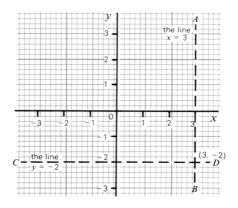

Exercise 10.2

1.   This is a table of values of a function

x	0	1	2	3	4	5
y	18	15	12	9	6	3

Represent the function by pairs of numbers.
Draw a graph, with x-axis labelled from 0 to 5, using 2 cm to represent 1 unit, and y-axis labelled from 0 to 18, using 1 cm to represent 1 unit.
Plot the points representing the function.
Check that they lie on a straight line, and draw the line, using a ruler.
Can you find the equation of the function in the form y = 'expression involving x' ?
If so, label the line with its equation.

2.   This is a table of values of a function.

x	-2	-1	0	1	2	3	4	5
y	-1	0	1	2	3	4	5	6

Represent this function by pairs of numbers.
Draw a graph with x-axis labelled from -2 to 5
and y-axis from -1 to 6. On both axes use a
scale of 2 cm to represent 1 unit.
Plot the points representing the function.
Check that they lie on a straight line, and draw the line, using a ruler.
If you can find the equation of the function, label the line with its equation.

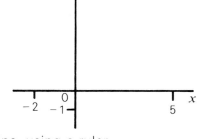

3.   Copy and complete the table of values for x = 0, 1, 2, 3, 4, 5, 6 for the
function $y = 3x$.

x	0	1	2	3	4	5	6
y							

Draw the graph of the function. Label the x-axis from 0 to 6, using a scale of
2 cm to represent 1 unit. Label the y-axis from 0 to 18, using a scale of 1 cm to
represent 1 unit. Plot the points representing the function. Check that they lie on
a straight line, and draw the line. Label the line $y = 3x$.

4.   Make a table of values for x = $-3, -2, -1, 0, 1, 2, 3, 4$, for the function $y = 2x - 1$.
Draw a graph of the function. Label the x-axis from -3 to 4, using a scale of
2 cm to represent 1 unit. Label the y-axis from -7 to 7, using a scale of 1 cm to
represent 1 unit. Plot the points representing the function. Check that they lie on
a straight line, and draw the line. Label the line $y = 2x - 1$.

5. Make a table of values for $x = -3, -2, -1, 0, 1, 2, 3, 4, 5$, for the function
    $y = 4 - x$.
    Draw a graph of the function. Label the x-axis from -3 to 5, and the y-axis from
    -1 to 7. On both axes use a scale of 2 cm to represent 1 unit. Plot the points
    representing the function. Check that they lie on a straight line and draw the line.
    Label the line $y = 4 - x$.

6. For each of the following functions, make a table of values.
    To draw the graph, decide on a suitable scale for the x-axis.
    Find the range of values of y, and decide on a suitable scale for the y-axis.
    Draw the axes, and plot the points representing the function.
    Check that the points lie on a straight line, and draw the line.
    Label the line with the equation of the function.
    1 $y = 5x$ x from -2 to 6
    2 $y = 4 - 3x$ x from 0 to 8
    3 $y = x + 7$ x from -4 to 4
    4 $y = 5 - 2x$ x from -1 to 5
    5 $y = 4x + 3$ x from -3 to 5

Exercise 10.3   Applications and Activities

1. Two children were playing a game of guessing functions.
    Lucy chose a function. Kirk asked for the y-value for a certain x-value. He chose,
    in turn, $x = 1, 5, 12, 9$ and 4, and the y-values which Lucy told him were as
    shown in the table.

Kirk chose x-value	1	5	12	9	4
Lucy said y-value	7	31	73	55	25

Kirk then thought he could guess the equation of the function.
What was it ?

Then it was Kirk's turn.

Lucy chose x-value	2	-3	4	-1	10
Kirk said y-value	8	18	4	14	-8

Lucy couldn't guess the function yet. Can you ?

She then chose more x-values.

Lucy chose x-value	0	5	− 10
Kirk said y-value	12	2	32

Then Lucy found the equation. What was it ?

Play this game with a friend. Here are other functions. Cover the numbers up and uncover them one at a time and see who can be first to discover the equation. You can check your answer by checking that all the remaining pairs of numbers satisfy the equation.

1

x	1	4	− 3	8	− 1	5	− 2	0
y	4	16	− 12	32	− 4	20	− 8	0

2

x	2	0	− 5	6	− 2	3	8	− 1
y	11	7	− 3	19	3	13	23	5

3

x	3	− 1	6	− 4	0	2	7	− 5
y	3	7	0	10	6	4	− 1	11

4

x	5	2	− 2	3	− 3	1	4	− 1
y	16	7	− 5	10	− 8	4	13	− 2

5

x	− 1	8	3	− 2	6	− 5	0	2
y	30	− 15	10	35	− 5	50	25	15

You can continue by choosing functions in turn. In order not to make it too easy you should ask for numbers which are not in any particular order.
Afterwards, you could draw the graphs of some of the functions.

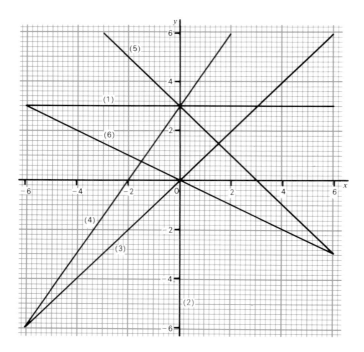

1 State the equations of the lines (1) and (2).

2 For line (3), copy and complete this table of values, reading the y-values from the graph.

x	-6	-4	-2	0	2	4	6
y	-6						

What is the equation of line (3) ?
Repeat this for lines (4), (5), (6) to find their equations.

3 Give the coordinates of the point where line (3) meets line (5).

3. **Related functions**

1 Using the same axes draw the graphs of $y = x$, $y = 2x$, $y = 3x$, $y = 4x$, $y = 5x$.
Draw the x-axis from -3 to 5, using a scale of 2 cm to 1 unit.
Draw the y-axis from -15 to 25, using a scale of 2 cm to 5 units, so that 2
2 mm squares represent 1 unit.
Plot the graphs for each function in turn, and label each one.
What do you notice about the graphs ?

2 Draw the graphs of $y = 2x$, $y = 2x + 3$, $y = 2x + 5$, $y = 2x - 2$, $y = 2x - 5$, using the same axes.
Draw the x-axis from -4 to 4, using a scale of 2 cm to 1 unit.
Draw the y-axis from -13 to 13, using a scale of 1 cm to 2 units.
Plot the graphs for each function in turn, and label each one.
What do you notice about the graphs ?

4. **What is this ?**

Draw the x-axis from -20 to 40, and the y-axis from -15 to 20, using a scale of 2 cm to 10 units on both axes.
Work out these functions for the values of x given, and draw the graphs for the range of x given. They are all straight lines.
Complete the picture by adding extra details, and colouring it.

1 $y = \frac{1}{10}x$

Use $x = -17, -10, 0, 10, 20, 30, 37$
Draw the line from $x = -17$ to $x = 37$

2 $y = \frac{1}{10}x + 5$

Use $x = -20, -10, 20, 30, 40$
Draw the line from $x = -20$ to $x = -10$ and from $x = 20$ to $x = 40$

3 $y = \frac{1}{10}x + 10.1$

Use $x = -11, 0, 19$
Draw the line from $x = -11$ to $x = 19$

4 $y = \frac{1}{10}x + 15$

Use $x = 0, 10$
Draw the line from $x = 0$ to $x = 10$

5 $y = \frac{1}{10}x + 16$

Use $x = 0, 10$
Draw the line from $x = 0$ to $x = 10$

6 $y = -12$

Draw the line from $x = -12$ to $x = 29$

7 $y = -15$

Draw the line from $x = -11$ to $x = 28$

8 $y = 2x - 71$

Use $x = 28, 35, 40$
Draw the line from $x = 28$ to $x = 40$

9 $y = -2x - 37$

Use $x = -20, x = -15, x = -11$
Draw the line from $x = -20$ to $x = -11$

10 $y = -5x - 46$

Use $x = -11, -10$
Draw the line from $x = -11$ to $x = -10$

11 $y = -5x + 107$

Use $x = 19, 20$
Draw the line from $x = 19$ to $x = 20$

12 $y = -6x + 16$

Use $x = 0, 1$
Draw the line from $x = 0$ to $x = 1$

13 $y = -6x + 77$

Use $x = 10, 11$
Draw the line from $x = 10$ to $x = 11$

5.　**Functions whose graphs are curves**

Not all functions have graphs which are straight lines.

1　The graph of $y = x^2$

Copy and complete the table of values, for values of x from 0 to 8.

x	0	1	2	3	4	5	6	7	8
y	0	1	4	9					

Draw the x-axis from 0 to 8, using a scale of 2 cm to 1 unit.
Draw the y-axis from 0 to 70, using a scale of 1 cm to 5 units (so that each 2 mm square represents 1 unit).
Plot the points on the graph.
Since the graph is not a straight line, you must not use your ruler to join the points, but must draw a curve, drawn freehand, making it as smooth as possible. You may find it helpful to plot an extra point $(7\frac{1}{2}, 56\frac{1}{4})$ as well.

2　Here is another table of values.

x	1.5	2	2.4	3	4	5	6	8
y	8	6	5	4	3	2.4	2	1.5

Can you discover the equation of the function represented ?
Draw both axes from 0 to 8, using scales of 2 cm to represent 1 unit.
Plot the points given, and join them by a smooth curve, drawn freehand.

3　Here is a doubling pattern.

x	1	2	3	4	5
y	2	4	8	16	32

Can you discover the equation of the function represented ?

By continuing the pattern backwards we also get these values.

x	-3	-2	-1	0
y	0.125	0.25	0.5	1

Draw the x-axis from -3 to 5, using a scale of 2 cm to 1 unit.
Draw the y-axis from 0 to 40, using a scale of 2 cm to 5 units.
Plot all 9 points, and also an extra point we have found using a calculator, $(4.6, 24.3)$
Join the points with a smooth curve, drawn freehand.

Nowadays, there are some calculators which will plot graphs of functions.
If you can use one of these you can plot the graphs of the functions given in this chapter, and compare them with the graphs you have drawn.
You may also have a program allowing you to plot graphs of functions on a computer.

PUZZLES

24.   Dad went to the dentist's this afternoon. On the way back he called at the Bank, then he bought me a record from the corner shop and got Mum some roses from the market stall. Dad gets paid on Thursdays and the Bank is open on Monday, Thursday and Friday. The dentist's is open every weekday but not on Saturdays.
The shops are closed on Thurday afternoons and there is no market on Tuesday or Friday. What day of the week was it ?

25.   Nine girls were arranged in a circle and Naseem chose four of them to be in her team, by starting counting at number 1 and counting clockwise a certain number.
The girl who was the last to be counted was chosen for the team, and she moved out of the circle. The counting was then repeated, starting at the next girl in the circle, until Naseem had completed her team.
What is the certain number that Naseem counted, so that she should get her four special friends in the team ? (These girls are standing in the positions marked x.)

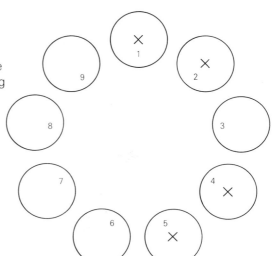

11 Thinking about solid figures

Basic shapes

What are the mathematical names of the shapes of these objects ?

Constructions

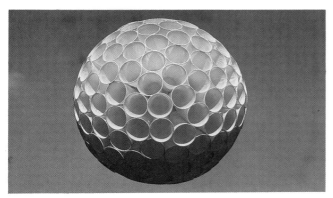

Office workers used their paper cups to make this sphere.

'The final stellation of the icosahedron'

Designs, old and new

Pyramids at Giza

Lincoln Cathedral

These 'golf balls', part of an early-warning station, are a familiar landmark on the North Yorkshire moors.

This modern building is the Sydney Opera House.

11 Solid Figures

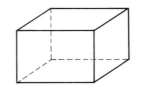
Cuboid, or Rectangular block

Cube

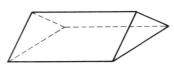
Triangular prism

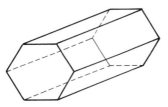
Hexagonal prism

Triangular pyramid, or tetrahedron

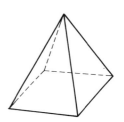
Pyramid with square base

Cylinder

Cone

Sphere

In your classroom, make a collection of objects which have these shapes, or a combination of these shapes. Arrange your collection carefully, and label the shapes. You can take a photograph of the display.

Exercise 11.1

1. **Practice in drawing cubes and cuboids**

   1   Cube

   Draw a square   Draw 4 parallel lines   Draw a square
                          of equal length   joining the 4 ends

             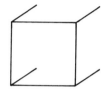   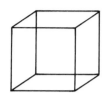

   Make some lines   or   Leave out the
   dotted lines   dotted lines

   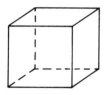   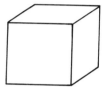

   2   Use a similar way to draw a cuboid.

   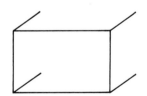   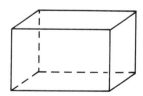

   3   Using isometric paper

   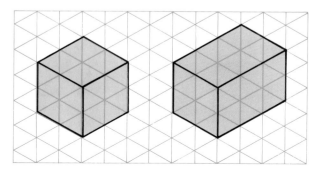

2.   Practise drawing a triangular prism, a triangular pyramid and a pyramid with a square base.
     If you find these difficult, use tracing paper to copy the drawings shown in this chapter.

3.   You can sketch a cylinder and a cone as follows:
     Begin with a rectangle, and an isosceles triangle.

Make curved lines at the top and bottom.

Rub out the straight lines, and make some of the curves dotted.

4.   Name the solid figures with these shapes.

1   2   3   4   5

  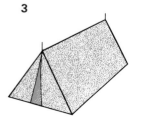  

5. Give an example of a common object, not shown in the last question, which has the shape of
    1   a cuboid,   **4**   a sphere,
    2   a cylindrical disc,   **5**   a prism.
    3   a cube,

6. Look at the drawings of the solid figures which have no curved faces, or look at actual objects if you have them available.
    Count the number of faces, vertices (corners) and edges on each.
    For example, this prism with pentagonal ends has 7 faces, 10 vertices and 15 edges.
    Copy and complete this table and add other solid figures to the list.

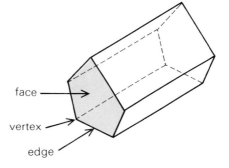

face ———▶
vertex ———▶
edge ▶

F = number of faces, V = number of vertices, E = number of edges.

Solid figure	F	V	E
cuboid			
triangular prism			
prism with pentagonal ends	7	10	15
tetrahedron			
pyramid on square base			

Can you discover the relationship between $F + V$ and E ?

7. A solid figure consists of a triangular pyramid fitted exactly on top of a triangular prism.
    State how many faces, vertices and edges the solid figure has.

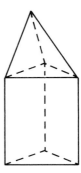

8. If small triangular pyramids are sliced off the corners of a cube, how many faces, vertices and edges has the remaining solid figure ?

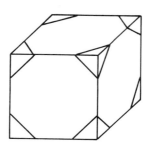

Nets of solid figures

These are patterns which when cut out and folded will make the figures.

Net of a cube

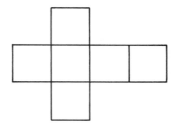

Making models from thin cardboard, using their nets

1   Draw the pattern of the net of the solid figure, on paper. Then place it over thin cardboard, with something underneath to protect the desk or table, and prick through the main points using the point of your compasses. Remove the pattern and join up the marks on the cardboard. (Keep the pattern for future use.)

2   Draw a tab on every alternate edge, i.e. starting at any edge, put tabs on edges 1, 3, 5, 7, . . . in order. Tabs can be drawn freehand. They should be large enough to stick easily.

tab

3   Score every line.
    This means making a nick in the line so that it folds neatly. Put your ruler along the line and drag your compass point along it. (When you fold the cardboard, always fold **away** from the side you scored on. Do not bend the cardboard backwards **and** forwards.)

4   Cut out the net and fold it along the scored lines.

5   Glue it together, doing one tab at a time and waiting until it has stuck before doing the next one, except at the last face where more than one tab may have to be glued at the same time. You may need to poke your compass point through a corner hole to help to make the last tab stick down properly.

To make a cube

Making the sides of the squares 4 cm long, copy the net of the cube shown on page 172 onto paper. (Graph paper or squared paper is useful.)
Carry out the instructions above for making the model.

To make a cuboid

Decide on the measurements your finished cuboid will have, and design and draw the net. Here is the net for a cuboid which will be 8 cm by 3 cm by 2 cm. Carry out the instructions for making the model.

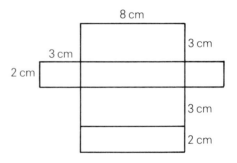

Here are nets for some other figures you can make. Decide which lengths on the nets should be equal.

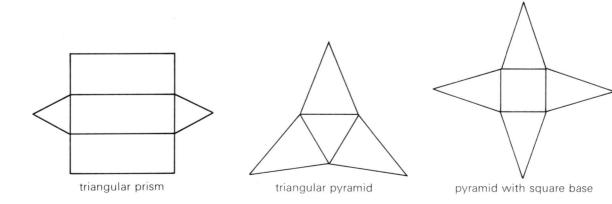

triangular prism   triangular pyramid   pyramid with square base

Exercise 11.2

1. The net of a cube can be arranged in several different ways. Which of these drawings of arrangements of 6 equal squares, if cut out and folded, would make a cube ?

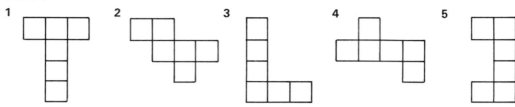

2. This net can be folded to make a triangular prism.
    Which letter(s) will point A join ?

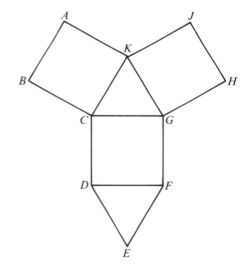

3. This drawing is part of a net for a cuboid with measurements 4 cm by 4 cm by 2 cm. Sketch the drawing and complete the net.

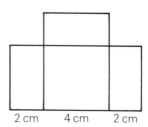

4. This is a triangular pyramid with all edges
    4 cm long.
    Since all the faces are equilateral triangles it
    can also be called a **regular tetrahedron**.

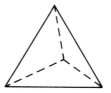

Which of these arrangements of 4 triangles can be used as nets of the pyramid ?

1   **2**   **3**

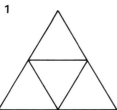   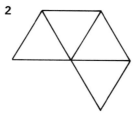   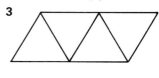

Draw a net of the pyramid accurately. (Isometric paper is useful.)
Make a model of the pyramid using cardboard.

5. To copy this net, begin by drawing the
    rectangle *ABCD*.
    Then use compasses with centres *C* and *D*,
    radius 5 cm, to find point *F*.
    Use compasses, centres *C* and *F*, to find
    point *E*, and similarly find point *H* and
    then *G*.
    Make a model, using cardboard.
    What is the name of the solid figure ?

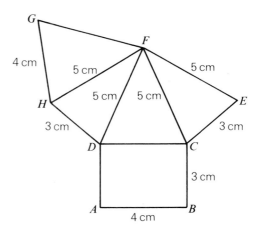

6. Name the solid figures made from these nets.

    1   **2**

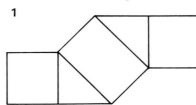   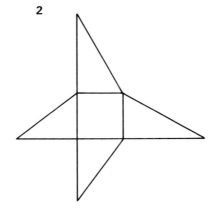

7.   **A model cylinder**, made from thin cardboard.

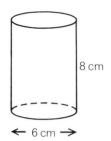

The circular ends are made from 2 circles,
radius 3 cm.
The curved surface is made from a
rectangle.
Length = 3.14 × diameter of cylinder
       = 3.14 × 6 cm = 18.8 cm
Breadth = height of cylinder = 8 cm
To stick the pieces together, tabs should
be added to the rectangle, as shown.
Score along the top and bottom edges
with tabs, but it is better not to score the
edge with the long tab.
Bend the rectangle carefully, and stick the
long tab behind the opposite edge.
Stick the circles onto the ends.

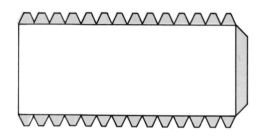

8.   **A model cone**, made from thin cardboard.

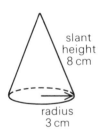

The base is made from a circle, radius 3 cm.
The curved surface is made from a sector
of a circle with radius 8 cm.
To find angle a, use the formula

$$a = \frac{\text{radius}}{\text{slant height}} \times 360°$$

In this case, $a = \frac{3}{8} \times 360° = 135°$

Tabs should be added to this piece, as
shown.
Score along the curved edge with tabs, but
it is better not to score the edge with the
long tab.
Bend the cone carefully, especially at its
point, and stick the long tab behind the
opposite edge.
Stick the circle onto the base.

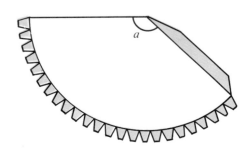

Exercise 11.3   Applications and Activities

1. Some cylindrical tins have radius $3\frac{1}{2}$ cm and height 6 cm. 70 tins are packed upright in 2 layers in a rectangular box, and just fit in. What are the inside measurements of the box ?

2. The circular cylinder has an axis of symmetry.
    Name another solid figure which has just one axis of symmetry.

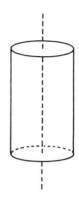

3. The diagram shows a plane of symmetry of the cylinder. How many planes of symmetry has a cuboid (whose faces are rectangular, not square) ?

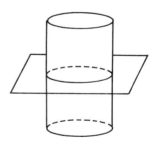

4. The diagram shows the net of a solid figure. Draw a sketch of the solid figure.

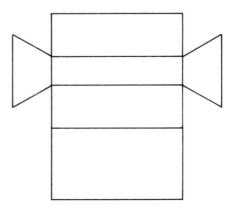

5. On a proper die, the numbers on opposite
    faces add up to 7.
    A cardboard cube was to be made into a
    die by labelling the squares on the net
    with the numbers 1, 2, 3, 4, 5, 6.

On these nets, some of the squares have been labelled. Sketch these diagrams
and label the other squares correctly.

1   **2**   **3**

                    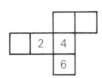

6. **Pentominoes**

    Pentominoes are arrangements of 5 equal squares which join together with
    edges of adjacent squares fitting exactly together, such as

     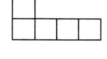

Pieces which would be identical if turned round or turned over are counted as the
same. Thus  is the same as

Draw the different arrangements on squared paper and try to find them all. There
are 12 altogether.
Now, some of these pentominoes if cut out and folded will make an open cubical
box. Find out which ones.

Hexominoes consist of 6 squares joined together. You may like to see how
many you can find, but there are 37 altogether.
11 of these will form the net of a (closed) cube. Try to find all of these, drawing
them on squared paper.

7. **Plans and Elevations**

This is a picture of a model cottage.

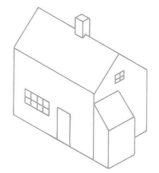

Seen from above, it looks like this.
This is a **plan** of the cottage.

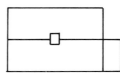

Seen from the front, it looks like this.
This is the **front elevation**.

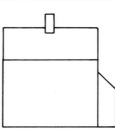

Seen from the side, it looks like this.
This is the **side elevation**.

Sketch the plans, front and side elevations of these objects.

1   2   3

      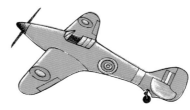

8. **The Regular Solid Figures**

These are solid figures made with regular polygons. There are
just five of them. You could make them and display them.
The smallest, the regular tetrahedron, is made with equilateral
triangles, with 3 triangles meeting at each point. See page 175,
question 4.
(The word **tetrahedron** means that it has four faces.)

If equilateral triangles are arranged with 4 triangles meeting at a point, an
octahedron is formed, and if there are 5 triangles meeting at a point, an
icosahedron is formed.
You can make these solid figures from their nets. (You may find it useful to copy
the patterns on isometric paper.)

net of octahedron

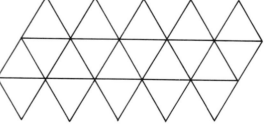

net of icosahedron

These are the only regular solid figures which can be made with equilateral
triangles.

The only regular solid figure made with squares is the cube.

The 5th regular solid figure is made from 12 regular pentagons, meeting 3 at a point. It is called a dodecahedron.

It can be made from its net, but as pentagons are not easy to draw, you may prefer to make it from separate pentagons.

Draw a regular pentagon carefully as a pattern and transfer it to cardboard 12 times by pricking through the main points.

Put a tab, drawn freehand, on each edge, and score along the edges. (You will only use half of these tabs, cutting the rest off when you know which ones are not needed.)

Glue two pentagons together, using one tab and cutting one off, and when the glue is dry glue two edges of a 3rd pentagon to these two, to make 3 pentagons meeting at a point. Add all the other pentagons in turn.

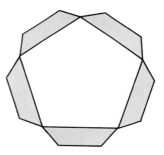

PUZZLES

26. **How many objects are there in a gross ?**

Think of a number, double it, add the number of pints in a gallon, multiply by the number of sides of a pentagon, take away ten times the number you first thought of. Now add on as many dozens as there are feet in a yard, double this number and take away the number of edges on a pyramid with a square base.
What is the answer ?

27. Wright and Co. sent Mr Johnson, a builder, a cheque for £300 to pay for work done. The cheque was stolen by a dishonest worker, Robert. He forged Mr Johnson's signature and took the cheque to a shop where he owed £200. He settled his debt with it and received the balance of £100 in cash.
Robert then left the district in a hurry. When the theft was discovered, the shop where Robert had settled his account was asked to refund to Wright and Co the £300 for the cheque, and it was then sent on to Mr Johnson, the rightful owner.
How much did the shop lose ?

12 Thinking about speeds

Journeys

Throughout the ages, the idea of speed has been important, but until very recently, the speeds involved were those of running and walking, the speeds of horses and, on water, the speeds of sailing ships. Journeys took days, rather than hours.

Stagecoach transport of 100 years ago

Modern transport

In the last 100 years or so, life has become much quicker and with transport by cars, trains, fast ships and planes being available, the importance of speed has increased. With modern vehicles it is possible to maintain regular speeds over long distances, and so the time a journey should take can be estimated quite accurately.

Make a list of vehicles and the speeds at which they normally can travel.

Intercity 225, high speed train

Speed limit signs on a Canadian road. What are the speeds in mph?

Speed limits

In the interests of safety on the roads, vehicles often have to limit their speeds.

Aircraft speeds

The first flight, made by Orville Wright in 1903, lasted for about 12 seconds. He flew 36.5 m at an airspeed of 48 km/h, ground speed 10.9 km/h.

Great Britain's 4 × 400 m relay team in Split, Yugoslavia, after setting a new European record, August, 1990.

The first men to set foot on the moon were Neil Armstrong and Edwin Aldrin, on 20th July, 1969.

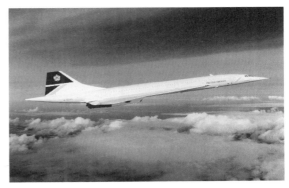

Concorde, the first supersonic airliner. It cruises at up to 2334 km/h.

Speed in sport

The idea of improving speeds forms an important part of many sporting events, whether it is the personal speed of an athlete, which can be improved by modern training methods, or of a machine such as a racing car, which can be improved by better design.

Make a list of sports in which speed plays an important part, and the speed records in those sports.

Recent developments

It is possible to send vehicles to outer space and by calculating their speeds, know in advance how long their journeys will take.

12 Speeds

The rate at which distance is travelled is called **speed**.

It is measured in units such as miles per hour, kilometres per hour, metres per second.

In many cases the speed varies. For instance, a train starts off from rest and gradually increases speed until it reaches its normal travelling speed. As it approaches a station it gradually reduces speed until it stops. You can work out the **average speed** of such a journey.

Finding speed

Examples

1   A ship sails at a steady speed, and in 5 hours travels 190 km. What is its speed ?

In 5 hours it sails 190 km
So in 1 hour it sails 190 ÷ 5 km = 38 km
Its speed is 38 km per hour.

2   A motorist drove from Aberystwyth to Manchester. The distance was 126 miles and he took $3\frac{1}{2}$ hours. What was his average speed for the journey ?

In $3\frac{1}{2}$ hours he travelled 126 miles
So in 1 hour he travelled 126 ÷ 3.5 miles = 36 miles, on average.
His average speed was 36 miles per hour.

You will notice that the speed was found by dividing the distance by the time. This means that we can write this as a formula:

$$\text{speed} = \frac{\text{distance}}{\text{time}} \qquad \text{or} \qquad \text{average speed} = \frac{\text{total distance}}{\text{total time}}$$

If the distance is measured in miles and the time in hours, the units for speed are miles per hour, which can be written as mph.
If the distance is measured in kilometres and the time in hours, the units for speed are km per hour, written as km/h.

In scientific work, the distance can be measured in metres and the time in seconds.
The units for speed are metres per second, written as m/s or ms^{-1}.
Other units can be used in a similar way.
To find the speed, you can use the method of examples **1** and **2** or you can use the formula.

3   A boy runs 100 m in 12.5 seconds. What is his average speed in m/s ?

$$\text{Average speed} = \frac{\text{total distance}}{\text{total time}}$$
$$= \frac{100}{12.5} \text{ m/s}$$
$$= 8 \text{ m/s}$$

Finding distance

4   A plane flies for $2\frac{1}{4}$ hours at 240 mph. How
far has it gone ?

240 mph means that in 1 hour it would go
240 miles,
so in $2\frac{1}{4}$ hours it goes $2\frac{1}{4} \times 240$ miles
$= 2.25 \times 240$ miles $= 540$ miles.

The distance was found by multiplying the speed by the time. This is a rearrangement
of the previous formula.

distance = speed × time

Again, the units must correspond. For instance, if the speed is in km/h the time must
be in hours to give the distance in kilometres. If the speed is in m/s the time must be
in seconds to give the distance in metres.

To find the distance, you can use the method of example **4** or you can use the formula.

5   A driver intends to go along a motorway at a speed of 100 km/h. If he wants to
stop for lunch in $3\frac{1}{2}$ hours time, how far can he go before then ?

$$\text{distance} = \text{speed} \times \text{time}$$
$$= 100 \times 3\frac{1}{2} \text{ km}$$
$$= 350 \text{ km.}$$

Finding time

6   A hiker has to walk 10 miles to a hostel. He
knows he can maintain an average speed of
4 mph. How long will it take him to reach
the hostel ?

He can go 4 miles in 1 hour
He can go 1 mile in $\frac{1}{4}$ hour
He can go 10 miles in $\frac{1}{4} \times 10$ hours $= \frac{10}{4}$ hours
$= 2\frac{1}{2}$ hours.

The time was found by dividing the distance by the speed, so the rearranged formula is

$$\text{time} = \frac{\text{distance}}{\text{speed}}$$

If the distance is in km and the speed in km/h, the time will be in hours.
If the distance is in metres and the speed in m/s, the time will be in seconds.
To find the time, you can use the method of example **6** or you can use the formula.

7   How long will it take a fishing-boat to sail 24 km if its speed is 10 km/h ?

$$\begin{aligned}
\text{time} &= \frac{\text{distance}}{\text{speed}} \\
&= \frac{24}{10} \text{ hours} \\
&= 2.4 \text{ hours} &\quad 0.4 \text{ hours} &= 0.4 \times 60 \text{ minutes} \\
&= 2 \text{ hours } 24 \text{ minutes.} &\quad &= 24 \text{ minutes}
\end{aligned}$$

(A sensible answer in practical terms would be 'about $2\frac{1}{2}$ hours'.)

Time in hours and minutes

Since there are 60 minutes in an hour you must take care with these units.
To change minutes into hours, divide by 60.
Times which are multiples of 3 minutes can be turned into exact decimals of an hour.

e.g.   3 min = 3 ÷ 60 h = 0.05 h
30 min = 0.5 h
42 min = 0.7 h

However, we often have times given in intervals of 5 minutes, and these are sometimes
better left as exact fractions.

e.g.   5 min = $\frac{5}{60}$ h = $\frac{1}{12}$ h

20 min = $\frac{20}{60}$ h = $\frac{1}{3}$ h

1 h 10 min = $1\frac{10}{60}$ h = $1\frac{1}{6}$ h

When you get times in hours, including decimals of an hour, you can turn the decimals into minutes by multiplying by 60.

e.g.   0.6 h = 0.6   × 60 min = 36 min
       0.15 h = 0.15 × 60 min = 9 min

Sometimes the answer may not be an exact number of minutes.

e.g.   0.125 h = 0.125 × 60 min = 7.5 min or $7\frac{1}{2}$ min

You may get times in hours and fractions of an hour. You can turn the fractions into minutes by multiplying by 60.

e.g. $\frac{2}{3}$ h = $\dfrac{2}{\cancel{3}_{1}} \times \cancel{60}^{20}$ min = 40 min

       $\frac{5}{12}$ h = $\dfrac{5}{\cancel{12}_{1}} \times \cancel{60}^{5}$ min = 25 min

Sometimes the answer may not be an exact number of minutes. You may need to give the answer as a decimal, or to the nearest minute, whichever seems more sensible.

e.g. $\frac{4}{7}$ h = $\frac{4}{7}$ × 60 min = $\frac{240}{7}$ min = 34.28 . . . min
                                   = 34 min, to the nearest minute,
                               or 34.3 min, to the nearest 0.1 minute.

Similar rules apply in turning seconds into minutes, when you divide by 60, or turning minutes into seconds, when you multiply by 60.

e.g.   4 min   = 4 × 60 seconds = 240 seconds
       0.3 min = 0.3 × 60 s   = 18 s
       $\frac{3}{4}$ min   = $\frac{3}{4}$ × 60 s   = 45 s
       12 s = $\frac{12}{60}$ min = 0.2 min
       14 s = $\frac{14}{60}$ min = $\frac{7}{30}$ min, if needed accurately,
                    = 0.23 min, if needed to 2 decimal places.

Exercise 12.1

1.   Find the average speeds of the following:

   1   A car travels 120 miles in 3 hours.
   2   A train travels 165 km in $2\frac{1}{2}$ hours.
   3   A runner races 200 m in 20 sec, (in m/s).
   4   A cyclist travels 18 km in $\frac{1}{2}$ hour.
   5   A fish swims 45 km in $1\frac{1}{2}$ hours.

2.   Find the distances travelled by the following:

    1   A motorist who maintains a speed of 70 mph for $\frac{1}{2}$ hour.
    2   A ship which steams for $3\frac{1}{4}$ hours at 20 km/h.
    3   A plane which travels at 320 km/h for $2\frac{3}{4}$ hours.
    4   A bird which flies at 30 mph for $\frac{1}{4}$ hour.
    5   A projectile which travels at 15 m/s for 5 seconds, (in metres).

3.   Find the times taken for these journeys:

    1   A motorist going 140 miles, if he maintains an average speed of 40 mph.
    2   A plane which travels at 800 km/h and makes a flight of 1400 km.
    3   A snail making a journey of 15 m at a speed of 30 m/hour.
    4   A train going at 75 mph, on a journey of 225 miles.
    5   A fishing boat going at 10 km/h, on a journey of 35 km.

4.   Change these times into hours, using decimals.

1	2 h 30 min		**4**	1 h 36 min
2	6 min		**5**	54 min
3	3 h 48 min			

5.   Change these times into hours, using fractions.

1	10 min		**4**	35 min
2	1 h 50 min		**5**	2 h 5 min
3	3 h 25 min			

6.   Change these times into hours and minutes.

1	3.25 h		**6**	$3\frac{1}{3}$ h
2	2.4 h		**7**	$1\frac{7}{12}$ h
3	1.75 h		**8**	$5\frac{1}{6}$ h
4	0.05 h		**9**	$1\frac{2}{3}$ h
5	2.7 h		**10**	$2\frac{5}{6}$ h

7.   **1**   Find the average speed if a train travels 72 km in 1 h 20 min.
    2   Find the distance if a fish swims for 10 min at a speed of 24 mph.
    3   Find the time taken by a runner who runs 1 km at an average speed of 15 km/h.
    4   Find the distance travelled by an antelope which moves for 5 min at a speed of 48 km/h.
    5   A snake has a maximum speed of about 6 km/h. How many metres could it travel in 1 minute ?

Exercise 12.2   Applications and Activities

1.   If a train is travelling at 90 km/h, how far does it go in 1 minute ?

2.   When Sheila visits her mother, the journey takes $1\frac{1}{2}$ hours if she goes at an average speed of 40 mph. If she reduces the average speed to 30 mph in wet weather, how much longer will her journey take ?

3.   A main road through a village has a speed limit of 30 miles per hour. A motorist covers the 2 mile section in $3\frac{1}{2}$ minutes. Did he break the speed limit ? On the return journey he travelled the 2 miles in $4\frac{1}{2}$ minutes. Do you know whether he broke the speed limit then ?

4.   A motorist normally made a journey of 90 miles in $1\frac{1}{2}$ hours. On one occasion road works reduced his average speed to 50 mph. How much longer than usual did the journey take ?

5.   A train starts at 2.30 pm and reaches the next stop at 3.15 pm. If its average speed is 72 km/h, what is the distance it has travelled ?

6.   A train travels 70 km at a speed of 100 km/h and then another 68 km at a speed of 85 km/h.
     1   What is the total distance travelled ?
     2   What is the total time taken ?
     3   What is the average speed for the whole journey ?

7.   A boat travels for $1\frac{1}{2}$ hours at 16 km/h and for the next $2\frac{1}{2}$ hours at 12 km/h.
     1   What is the total distance travelled ?
     2   What is the total time taken ?
     3   What is the average speed for the whole journey ?

8.   On a journey to work, Mrs Mistry drove 7 miles through town in 30 minutes and then 18 miles along the motorway in 20 minutes. What was her average speed over the whole journey ?

9. A lorry driver travels from Carlisle to Manchester and then on to London, at an average speed of 45 mph.
Find, to the nearest $\frac{1}{4}$ hour, how long the journey takes.
On the return trip from London to Carlisle he has to go via Oxford and Birmingham. How long will this journey take, if he still keeps to an average speed of 45 mph ?
The chart gives distances between the towns, in miles.

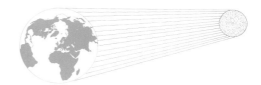

Birmingham				
197	Carlisle			
89	120	Manchester		
62	264	155	Oxford	
120	313	204	56	LONDON

10. The sun is 93 000 000 miles away. Light travels at 186 000 miles per second. How long does it take light from the sun to reach us ?

11. The turning of a wheel can be measured in revolutions (revs) per minute. If a wheel makes 20 revs per minute, how many revs does it make in an hour ? How long would it take to make 18 000 revs ?

12. **Thunder and lightning**

You probably know that light travels faster than sound, which is why we see the lightning before we hear the thunder. You can get some idea of how far away the storm is by timing the gap between the lightning and the thunder.
The light travels so fast that you can assume that you see the lightning immediately. The sound of thunder travels at about 1100 feet/second in air.
So you can make a list giving the distance of the storm from you, to the nearest 0.1 mile.
(To turn feet to miles divide by 5280.)

Time gap in seconds	Distance in miles
1	0.2
2	
.	
.	
.	
10	

13.   **Personal speed records**

With your friends to help you, you could work out a list of these, beginning by finding the times you take to run 100 m, 200 m, etc. and working out your speed over these distances.

If you can swim, you could add the speeds for various distances, and swimming strokes, to your list.

Then there are speeds for cycling, skating, skateboarding, and other activities, which you can add to your list.

Be careful, however, to travel at safe speeds. You do not want to cause any accidents to yourself, or to others, by trying to go too fast for safety.

14.   **Speeds of animals**

Look in reference books to find the speeds of various animals. You can decide whether to include birds, fish, etc. as well. Make a poster to show these. You can show the speeds on a bar chart, although it will be difficult to choose a scale to range from the speed of a swift, 171 km/h, to a snail, 0.05 km/h.

If the speeds are given in miles/hour you can convert them to km/h by multiplying by 1.609.

15.   **Speed records**

Look in reference books to find the present-day speed records for various forms of transport such as cars, ships, trains, aircraft. Make a poster to illustrate these speeds. It is also interesting to see how these speed records have increased over the years.

PUZZLE

28.   Here are two division sums, where A, B, C and D stand for different figures.
What are the correct figures ?

$CD \div AB = 3$, remainder 3

$AB\mathbf{0} \div CD = 3$, remainder 3

Miscellaneous Section B

These aural excercises, B1 and B2, should be read to you, probably by your teacher or a friend, and you should write down the answers only, doing any working out in your head. You should do the 15 questions within 10 minutes.

Exercise B1

1. £60 is shared between two people, Jack and Jill, so that Jack gets twice as much as Jill. How much does Jack get ?

2. In the function $y = 10 - 2x$, what is the value of y when $x = 1\frac{1}{2}$?

3. When throwing two ordinary dice, what is the total score which is most likely to occur ?

4. A plane left Manchester at 12.55 pm and arrived at Palma at 3.25 pm. How long did the journey take ?

5. How many hundredths are there altogether in the number 0.36 ?

6. All the angles of a hexagon are equal, and the sum of the angles is 720°. How big is each angle ?

7. A motorist travels at an average speed of 50 miles per hour for 3 hours. How far does he travel in this time ?

8. How many edges has a cube ?

9. The probability of Kevin winning his next match is 0.7. What is the probability of him not winning ?

10. What is the ratio of weights, in its simplest form, of two packets weighing 750 g and 1 kg ?

11. What is the lowest number into which 2, 3, 5 and 10 all divide ?

12. Out of a batch of 500 oranges, 20% were bad. How many were fit to sell ?

13. What word describes a polygon which has all its sides equal and all its angles equal ?

14. A cricketer scored 10, 20, 25 and 45 runs in four innings. What was his average score ?

15. Mark is normally paid at the rate of £4 per hour. On Saturdays he is paid at $1\frac{1}{2}$ times this rate. How much does he earn for 3 hours work on a Saturday ?

Exercise B2

1. What is the name of the solid figure with the shape of a tennis ball ?

2. Simplify the expression $15c - c$.

3. If 300 g of cooked meat is sufficient to make sandwiches for 4 people, how much should be bought to make sandwiches for 6 people ?

4. The function $y = 4x + 7$ is plotted on a graph. What is the x-coordinate of the point on the graph where $y = 15$?

5. In a bag there are 10 discs. 5 are red, 3 are blue and 2 are yellow. What is the probability of **not** drawing a yellow one ?

6. How many sides has an octagon ?

7. A motorist drives 75 miles at 50 miles per hour. How long does the journey take ?

8. If $x = 10$, what is the value of $x^2 - 2x + 1$?

9. How many vertices has a triangular prism ?

10. A line 50 cm long is divided in the ratio 2 : 3. How long is the shorter part ?

11. How many quarters are there in $3\frac{1}{2}$?

12. Each side of a regular pentagon is 8 cm long. What is the perimeter of the pentagon ?

13. Which of these answers is likely to be the correct one for 16 × 29; 264, 364 or 464 ?

14. Write down **an equation** which could be used to solve this problem, with x for the unknown number. 'I think of a number, halve it and then add 3. The result is 11.'

15. A child who was 1 m tall increased in height by 4% during the year. How tall is he now ?

Exercise B3   Revision

1. How many souvenir mugs costing £1.65 each can be bought for £100 ?

2. State the numbers of faces, vertices and edges on these solid figures:
    1   a cuboid,
    2   a pyramid on a square base,
    3   a triangular prism,
    4   a hexagonal prism.

3. Using your calculator, copy and complete this number pattern to the line
    beginning with 3333, then deduce the next three lines by following the pattern.

n	n^2
3	9
33	1089
333	. . .
3333	
. . .	

4. 250 kg of metal is used in making 60 metal components each weighing 4.1 kg.
    What amount of metal is wasted ?
    What percentage of metal is wasted ?

5. In this regular 12-sided polygon with
    centre O,
    1   find the size of angle a.
    2   What kind of triangle is $\triangle OBC$?
    3   Find the size of angle b,
    4   find the size of angle c ($\angle BCD$).

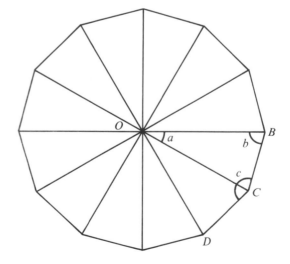

6. Brass contains copper, tin and zinc in the ratio 64 : 7 : 1. How much zinc is there
    in a brass ornament which weighs 2.16 kg ?

7. Two men play a game of chess. The probability of Derek winning is $\frac{2}{9}$. The probability of Stephen winning is $\frac{1}{9}$. If neither wins the game is a draw. What is the probability of a draw ?

8. From the diagram, write down an equation and solve it to find the value of x.
    Hence find the sizes of the angles A, B and C.

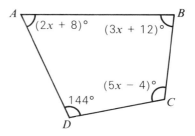

9. Explain how you can tell, without actually dividing it, that the number 11 550 divides by 2, 3, 5 and 25, and that it does not divide by 4 or 9.
    Does it also divide by 7, and by 11 ?

10. $ABCD$ is a rhombus with $\angle ABC = 60°$.
     What sort of triangle is
     1 $\triangle ABC$,
     2 $\triangle ABD$,
     3 $\triangle ABX$?

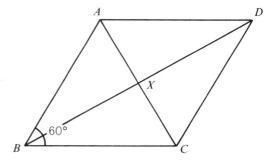

11. What is the ratio of £4.90 to 35p expressed in its lowest terms ?

12. This is the net of a triangular prism. When it is cut out and folded, which letter(s) will point A join ?

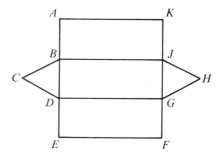

13. On graph paper, using the same scale on both axes, plot the points A $(-4, -3)$, B $(1, -2)$, C $(3, 4)$, D $(-2, 3)$. Join AB, BC, CD, DA.
     What sort of figure is $ABCD$?
     If its diagonals intersect at E, write down the coordinates of E.

14. A car passes a junction A at 2.55 pm and reaches a village B, 6 miles distant, at 3.05 pm. What is the average speed of the car ?

15. Last year Mr Yates, a car dealer,
     sold 263 new cars and 369 second-hand
     cars. He also sold 155 new vans and
     87 second-hand vans.
     Design a table to show all this
     information. It should also show the total
     numbers of cars sold, vans sold, new
     vehicles sold, second-hand vehicles sold,
     and a final total of all vehicles sold.

16. A regular tetrahedron with numbers 1, 2,
     3, 4 on its faces is used as a die. The
     number on the face which rests on the
     ground and therefore cannot be seen is
     taken as the score.
     Make a table showing the possible total
     scores when two of these dice are
     thrown.

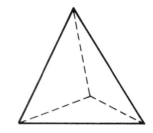

     How many equally likely outcomes are there ?
     What is the probability that the total score is greater than 6 ?

17. Three women invest £1000, £1500 and £2500 respectively into a business
     venture. What is the ratio of their investments, in its simplest form ?
     In the first year the business made a profit of £1200. The women agree to share
     this profit in the same ratio as their investments. How much does each woman
     get ?

18. Copy and complete the table for the function $y = 2x - 3$.

x	-3	-2	-1	0	1	2	3
y	-9						

     Identify the function below, giving the equation as $y = $ 'expression in x'.

x	-1	0	1	2	3
y	3	0	-3	-6	-9

     Represent the two functions on the same graph, drawing the x-axis from -3 to
     3 and the y-axis from -9 to 3.
     State the coordinates of the point where the two lines intersect.

19. **1**   What is the sum of the exterior angles of a polygon ?
     2   If the polygon is a regular polygon with 30 sides, what is the size of each
              exterior angle ? What is the size of each interior angle ?

20. A rubber ball bounces back $\frac{4}{5}$ of the height from which it is dropped.
     If it is dropped out of an upstairs window 5 m above the ground, how far does it
     rise after
     1   the first bounce,
     2   the second bounce,
     3   the third bounce ?

Exercise B4   Activities

1. **Feed yourself for £1**

    Plan a proper meal to make for yourself, with food and drink costing not more
    than £1. You may find it easier to plan for yourself and the family or a few
    friends, spending not more than £1 per person.
    The meal should have two or three courses, not just be a snack of bread and jam.
    You have to include the cost of all the main ingredients, although you can
    assume that you don't need to pay for small items like salt, which are already in
    the house, and you don't have to include the cost of the gas or electricity used in
    cooking the food. Try to have a balanced, healthy menu.
    Perhaps in the holidays you will be able to do this practically, possibly with your
    family or friends, including shopping for the food, preparing and cooking the
    meal, eating it, washing up and tidying things away afterwards.

2. **Buying a tool kit**

    Imagine you have £100 to spend to buy a basic tool kit for yourself or for the
    family. You will begin by thinking of the most useful tools such as screwdrivers,
    pliers and a hammer. Use a shopping catalogue, or visit the local shops, to make
    a list of useful tools and their cost. Try to include most things that are needed in a
    house to do simple repairs or DIY jobs.

    (If you are not the DIY expert at home and would have no idea where to begin
    with this list, then change the activity to suit your own interests. For instance,
    you could choose to buy a set of gardening tools, or kitchen equipment.)

3.   **The Laws of Growth or Decay**

If an amount of money is increased each year by a constant percentage, then the increase also gets bigger each year.
With your calculator you can investigate such growth.
Suppose you begin with £1000 and it increases by 10% each year.
The increase in the first year is 10% of £1000, which is £100.
The amount at the end of the first year is £1100.
Now in the second year it increases by 10% of £1100, which is £110.
The amount at the end of the second year is £1210.
You can continue working out the amounts in this way.
However, to find the amount at the end of any year, you are finding
100% + 10% = 110% of the amount at the beginning of the year. So you can multiply by the number 1.1 each time.
So on your calculator press 1.1 $\times$ 1000 $=$ $=$ $=$ $=$ . . .
and you will get the amounts at the end of 1 year, 2 years, 3 years, . . .
How many years will it be before the money is doubled, to over £2000 ?

Show your results on a line-graph, but joining the points with a smooth curve, drawn freehand.
These amounts are called the amounts at compound interest. If you subtract the original amount, £1000, the amount remaining is the **compound interest**.

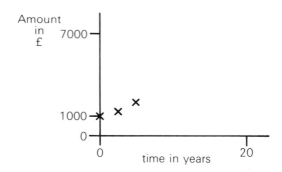

You can also investigate the effects of different rates of interest. Try 2%, 4%, 6%, 8%, 12%, etc. (For 2% you will multiply by 1.02)
You can show all these results on one graph using different colours for the different rates.

Also show on a bar chart the amounts after 5 years, if £1000 is invested at each rate of interest.
Comment on the results.

Find out what rates of interest are being paid by the main banks and building societies at the present time.
Find out about **inflation**.
See if you can find out about wages and prices 20 years ago. Why have they risen so much ?

The same effect applies to population growth, with humans, animals or bacteria. If an island had a population of 10 000, and the population grew at 2% each year, what would the population be in 50 years time ? Give some reasons why such an increase might not happen.

The opposite effect is the law of **decay**.
For instance, the value of a machine **depreciates** each year. If the rate of depreciation is 8% and a machine is worth £1000 now, what will it be worth in 5 years time ?
In the first year it will lose 8% of £1000, that is £80, and at the end of the year it will be worth £920.
In the second year it will lose 8% of £920, and so on.
To find the amounts at the end of each year, you need 100% − 8% = 92% each time.
On your calculator press 0.92 ×̲ 1000 =̲ =̲ =̲ =̲ . . .
and you will get the values at the end of 1 year, 2 years, 3 years, . . .
At the end of 5 years it will be worth £659.
In how many years is its value reduced to less than half ?

You can show these results on a line graph (but joining the points with a smooth curve), and add different curves for different rates of depreciation.
Why does the value never actually reach zero ?

A most important application of the law of decay is the decrease of radioactivity in a radioactive material. You can try to find out more about this. What is meant by the **half-life** of a radioactive element ?

4. **A Year's Work**

Here are some examples of activities based on the year with number 1992, but if you are doing this in a different year, just amend it.

Time and the calendar

1   Write 1992 in Roman numerals.
2   Is it a leap year ?
3   On which day of the week does the year begin ?
4   On which day of the week is your birthday ?
5   On which day of the week is Christmas Day ?
6   On what date is Easter Sunday ?

7   You may have dates special to other religions which you wish to note here, for instance, the dates of Ramadan, or Diwali.

8   In which months is there a 'Friday the thirteenth' ?

9   Which special sporting events are taking place in the year ? For instance, the Olympic Games ?

10   Are there any special political, nationwide or local events taking place ?

1992 units

11   What were you doing, or when was, 1992 seconds ago, 1992 minutes ago, 1992 days ago, 1992 weeks ago, 1992 months ago ?

12   How far from where you are now is 1992 mm, 1992 cm, 1992 m, 1992 km ?

13   Describe the heaviness of 1992 g, 1992 kg, and how much space 1992 litres of liquid occupies.

14   Can you and your friends collect 1992 pennies altogether ? Afterwards, you can give them to a favourite charity.

Numbers

15   Is 1992 a prime number ? If not, what factors has it ?

16   What is 1992^2 ? What is $\sqrt{1992}$?

17   Can you add up some square numbers to make 1992 ?

18   Can you add up some cube numbers to make 1992 ?

19   Can you add up some triangular numbers to make 1992 ?

20   How can you make 1992 by adding some of the numbers of the doubling sequence 1, 2, 4, 8, . . . (using each number once only) ?

21   How can you make 1992 by using some numbers of the sequence 1, 3, 9, 27, . . . (using each number once only, but using addition or subtraction) ?

22   Here is one way to get to 1992 just using the figure 2.
$$1992 = 2222 - 222 - (2 \times 2 \times 2)$$
Try to get to 1992 just using each of the figures 3 to 9 in turn.

23   1991 is a palindromic number, that is, it is the same backwards as forwards. Can you make 1992 into a palindromic number, by continually reversing and adding ? (If the numbers get very big, abandon your attempt.)

	1992
reversed	2991
add	4983
reversed	3894
add	8877
	. . . .

24   Using the numbers 1, 9, 9, 2 in that order, and using mathematical signs, see how many other numbers you can represent.

e.g. $16 = 1 + 9 + (\sqrt{9} \times 2)$
$810 = (1 + 9) \times 9^2$
$1748 = 19 \times 92$

What is the largest number possible ? (Don't try to work it out if it is too big!)

Geometrical patterns

25   Go 1 step North, 9 East, 9 South, 2 West, and starting from where you finished, repeat several times. (Or you can draw the route on a large sheet of paper. You can also try similar patterns on isometric paper.)

26   Start with a circle and mark 24 equally-spaced points around the circumference. (Use a circle with a radius just larger than that of your protractor and you can use your protractor to mark off points every 15° round the circumference.)

Start from any point, count 1 point and join these two points with a straight line, using a ruler.
Continuing from the point you finished at, count round 9 points and then join the two points at the beginning and end of the counting with a line.
Carry on with another 9 points, then 2 points.
Repeat the sequence 1, 9, 9, 2 until you arrive back at the starting point after having counted 2.
You could do this with nails and cotton, making a string-art picture. (1993 makes a more interesting pattern than 1992.)

Invent your own activities, based on the year.

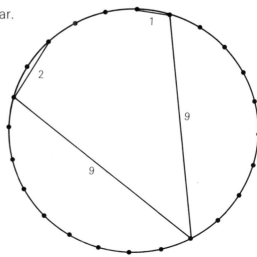

5.   **Probability experiments**

Use 6 cards of which 2 are picture cards (or are marked in some way differently to the others).

1   If you mix them up, and then deal them out in a row, what is the probability that the two picture cards are next to each other ?

successful   **not successful**

Make a guess, giving the answer as a simple decimal or fraction.
Now carry out the experiment, doing it at least 100 times.

The probability, worked out by experiment, $= \dfrac{\text{number of successful trials}}{\text{total number of trials}}$

Was your guess a good one ?

2   Now try a second experiment. This time you deal the cards out in a circle. What is the probability now that the two picture cards are next to each other ?

successful   **not successful**

Make a guess, and then carry out the experiment and work out the probability. Was your guess a good one ?

If you are interested in seeing how your experimental results for the probabilities compare with the theoretical probabilities, you may like to try to calculate the theoretical probabilities, using these methods.

For part **1**, imagine that you deal out just 5 of the cards, keeping hold of one of the picture cards. Now you are going to fit this card in, at any place in the row, making a space for it. How many places are there for it to go ? These are equally likely to occur. How many of these places are next to the other picture card, and thus successful ?
So what is the theoretical probability ?
Repeat the calculation for part **2**.

Finally, comment on whether your experimental results match the theoretical ones.

6. **Diagonals of polygons**
   A diagonal is a line which joins two non-adjacent points.
   Here are sketches of a triangle, a quadrilateral and a pentagon with the diagonals shown by dotted lines.

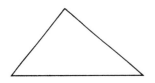 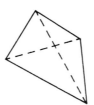 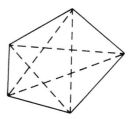

Copy and complete the table.

Number of sides of polygon	3	4	5	6
Number of diagonals	0	2	.	.

Sketch a polygon with 10 sides, and no angles greater than 180°. From one point, how many diagonals can be drawn ? To find the total number of diagonals, multiply this number by 10, because you can draw diagonals from each of the 10 points, then divide by 2 because using this method you have counted every diagonal twice. How many diagonals are there ?
Can you find a formula for the number of diagonals d of a regular polygon with n sides ?
If so, use your formula to find the number of diagonals of a regular polygon with 20 sides.

7. **Using a network map, the London Undergound**

Elizabeth and her French pen-friend, Janine, are planning a sightseeing
expedition to London. They will stay two nights and can plan to visit places on
three days. They have made a list of some of the places they would like to see,
together with the nearest Underground station.

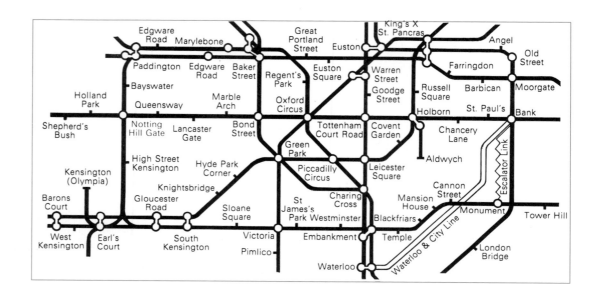

Place	Underground Station
Buckingham Palace	Victoria or St James's Park or Green Park
Tower of London	Tower Hill
Trafalgar Square	Charing Cross
Hyde Park	Hyde Park Corner or Marble Arch
Covent Garden	Covent Garden
Houses of Parliament	Westminster
British Museum	Tottenham Court Road or Goodge Street
Science Museum	Gloucester Road
Museum of London	Barbican, St Paul's or Moorgate
Shops in Oxford Street	Bond Street
Harrods	Knightsbridge
Madame Tussauds	Baker Street

Place	Underground Station
Place	**Underground Station**
Piccadilly Circus	Piccadilly Circus
Westminster Abbey	Westminster
St Paul's Cathedral	St Paul's
Tower Bridge	Tower Hill
London Bridge	London Bridge or Monument
Exhibition at Olympia	Olympia
Royal Festival Hall	Waterloo
The Monument	Monument

Perhaps you can think of other interesting places which could be added to the list.

Their hotel accommodation is near Great Portland Street Underground station and so they will start out from there each time, and finish there each day.

Plan suitable routes for them to follow, using the Underground for transport, for the afternoon of the first day and on the mornings and afternoons of the second and third days, so that they can see as much as possible in the time. They may not be able to fit everything in.

In your list of visits, include instructions for travelling by Underground, including stations where they have to change from one line to another. If you can use a proper Underground map, which will be in colour, you can give a more complete answer, including the names of the lines.

8. **The Fibonacci Sequence (4)**

    Links with a pentagon

    Draw a regular pentagon and join its
    diagonals.

    Find the ratios $\dfrac{AB}{BC}$, $\dfrac{AC}{AB}$ and $\dfrac{AD}{AC}$, by

    measuring, i.e. find $AB \div BC$ and give the
    answer in decimal form, etc.

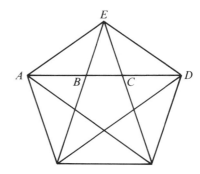

    In fact, these equal $\frac{1}{2}(\sqrt{5} + 1)$ exactly.
    Work out the value of this, to 3 decimal places.
    Do your answers match this ?

    Find the ratios $\dfrac{BC}{AB}$, $\dfrac{AB}{AC}$ and $\dfrac{AC}{AD}$.

    These equal $\frac{1}{2}(\sqrt{5} - 1)$ exactly.
    You can work this out, to 3 decimal places, and check your answers.
    Is there a link with the ratios from consecutive terms of the Fibonacci sequence ?
    (See page 49 to remind you of these.)

    The ratio 1.618 : 1 or 1 : 0.618 is known as the **Golden Section ratio**.

    Draw 4 rectangles with the measurements shown here, on a sheet of paper.
    Which one would you prefer for the shape of a picture ? Ask other people which
    they would prefer, and make a list of the replies. (It is better not to let them hear
    other people's replies before they choose.)

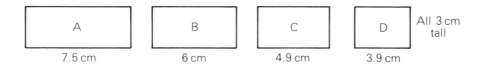

    Repeat this using rectangles for upright pictures.

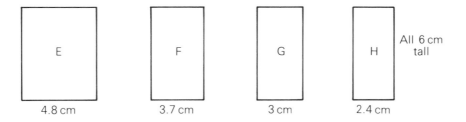

The rectangular shape with sides in the ratio of the Golden Section is a pleasing shape which is often used in Art, and in the proportions of some ancient buildings, and also some modern buildings.

Which of the rectangles A, B, C, D and which of E, F, G, H, had measurements in the Golden Section ratio ? Did most people choose those two, or not ? Did you ?

As well as the measurements of the whole picture, in order to get a pleasing composition, the artist often uses the golden section ratio within the picture.

Measure above and below the skyline in various pictures.

Find the ratio $a : b$ (or $a + b : a$) in the form of a decimal and see how close it is to 1.618.

Divide the width of the picture in the golden section ratio.
e.g. If the picture is 30 cm wide, then
$30 \div 1.618 = 18.5$, and the two parts are
18.5 cm and 11.5 cm.
Measure 18.5 cm or 11.5 cm from either edge and see if at this distance there is an important feature of the picture.

9. **The semi-regular solid figures**

(These are also called the Archimedian polyhedra.)

If you have made the 5 regular solid figures you may like to add to your
collection these 13 solid figures, which are made with combinations of regular
polygons, e.g. equilateral triangles and squares, or squares and regular hexagons,
etc.
It will take a long time to make all of these, so you may prefer to work with a
group of friends, doing one or two each.
You can make them from their nets and the nets of two of them are given here.
Follow the general instructions given for making models, on page 172.

Net of truncated tetrahedron

(Draw the pattern on isometric paper.)

Net of rhombicuboctahedron

(Draw the pattern of squares on squared paper and use compasses to find the 3rd
points of the triangles.)

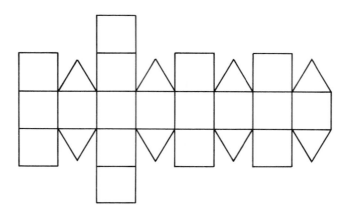

For the others, we suggest that you use the method described for the regular dodecahedron (page 181), making separate faces with tabs on each edge, and cutting off half the tabs when you find out which ones are not needed.

All polygons have edges of the same length, so begin by making patterns for an equilateral triangle, a square, a regular pentagon, a regular hexagon, a regular octagon and a regular decagon (10 sides).

You can then make as many copies as you need, from cardboard, by pricking through the points.

The list on the next page gives instructions for the other 11 models.

You can paint the models using different colours for the different sorts of polygons, and they look very attractive.

Put your models on display, and take a photograph of them.

Name	Polygons used All regular, and all sides the same length	Arrangement at each vertex
Truncated cube	8 triangles 6 octagons	2 octagons and 1 triangle
Truncated octahedron	6 squares 8 hexagons	2 hexagons and 1 square
Truncated dodecahedron	20 triangles 12 decagons	2 decagons and 1 triangle
Truncated icosahedron	12 pentagons 20 hexagons	2 hexagons and 1 pentagon
Cuboctahedron	8 triangles 6 squares	square, triangle, square, triangle, in order
Icosidodecahedron	20 triangles 12 pentagons	pentagon, triangle, pentagon, triangle, in order
Rhombicosidodecahedron	20 triangles 30 squares 12 pentagons	pentagon, square, triangle, square, in order
Truncated cuboctahedron or Great rhombicuboctahedron	12 squares 8 hexagons 6 octagons	octagon, square, hexagon in either clockwise or anticlockwise order
Truncated icosidodecahedron or Great rhombicosidodecahedron	30 squares 20 hexagons 12 decagons	decagon, square, hexagon in either clockwise or anticlockwise order
Snub cube	32 triangles 6 squares	1 square and 4 triangles. Counting triangles from the square in anticlockwise order, another square is stuck on the free edge of the 2nd triangle. Triangles are joined to the other free edges.
Snub dodecahedron	80 triangles 12 pentagons	1 pentagon and 4 triangles. Counting triangles from the pentagon in anticlockwise order, another pentagon is stuck on the free edge of the 2nd triangle. Triangles are joined to the other free edges.

10.   **Using the computer**

Here are some more suggestions.

1   Investigate various functions and plot
their graphs.
You can see the effect of changing
the equation of a function by drawing
several graphs in turn.
e.g. $y = x$, $y = 2x$, $y = \frac{1}{2}x$, etc.
$y = 3x$, $y = 3x + 2$, $y = 3x - 2$, etc.
$y = 2x$, $y = -2x$

You can look at functions involving x^2, x^3 or $\frac{1}{x}$, whose graphs are curves.

Again, you can compare graphs.
e.g. $y = x^2$, $y = x^2 + 10$
$y = x^2$, $y = -x^2$
$y = x^3$, $y = x^3 - x$

2   Investigate polygons and other shapes by using a LOGO program.
What interior angles are possible for a regular polygon ?

3   Use the computer to generate random numbers instead of tossing coins,
throwing dice, etc. for probability experiments.
e.g. With a suitable program you can get a list of scores when two dice are
thrown, work out the sum of the scores in each case, and plot the
frequencies of the various sums on a vertical bar chart or histogram.
If there is a more remote event, such as getting faulty components when, on
average, 5% of all components are faulty, then using random numbers you
can investigate experimentally the probabilities of getting 0, 1, or 2 or more,
faulty ones in a batch of 100 components.

PUZZLE

29.   The other evening the Stewart family were checking up their savings in the Holiday Fund.
Father, mother, their son and two daughters had a total of £178 in their accounts.
Father's and mother's savings totalled £124. Pauline's savings equalled Debbie's and
Timothy's combined.
Mother had three times as much as Debbie had saved. Pauline and Timothy combined
held savings of half the amount their father had saved.
How much had each person saved ?

13 Thinking about bearings

Compass directions

In the days of sailing ships and other rather slow forms of transport it was sufficient to use compass directions for deciding on the direction in which to travel.

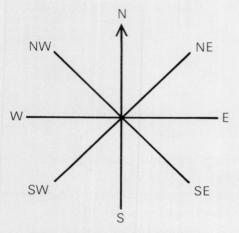

8-points compass directions

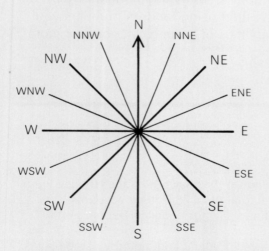

16-points compass directions

The Mayflower II, the replica of the original Mayflower, arriving in New York Harbour, in 1957.

32-points compass directions

Bearings

As the speed of travel has increased, more accurate measurements are needed. At first these were based on the main directions of North and South, tuning a certain number of degrees East or West. But if the communication system was not clear, instructions could be mis-heard and mistakes could be costly.

The present system is based on **always** starting from the North direction and **always** turning clockwise, so there is no need to transmit those details. The angle is given as a 3-figure number so that if, for instance, radio communication is distorted and only 2 figures are received, it is clear that the information is incomplete.

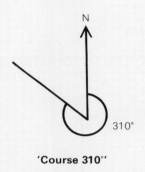

'Course 310°'

Airbus A320 cockpit

Using a compass

If you are walking in difficult country, you are strongly advised to take a compass with you.

It is useful in checking your direction of travel, and finding your position. You will use it, together with your map, looking at landmarks you can see such as church towers, peaks of hills, streams, etc. If you are lost in a mist or a snowstorm, or if it goes dark, the compass could be vital for your safety.

13 Bearings

3-figure bearings

Bearings (directions) are measured from North, in a clockwise direction. They are given in degrees, as 3-figure numbers.

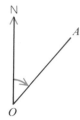

Examples

1 Show the directions given by the bearings 040°, 310°.

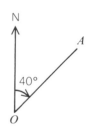

Direction *OA* has a bearing of 040°

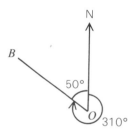

Direction *OB* has a bearing of 310°

Opposite directions

To face the opposite direction, you turn through 180°. So to find the bearing of a reverse direction, add 180°. If this comes to 360° or more, subtract 180° instead.

2 Find the bearings of the directions *AO* and *BO* from example **1**.

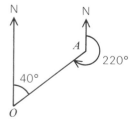

The bearing of *A* from *O* is 040°
The bearing of *O* from *A* is 040° + 180°
= 220°

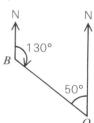

The bearing of *B* from *O* is 310°
The bearing of *O* from *B* is 310° − 180°
= 130°

Exercise 13.1

1. Find the bearings given by the directions *OA*, *OB*, *OC*, *OD* and *OF*.

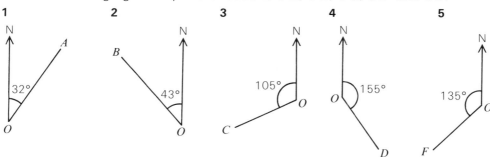

2. Draw sketches to show the directions given by the bearings
    1   190°   **2**   030°   **3**   280°   **4**   115°   **5**   005°

3. Find the bearings of the directions *AO*, *BO*, *CO*, *DO* and *FO* in question 1.

4. By measuring with your protractor, find the bearings given by the directions *OA*,
    OB, *OC*, *OD*, *OF* in these scale drawings.

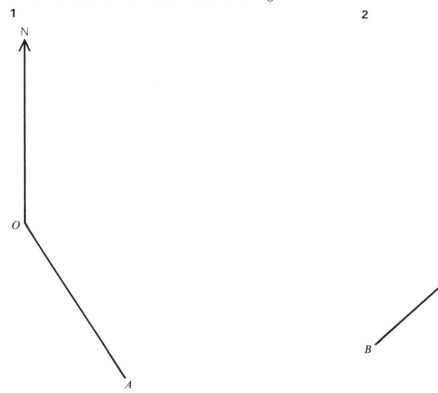

4.   **3**   **4**   **5**

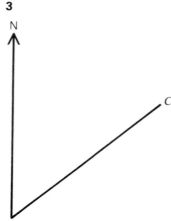      

5.   Find the bearings of these places from a point *O*.
     1   *A* is south-west of *O*,   **4**   *D* is north-east of *O*,
     2   *B* is east of *O*,   **5**   *F* is west of *O*.
     3   *C* is north-west of *O*,

6.   **1**   The bearing of *P* from *Q* is 060°. What is the bearing of *Q* from *P* ?
     2   The bearing of *P* from *Q* is 145°. What is the bearing of *Q* from *P* ?
     3   The bearing of *P* from *Q* is 220°. What is the bearing of *Q* from *P* ?
     4   The bearing of *P* from *Q* is 025°. What is the bearing of *Q* from *P* ?
     5   The bearing of *P* from *Q* is 123°. What is the bearing of *Q* from *P* ?

7.   **1**   Find the bearings of *B* and *C* from *A*.

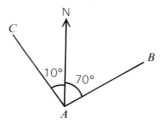

     2   Find the bearings of *B* and *C* from *A*.

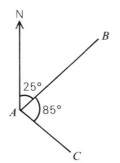

3   The bearing of *B* from *A* is 055° and
the bearing of *C* from *B* is 140°.
Find the size of ∠*ABC*.

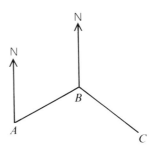

4   The bearing of *B* from *A* is 060° and
∠*ABC* is 100°.
Find the bearing of *B* from *C*.

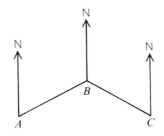

5   Find the bearing of *C* from *A*, and of
C from *B*.

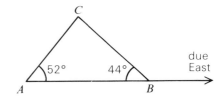

8. **Revision practice in drawing parallel lines**

Copy the drawing with points *A*, *B* and the
north line, on tracing paper.
Use your set-square and ruler to draw lines
parallel to the north line through *A* and *B*.
Join *AB*.
Find, by measuring with your protractor,
1   the bearing of *B* from *A*,
2   the bearing of *A* from *B*.

Exercise 13.2   Applications and Activities

1.   A ship sailing in the direction 058° alters course to sail in the opposite direction. What is its new course ?

2.

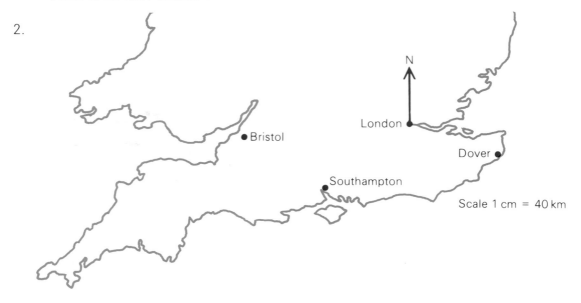

Use tracing paper to mark the positions shown by London, Bristol, Dover and Southampton, and also mark the North direction.
Find the distances, to the nearest 20 km, and the bearings of

1   Dover from London,
2   Southampton from London,
3   Bristol from Southampton,

4   Dover from Bristol,
5   Dover from Southampton.

3.   A boat leaves a harbour *A* and sails 5 km south-west to a point *B*, and then 3 km south to a point *C*.
On what bearing must it sail to head directly back to harbour and how far has it to sail ?
(Draw an accurate scale drawing using a scale of 1 cm to represent 1 km. Show *AB* and *BC*. Join *CA* and find the bearing and distance.)

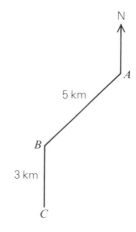

4.

Use tracing paper to mark the positions shown for the school, church, castle, wood and farm, and also mark the North direction.
Find the bearings of

1   the church from the school,   **4**   the farm from the church,
2   the farm from the wood,   **5**   the castle from the farm.
3   the wood from the castle,

5.   A fishing boat leaves a harbour and sails for $3\frac{1}{2}$ hours at a speed of 20 km per hour on a bearing of 160°. It then sails due East for 3 hours at a speed of 15 km per hour. Then the skipper hears a storm warning on the radio. How far is the boat from the harbour, on what bearing should the boat be headed, and how long will it take to reach harbour, if it resumes its speed of 20 km per hour ?

6. Two ships leave a port A. The first ship
    sails on a bearing of 062° and at noon it is
    at position B, 25 km from A. The second
    ship sails on a bearing of 312° and at noon
    it is at a point C, 18 km from A.
    Draw an accurate scale drawing, using a
    scale of 1 cm to represent 2 km, and join
    BC.
    How far apart are the ships, at noon ?

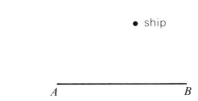

7. There are 2 coastguard stations, A and B,
    50 km apart, with B being due East of A.
    A ship is shown on radar on a bearing of
    058° from A, and on a bearing of 326°
    from B.
    Draw an accurate scale drawing showing
    A, B and the ship, and find how far the
    ship is from A, and from B.
    (Use a scale of 1 cm to represent 5 km.)

8. **Alternative Notation for Bearings**

    You may still find instances where the old method of stating bearings is used, so
    here are some examples of how the method works.

    Bearings are measured from North or South, whichever is the nearer direction,
    and they are measured towards the East or towards the West.
    N 20° E means measure 20° from the North, turning towards the East.

    Examples

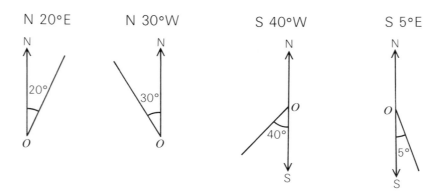

Using this notation, find the bearings given by the directions *OA, OB, OC, OD, OF*.

1   **2**   **3**

   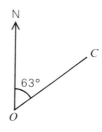   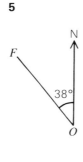

4   **5**

Draw sketches to show the directions given by the bearings

6   N 30° E   **7**   S 65° W   **8**   N 70° W   **9**   N 5° E   **10**   S 60° E

PUZZLES

30.   Decode this bill. Each capital letter stands for a figure and each figure stands for the corresponding letter.

				£
T	376034	at	£C each	I D
SB	90819731	at	£SB each	S DD
I	384501	at	£SS each	I I
D	4371171	at	£BD each	T C
R	60891	at	£AE each	B C S
				C S O

31.   Two trucks in the desert travel directly towards each other. They start out 120 km apart. One travels at 40 km/h, the other at 20 km/h.
      How far apart are they 1 minute before they meet ?

14 Thinking about perimeter, area

Perimeter

If you had a plot of land which needed fencing to keep animals out, you would have to measure the perimeter to see how much fencing was needed.

The perimeter is the total distance round the boundary of the plot.

What is the perimeter of this plot ?

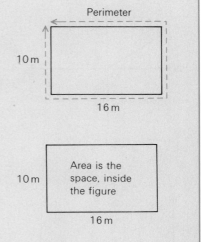

Area

When you wanted to put fertilizer on the land, you would have to know the area of the plot, to see how much fertilizer was needed.

We compare areas with a square of edge 1 cm, and we call that area 1 square centimetre, (written 1 cm^2).
For larger areas we use 1 m^2 or 1 km^2.

How many 1 m^2 squares would fit into the plot above ?
What is the area of the plot ?

(Land is sometimes measures in hectares.
1 hectare = 10 000 m^2)

The British system for areas of fields

Fields in the Middle Ages used to be divided into strips, which were ploughed using oxen. A rod or pole was used to prod the oxen.
4 rods wide was the width of the strip, and the length was 40 rods, which was called a furrow-length (a furlong). This was the distance the oxen went without a rest.
The area of the strip was called an acre and was the amount that could be ploughed in a day.
Even when oxen were replaced by horses, it was still judged that it took a day to plough an acre of land.
Since a rod is $5\frac{1}{2}$ yards long, there are 4840 square yards in an acre and 640 acres in a square mile.

4 rods	1 acre
	40 rods

Using area at work

How would these people use perimeters and areas in their work ?
Farmers or gardeners,
carpet suppliers,
builders.

and volume

Volume

Which tank holds the most water ?

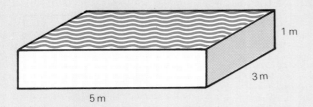

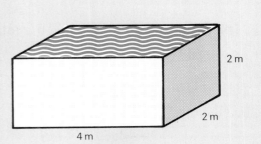

We measure volume by comparing the space with that of a cube with edge 1 cm.
This is called 1 cubic centimetre, (written 1 cm³).
Larger volumes can be compared with 1 m³.
We also need a connection with capacity.
1 litre = 1000 cm³.

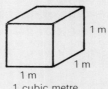

1 cubic metre

Firemen at work

Sculpture of Archimedes, by Thompson Dagnall, at UMIST

Using volumes

How would these people use volume in their work ?
Firemen,
removal firms,
fridge manufacturers,
architects.

Archimedes' Principle

Archimedes, who lived from 287 to 212 BC, and who was one of the greatest mathematicians of all time, was said to have jumped out of the bath and run down the street shouting 'Eureka', (I have found it). What had he discovered ?

14 Perimeter, Area and Volume

Perimeter

The **perimeter** of a figure is the total length of the edges.

Perimeter of a rectangle
- = sum of lengths of its 4 sides
- = 2 × (length + breadth) = $2(l + b)$

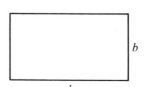

Perimeter of a triangle
- = sum of lengths of its 3 sides
- = $AB + BC + CA$

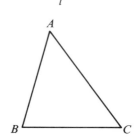

Examples

1 Find the perimeter of the rectangle.

Perimeter = $2(l + b)$
$= 2 × (10 + 8)$ cm
$= 2 × 18$ cm
$= 36$ cm

2 Find the perimeter of an equilateral triangle
with side 6 cm.

Perimeter = 6 cm + 6 cm + 6 cm
$= 18$ cm

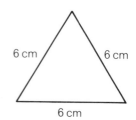

Area

When we measure area we compare it with a unit area.
We use the area of a square of side 1 cm for the unit.
This is called 1 square centimetre, and written as 1 cm².
If we are measuring larger areas we compare them with 1 square metre (1 m²) or
1 square kilometre (1 km²)

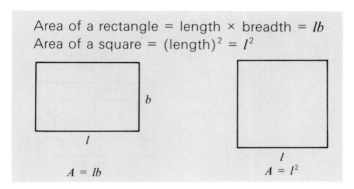

Area of a rectangle = length × breadth = lb
Area of a square = (length)^2 = l^2

$A = lb$ $A = l^2$

Examples

3 Find the area of the rectangle.

Area = lb
   = 9 × 7 cm^2
   = 63 cm^2

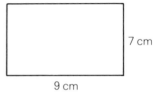

7 cm

9 cm

4 Find the area of the square.

Area = l^2
   = 6^2 cm^2
   = 36 cm^2

6 cm

5 Find the area of a path 2 m wide round a rectangular lawn 10 m by 5 m.

1st method

The complete rectangle is 14 m long and 9 m wide.

Total area of lawn and path = lb
                           = 14 × 9 m^2
                           = 126 m^2
Area of lawn   = 10 × 5 m^2
                           = 50 m^2
Area of path   = (126 − 50) m^2
                           = 76 m^2

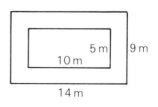

5 m   9 m
10 m

14 m

2nd method

Split the path into 4 rectangles, which are all 2 m wide.

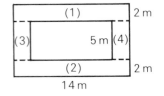

Area of (1) = 14 × 2 m^2 = 28 m^2
Area of (2) = 14 × 2 m^2 = 28 m^2
Area of (3) = 5 × 2 m^2 = 10 m^2
Area of (4) = 5 × 2 m^2 = 10 m^2
  Total area = (28 + 28 + 10 + 10) m^2
        = 76 m^2

6   Tiling

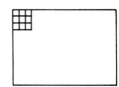

A floor is 4 m long and 3 m wide. How many tiles should be bought to cover it if the tiles are square, with sides 25 cm long ?
If the tiles are sold in boxes, with 25 tiles in a box, how many boxes should be bought ?

The number of tiles which will fit along the side 4 m long is 4 m ÷ 25 cm

$$= \frac{400 \text{ cm}}{25 \text{ cm}} = \frac{400}{25} = 16$$

The number of tiles which will fit along the side 3 m long is 3 m ÷ 25 cm

$$= \frac{300}{25} = 12$$

The total number of tiles needed = 16 × 12 = 192
The number of boxes needed = 192 ÷ 25 = 7.68
So 8 boxes must be bought.

Exercise 14.1

1.   Find the perimeter and area of these figures.

1

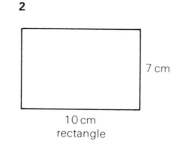

12 cm

square

2

7 cm

10 cm
rectangle

2. Sketch these figures.
    Find the perimeters, and find the areas by dividing them into rectangles. All
    angles are right angles.

1
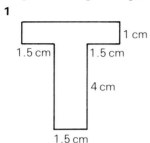

2
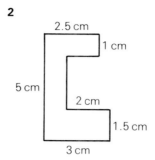

3. Find the area and perimeter of a rectangular lawn 6 m long and 5 m wide.

4. **1** If the perimeter of a square is 44 cm, what is its area ?
    2 If the area of a square is 900 cm², what is its perimeter ?

5. A rectangle 9 cm by 6 cm is cut out of the corner of a square piece of paper of
    side 10 cm. What area is left ? What is the perimeter of the piece that is left ?

6. There is a path 1 m wide all round a
    rectangular lawn of size 10 m by 7 m.
    Find the area of the path.

7. Find the areas and the perimeters of these figures. They are drawn full size.
    Make any measurements you need, measuring in cm, to the nearest ½ cm.

1
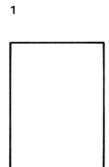

2
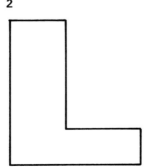

3
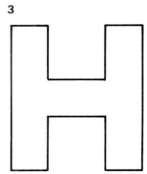

8. A rectangular floor measures 5 m by 3 m. What is its area ?
    A carpet costs £20 per square metre. What is the cost of carpet for the floor ?

9.   A floor 10.5 m long and 6 m wide is to be
      covered by tiles 30 cm square. How many
      tiles will be needed ?

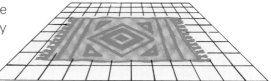

10.   A fence is erected round a rectangular field which is 100 m long and 70 m wide.
      What is the total cost of the fence, if it costs £8 per metre of length ?

11.   **1**   A rectangle is 8 cm long. Its perimeter is 20 cm. What is its width ?
      2   A rectangle is 5 cm wide. Its area is 35 cm². What is its length ?
      3   A square has side 6 cm. A rectangle is 4 cm wide and has the same area as
             the square. What is its length ?
      4   A square has side 7 cm. A rectangle is 3 cm wide and has the same
             perimeter as the square. What is its length ?

12.   A rectangle has an area of 30 cm².
      The length of each side is a whole number of centimetres. One possible
      rectangle would be 1 cm wide by 30 cm long.
      Write down the sizes of all the other possible rectangles.
      Which of these rectangles has the least perimeter ?
      Another rectangle with the same area has a width of 4 cm.
      What is the length of this rectangle ?
      What is the perimeter of this rectangle ?

13.   Sarah measures the edges of a photograph and finds that they are 14.9 cm
      and 10.1 cm.
      Find the area of the photograph, giving your answer correct to 3 significant
      figures.

14.   **To find the area of a triangle**

      1   A right-angled triangle.

             The rectangle *ABCD* has been
             divided into two triangles.
             What is the area of the shaded
             triangle ?
             Can you state a general method or
             formula for finding the area of a
             right-angled triangle ?

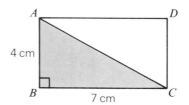

2 The shaded triangle has been enclosed in a rectangle as shown. What fraction of the area of the rectangle is the area of the shaded triangle ?
What is the area of that triangle ?
Can you give a general method or formula for finding the area of a triangle ?

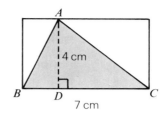

3 Use the method of **1** above to find the areas of $\triangle ACD$ and $\triangle ABD$.
Hence find the area of $\triangle ABC$.
The line AD is called the **perpendicular height** or **altitude** of $\triangle ABC$.
Can you find a formula for the area of $\triangle ABC$ when you know the measurements of the base BC and the perpendicular height AD ?

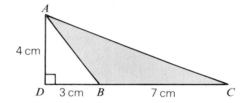

15. **To find the area of a parallelogram**

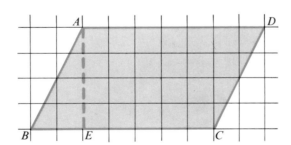

Copy the parallelogram $ABCD$ onto squared paper and draw the perpendicular line AE from A to the base BC.
Cut out the parallelogram.
Cut off the triangle ABE and rearrange the two pieces to form a rectangle.
Find the area of the rectangle and hence say what the area of the parallelogram is.
Can you find a formula for the area of a parallelogram when you know the measurements of the base BC and the perpendicular height AE ?

Area formulae

Area of a triangle $= \frac{1}{2} \times$ base $\times$ perpendicular height $= \frac{1}{2}bh$
Area of a parallelogram = base $\times$ perpendicular height $= bh$
Area of a trapezium $= \frac{1}{2} \times$ sum of the parallel sides $\times$ the perpendicular distance
between them $= \frac{1}{2}(a + b)h$

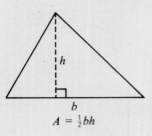
$A = \frac{1}{2}bh$

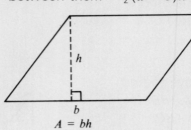
$A = bh$

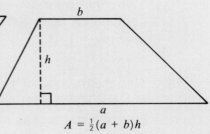
$A = \frac{1}{2}(a + b)h$

Examples

1   Triangle

Area $= \frac{1}{2}bh$
$\quad\quad = \frac{1}{2} \times 12 \times 8$ cm^2 = 48 cm^2

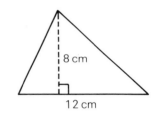

2   Parallelogram

Area $= bh$
$\quad\quad = 11 \times 7$ cm^2 = 77 cm^2

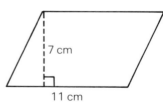

3   Trapezium

Area $= \frac{1}{2}(a + b)h$
$\quad\quad = \frac{1}{2} \times (13 + 7) \times 6$ cm^2
$\quad\quad = \frac{1}{2} \times 20 \times 6$ cm^2 = 60 cm^2

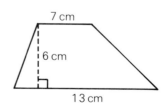

4   Find the area of this figure, which shows the side of a shed.

Area of rectangle $= lb$
$\quad\quad\quad\quad\quad\quad = 8 \times 6$ m^2 = 48 m^2
Area of triangle $\quad = \frac{1}{2}bh$
$\quad\quad\quad\quad\quad\quad = \frac{1}{2} \times 8 \times 3$ m^2 = 12 m^2
Total area $\quad\quad\quad = (48 + 12)$ m^2 = 60 m^2

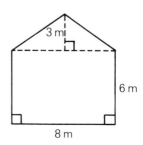

Exercise 14.2

1.   Find the areas of these figures.

1   **2**   **3**

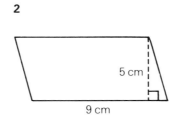
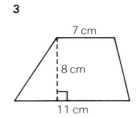

2.   Find the areas of these triangles, assuming that the edges of the squares are 1 cm long.

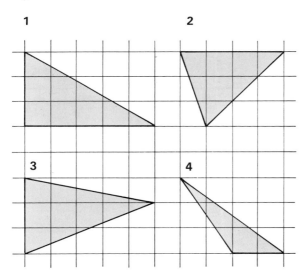

3.   The measurements of the rectangle are 4.65 cm by 2.15 cm.
     What is the area of the shaded triangle, correct to 2 significant figures ?

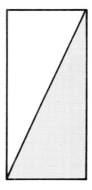

4. Find the areas of the parallelogram and the trapezium, assuming that the edges of
    the squares are 1 cm long.

    1   **2**

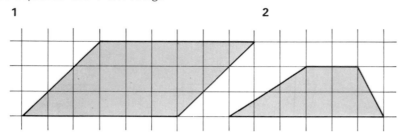

5. Find the areas of these figures. They are drawn full size. Make any measurements
    you need, measuring in cm, to the nearest $\frac{1}{2}$ cm.

    1   **2**   **3**

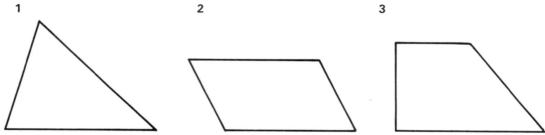

6. Find the total area of the quadrilateral
    ABCD.

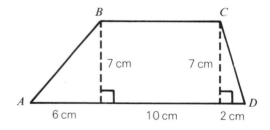

7. Find the shaded area by finding the areas
    of $\triangle ADE$ and $\triangle BCE$.

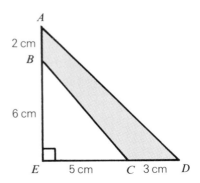

Volume

When we measure volume we compare it with a unit volume.
We use the volume of a cube of side 1 cm for the unit.
This is called 1 cubic centimetre and written as 1 cm³,
sometimes as 1 cc.

1 cm

If we are measuring larger volumes we will compare them with 1 cubic metre (1 m³).

It is useful to know that:
1 litre = 1000 cm³
1 litre of water or 1000 cm³ of water weighs 1 kg
1 cm³ of water weighs 1 g.

Volume formulae

Volume of a cuboid = length × breadth × height
$$= lbh$$

Volume of a cube = (length)³ = l^3

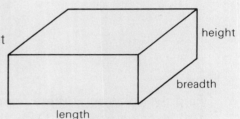

height

breadth

length

Surface area

The surface area of a cuboid or cube is the sum of the areas of the 6 faces.

Example

Find the volume, surface area and total
length of the edges of this cuboid.

Volume = lbh
$$= 10 × 7 × 4 \text{ cm}^3 = 280 \text{ cm}^3$$

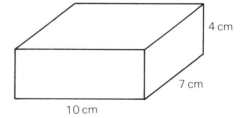

4 cm

7 cm

10 cm

Area of front or back = 10 × 4 cm² = 40 cm²
Area of each side = 7 × 4 cm² = 28 cm²
Area of top or bottom = 10 × 7 cm² = 70 cm²
Total area = 2 × (40 + 28 + 70) cm² = 276 cm²

There are 4 edges of length 10 cm, 4 of 7 cm and 4 of 4 cm.
Total length = 4 × (10 + 7 + 4) cm = 84 cm

Exercise 14.3

1. Find the volumes of these figures, if they are built with cubes of edge 1 cm, by working out how many cubes are used.

    1   **2**

    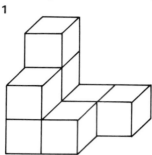   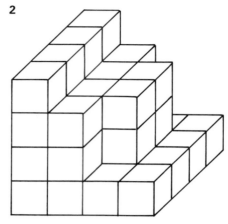

2. Find the volumes of these figures.
    1   A rectangular box 11 cm by 10 cm by 6 cm,
    2   a cube of edge 6 cm,
    3   a rectangular room 6 m by 5 m with height $2\frac{1}{2}$ m,
    4   a matchbox 7.5 cm by 4 cm by 1.5 cm,
    5   a case 65 cm by 40 cm by 18 cm.

3. Find the total surface area of these figures.
    1   A rectangular box 12 cm by 6 cm by 2 cm,
    2   a cube of edge 4 cm.

4. The sum of the lengths of the edges of a cube is 84 cm. How long is one edge ? What is the volume of the cube ?

5. A box has a square base of side 9 cm. The volume of the box is 405 cm³. Find the height of the box.
    Find the total surface area of the box.

    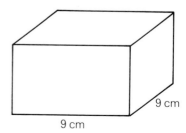

    9 cm

    9 cm

6. A large cube is built of 125 small equal cubes. How many small cubes lie along one edge of the large cube ?

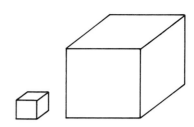

Density

If we want to compare two substances to decide which is heavier, we must use equal volumes of each. We can give each substance a numerical measurement called **density**.

The density of a material = the mass per unit volume.

The formula is: Density $= \dfrac{\text{mass}}{\text{volume}}$

(In Physics it is important to use the exact word 'mass', but in Mathematics we often use the more everyday word 'weight' to mean mass.)

From rearranging the formula we can work out the mass if the volume and density are known.

$$\text{Mass} = \text{volume} \times \text{density}$$

Or we can find the volume if the mass and density are known.

$$\text{Volume} = \frac{\text{mass}}{\text{density}}$$

The units in these formulae must correspond. If the mass is in grams, the volume in cm^3, the density is in g/cm^3, (grams per cubic cm). If the mass is in kg, the volume in m^3, the density is in kg/m^3.

Examples

1 If a piece of metal has a volume of $16\,cm^3$ and a mass of $128\,g$, what is its density ?

Density $= \dfrac{\text{mass}}{\text{volume}} = \dfrac{128}{16}\ g/cm^3 = 8\,g/cm^3$

2 If copper has density of $8.9\,g/cm^3$, what will be the mass of a rectangular block of copper, with measurements $5\,cm$ by $3\,cm$ by $2\,cm$?

Volume $= lbh = 5 \times 3 \times 2\ cm^3 = 30\,cm^3$
Mass $\quad= \text{volume} \times \text{density} = 30 \times 8.9\ g = 267\,g$

3   If petrol has density of 0.8 g/cm³, and the petrol in a can weighs 4 kg, how much petrol, in litres, does the can contain ?

$$\text{Volume} = \frac{\text{mass}}{\text{density}} = \frac{4000}{0.8}\,\text{cm}^3 = 5000\,\text{cm}^3$$

(The mass had to be expressed in grams to match the density in g/cm³.)
Now 1000 cm³ = 1 litre, so there are 5 litres of petrol in the can.

Exercise 14.4

1.   Find the density of silver if a rectangular bar 6 cm by 5 cm by 0.5 cm weighs 159 g.

2.   Find the density of a cube of wood which weighs 75 g and has edges of length 5 cm.

3.   A bar of steel is 5 m long and the cross-section is 5 cm by 2 cm.
What is its volume, in cm³ ?
If its density is 7.8 g/cm³, what is the weight of the bar ?

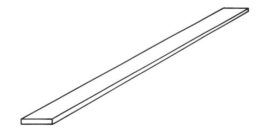

4.   A rectangular block of stone has to be transported.
If it measures 2.4 m by 1.5 m by 1.2 m, and its density is 2800 kg/m³, how much will it weigh ?

5.   154.4 g of gold, which has density 19.3 g/cm³, is to be melted down and shaped into a cube.
What is the volume of the gold ?
What is the length of an edge of the cube ?

Exercise 14.5 Applications and Activities

1. The plan shows the ground floor of a
   house.
   1 cm represents 1 m.
   Use the plan to find
   1 the length and width of the lounge,
         in m,
   2 the area of the lounge, in m².
   3 What is the cost of a carpet for the
         lounge, when a square metre of
         carpet costs £24 ?

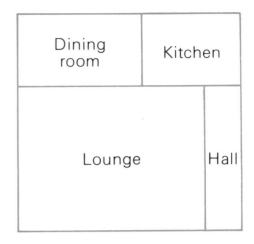

2. How many tiles 15 cm square will be needed to tile a wall which is 7.5 m long
   and 1.5 m high ?
   If the tiles are sold in boxes of 25 tiles for £8, how many boxes must be bought
   and what will they cost ?

3. A wooden box is 1 m long, 80 cm wide and 50 cm high. The outside of the box
   is to be painted. Find the area, in cm², of each surface, and hence find the total
   area to be painted.

4. In a large hall, the floor is covered by a carpet except for a
   border 1 m wide round the carpet, which is covered by
   non-slip tiles. The room is 15 m long and 12 m wide. Find
   its area.
   Find the measurements of the carpet, and its area.
   What is the total area of the tiled part of the room ?

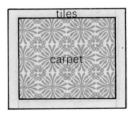

5. A rectangular lawn is 9 m long and 6 m wide. The gardener wants to use 50 g of
   fertilizer for each square metre. How much fertilizer does he need ?
   Boxes of fertilizer contain 2.5 kg. The gardener decides to buy one box and he
   spreads the contents evenly over the lawn. On average, how much fertilizer is
   there on each square metre of the lawn ? Give your answer to the nearest 5 g.

6. Rabia has a rectangular sheet of cardboard which measures 70 cm by 50 cm.
   She is going to use this to make rectangular tickets for a coffee evening. The
   tickets will measure 10 cm by 7 cm.
   What is the largest number of tickets that she can cut from the cardboard ?

7. A farmer wants to make a rectangular
    paddock by bounding three sides by
    fences, the fourth side being bounded by
    a river. He has 80 m of fencing available.
    He wants to enclose as large an area as
    possible.

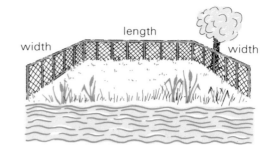

    Copy and complete this table.

length (m)	10	20	30	40	50	60	70
width (m)	35						
area (m²)	350						

Draw a graph, with length on the horizontal axis from 0 to 80 m, using a scale
of 2 cm to 10 m, and area on the vertical axis from 0 to 800 m², using a scale of
2 cm to 100 m².
Plot the points for length and area given in the table, e.g. (10, 350), and plot
also (0, 0) and (80, 0). Join the points with a smooth curve, drawn freehand.
Find the highest point on the graph.
What is the largest area the farmer can enclose ? What measurements should his
paddock have to enclose this area ?

8. *ABCD* is a square. How long is each
    side ?
    Find the areas of
    1   the square *ABCD*,
    2   △*CFE*,
    3   △*ABE*,
    4   △*ADF*.
    5   Use these answers to find the
          shaded area.

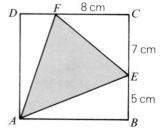

9. Draw these figures full size.
    1   A triangle with base 8 cm and height 6 cm,
    2   a square with side 4.8 cm,
    3   a rectangle with length 7 cm and breadth 3.5 cm.
    Decide by estimation which of these three shapes has the largest area, and
    which has the smallest area. Calculate the areas to verify your estimates.

10. A room is 4 m wide, 3 m long and $2\frac{1}{2}$ m high. What is the total area of the four
    walls ?

11. Find the areas of these figures, assuming that they are drawn on a grid of squares of edge 1 cm.

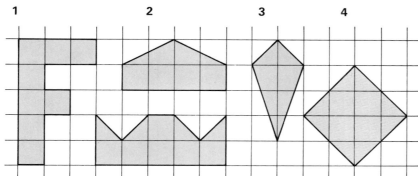

1   **2**   **3**   **4**

12. This is the plan of a plot of land.
    1   Find its total area,
    2   find its perimeter.

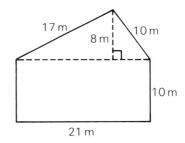

13. This swimming pool is 2.5 m deep. Find the volume of water which is needed to fill it.

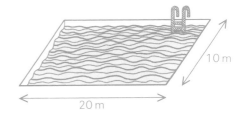

14. This is a rectangular drinks container. How many litres of liquid will it hold ?

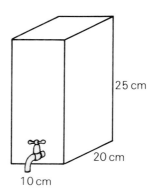

15. How many cubic metres of concrete will be needed to make a path 30 metres long, 0.5 metres wide, if the concrete is to be laid to a depth of 0.1 m ?

16. Here is the net of a cuboid. When the cuboid is constructed, what is its volume ?

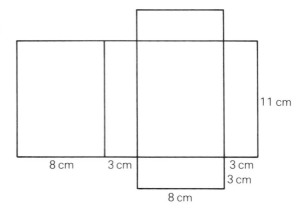

17.

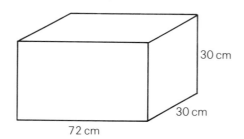

The box has measurements shown. It is filled with packets of tea, stacked upright in the box.
1   How many packets of tea fit onto the base of the box ?
2   How many layers of packets of tea are there in a full box ?
3   How many packets of tea altogether fit into the box ?

18. To find the density of mercury, a small glass which could hold 20 cm³ of liquid was used. The empty glass weighed 65 g, and when it was filled with mercury the full glass weighed 337 g.
1   What was the mass of the mercury ?
2   What is the density of mercury ?

19. A rectangular pool with length 20 m and width 10 m has a layer of ice on top of the water, of thickness 10 cm. What is the volume of the ice, in m³ ?
What is the weight of the ice, if its density is 900 kg/m³ ?

20.   You can work out the density of several substances.

For types of wood, you can cut the wood into a cuboid shape, to calculate the volume. You can also weigh the piece of wood.

Then using the formula Density $= \dfrac{\text{mass}}{\text{volume}}$, you can find the density of the wood.

For types of metal, which are heavier than water, you can find the volume by sinking the object in water, and finding the volume of water which is displaced. This will equal the volume of the object. You can also weigh the metal.

For liquids, you can measure the volume directly, but you must decide how to find the weight.

Make a list of the results, in order of density, from the lightest to the heaviest substance.

PUZZLE

32.   How many mathematical words can you find, reading horizontally, vertically or diagonally, in both directions ?

E	B	P	C	D	I	M	A	R	Y	P	R	E
Q	U	A	D	R	I	L	A	T	E	R	A	L
U	N	R	C	H	O	R	D	B	A	O	D	G
A	O	A	O	L	D	E	U	T	E	B	I	N
T	G	L	N	A	E	C	I	G	D	A	U	A
I	A	L	E	M	F	O	A	P	I	B	S	T
O	T	E	U	I	D	T	E	O	S	I	P	C
N	C	L	G	C	N	D	R	L	U	L	H	E
H	O	O	A	E	R	A	A	Y	B	I	E	R
V	K	G	C	D	L	A	U	G	M	T	R	K
F	O	R	M	U	L	A	Q	O	O	Y	E	I
B	E	A	R	I	N	G	S	N	H	N	E	T
P	M	M	U	I	Z	E	P	A	R	T	N	E

15 Thinking about scatter graphs

A scatter graph

Is there any connection between being good at Maths and being good at Science ?
For a set of pupils, we can plot their exam marks in Maths, and exam marks in Science, on a graph called a scatter graph or a scatter diagram.
It might look like this, showing that some pupils are good at both subjects, many pupils are round about average in both subjects, and some pupils are poor at both subjects.

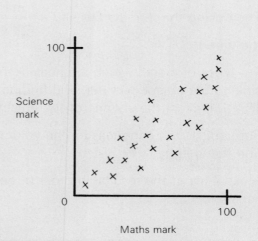

There is no-one who is very good in one subject and very poor in the other.
We could assume that people who are good at Maths are also good at Science.
The mathematical word for this sort of connection is called **correlation**.

Your own investigations

If you have marks available in your class from a recent exam you could plot them on a scatter graph.
It might not look like the one above. There could be many reasons for this, even though it is generally assumed that pupils' ability in Maths ought to be matched by their ability in Science.

You could draw similar scatter graphs to see if there is any correlation between other subjects.

ENGLISH	60	Good steady work
HISTORY	52	Satisfactory
GEOGRAPHY	66	A good term's work
FRENCH	58	A good beginning in this subject.
MATHEMATICS	86	Very good
SCIENCE	80	Very good
P.E.		GOOD USUALLY

Is expensive advertising effective ?

Would reducing speeds reduce accidents ?

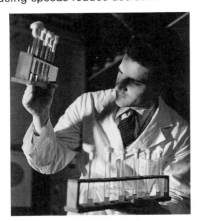

Work at Balaton Lodge, the research hospital for horses' complaints

Uses of correlation

The idea of correlation is very important in all sorts of research, e.g.

- medical research—causes of illness and methods of treatment,

- scientific research,

- research on family spending, etc.,

- industrial research on methods, costs and profits,

- research on the costs and results of advertising,

- financial research,

- research on education,

- research on accidents linked to amount of traffic or speeds of vehicles.

The measurements can often be affected by other factors as well as those being measured, so that it is rare for there to be an exact relationship shown. So when evidence of correlation is found, the next thing to be done is to see whether there is a genuine connection or whether it is just coincidence that as one set of readings goes up, so does the other.

15 Scatter Graphs

This kind of graph can be drawn to look at the relationship between 2 sets of data.

Examples

1   Is there any relationship between the number of goals scored by the home team and the number of goals scored by the away team in football matches ?

Draw and label the axes like this.

If the first score is 4-1, put a cross in the space which represents 4 goals by the home team and 1 by the away team.

Here is the graph showing the results on one particular Saturday, in the 4 divisions of the football league.

On a different Saturday, these were the results:

1-0	1-0	1-0	1-1	1-3	0-1	2-0	1-2	1-1	2-2
0-2	3-2	1-2	2-1	3-3	0-0	0-0	1-2	2-1	0-1
2-1	3-1	1-1	2-2	3-3	2-0	2-3	1-2	1-1	0-2
2-2	1-0	1-0	1-0	2-1	1-1	0-2	4-2

Make a scatter graph of these results and compare your graph with the one above.
Can you comment about any relationship shown by the graphs ?
Use the latest results from a recent newspaper, draw a graph and compare it with
the previous two.

These examples use a few whole numbers only, on each axis, and these were
represented in blocks.

When the numbers have a bigger range, or if the data involves measurements, we label
the axes in a different way.

2   Do tall fathers have tall sons, and smaller fathers smaller sons ?

The heights of 10 boys and their fathers are given in this table.

Height of father (in cm)	167	168	169	171	172	172	174	175	176	182
Height of son (in cm)	164	166	166	168	169	170	170	171	173	177

To plot the points on a scatter diagram we will use the horizontal axis for the heights
of the fathers. (It is usually best to plot the 1st set of data on the horizontal axis.) The
fathers' heights range from 167 to 182 cm so it is unnecessary to extend the labelling
much beyond these values.

We then use the vertical axis for the heights of sons. These range from 164 to 177 cm.
It is not essential to keep the same scale on both axes but it is suitable in this question.

The small cross shows the 1st pair of data
which is 167 cm (father) and 164 cm (son).

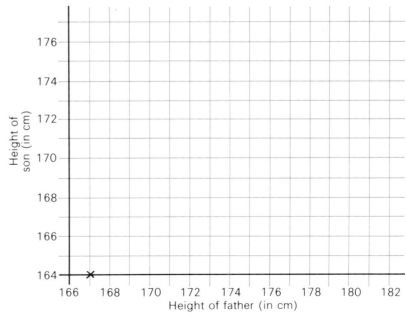

Draw the graph for yourself, using graph paper or squared paper, and put in the other 9 crosses.

Do you think there is any connection between the heights of fathers and sons ?

You could investigate this further by collecting data from some of the boys in your class, and their fathers. The boys should be nearly the same age. (Why ?)

You could also investigate to see if there is any connection between heights of daughters and their mothers.

Correlation

The relationship between 2 sets of variables is called **correlation**.
Here are some pictures of scatter graphs with axes not labelled.

This shows that there is good (positive) correlation between the variables.

Here there is an exact relationship. This can be described as perfect correlation.

There is some correlation but it is not very close.

This is a relationship where as one variable increases, the other decreases.
This is said to be inverse or negative correlation.

Perfect inverse correlation.

There does not seem to be any relationship. There is no correlation, or there is zero correlation.

Statisticians use a formula to work out a numerical value for correlation. They would not make any assumptions about whether two variables have correlation unless they had at least 30 pairs of data. However, we have used less items here, so that the questions do not take too long.

When there is evidence of correlation between two sets of data, you have to decide if they are really connected, or whether they are both linked to a third item.

For example, someone found a strong positive correlation between size of feet and maths ability, but the real reason for the connection was that the boys with the bigger feet were older boys, and they had learnt more maths. Both these items, size of feet, and maths knowledge, would show some correlation with age of boys, but there is no other connection.

size of feet

Exercise 15.1

1. The marks out of 10 for some children in two tests are given below.
    Draw axes like these and put crosses in
    the squares to represent the marks.
    Comment about the relationship shown by
    the graph.

    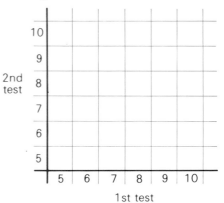

    The marks are given for each child in turn. 6, 7 means 6 in the first test and 7 in
    the second test.

5, 6	8, 7	6, 5	8, 6	6, 7	6, 7	10, 10	7, 8	9, 9
8, 8	6, 8	8, 9	9, 8	9, 9	7, 6	9, 10	8, 9	5, 7
6, 6	10, 10	9, 9	8, 9	6, 9	7, 7	8, 8	8, 8	9, 10
9, 9	7, 8	9, 9	10, 10	9, 9	7, 7	8, 7	7, 9	8, 8
9, 10	8, 9	9, 8	9, 8	7, 8	7, 8	9, 9	8, 7	9, 9

2. The marks of 10 students in 2 Maths exams were as follows:

1st year	70	68	60	55	49	46	43	40	36	30
2nd year	65	63	55	55	50	45	46	44	39	40

    Plot the points on a scatter diagram and comment on the correlation.

3. The heights and weights of 8 young men are given in this table.

Height (in cm)	167	169	172	178	182	183	184	186
Weight (in kg)	68	70	70	74	75	76	78	79

    Plot the points on a scatter diagram and comment on the correlation.

4. Here are the lengths and widths of 11 leaves from a bush.

Length (in cm)	7.5	6.7	7.3	6.8	6.6	5.6	5.1	4.7	5.5	6.2	6.4
Width (in cm)	3.9	2.8	3.4	3.7	3.1	2.1	2.3	1.5	2.2	2.6	2.6

Plot the points on a scatter diagram and comment on the correlation.

5. A group of 8 children held a money-raising event and raised £150, which they decided to split between 2 charities X and Y.

They all wrote down the amounts they wanted to send to each charity.

	Jane	Sarah	Rishi	Leela	James	Naomi	Daniel	Hugh
To charity X	50	10	20	40	75	30	90	150
To charity Y	100	140						

Copy the table and complete the last line.
Plot the data on a scatter diagram with the money for charity X on the horizontal axis and for charity Y on the vertical axis.
Describe the type of correlation.
Suggest a way for the children to decide how much to send to each charity.

6. In each of the following cases say whether you think that the correlation would be positive, negative or zero.
Give reasons and sketch the kind of scatter diagram you would expect.
1   The daily air temperature, and the amount of ice-cream sold.
2   The number of empty seats, and the number of occupied seats in a theatre each evening during the performances.
3   The marks obtained by children in a test, and their house numbers.
4   The distances that children live from school, and their journey times to school.
5   The daily air temperature, and the amount of electricity used by households in a certain city.

7. Sets of values of two related variables x and y are given below.
Plot the values on scatter diagrams, with x on the horizontal axis from 0 to 8, and y on the vertical axis from 0 to 80.
Describe the relationship under these headings:
perfect positive correlation, positive correlation, no correlation, negative correlation, perfect negative correlation.

1

x	0	1	2	3	4	5	6	7	8
y	80	65	60	50	30	20	15	10	5

7.

2

x	0	1	2	3	4	5	6	7	8
y	80	50	20	50	60	20	40	70	50

3

x	0	1	2	3	4	5	6	7	8
y	0	5	15	20	35	35	45	60	70

4

x	0	1	2	3	4	5	6	7
y	70	60	50	40	30	20	10	0

5

x	0	1	2	3	4	5	6	7	8
y	15	20	25	30	35	40	45	50	55

Exercise 15.2   Applications and Activities

1.   Here are the figures for current television licences, and admissions to cinemas, over a period of 11 years.

Year	67	68	69	70	71	72	73	74	75	76	77
TV licences (millions)	14	15	16	16	17	18	20	23	25	26	30
Cinema admissions (Ten millions)	27	24	22	19	18	16	13	14	12	10	10

Plot these figures on a scatter diagram.
Do you think that television was responsible for the falling attendances at cinemas in that period ?

2.   Here are the figures for the number of vehicles on the road, and the deliveries of motor spirit, in Great Britain, for 8 years.
('Motor spirit' means petrol and other fuels for vehicles.)

Year	67	68	69	70	71	72	73	74
Vehicles (millions)	14.1	14.4	14.8	15.0	15.5	16.1	17.0	17.3
Motor spirit (Million tons)	12.3	13.0	13.4	14.2	15.0	15.9	16.9	16.5

Plot these figures on a scatter diagram, and comment on the relationship.

3.   Carry out an investigation with data with which you expect to find some kind of
      paired relationship.
      Collect the data and represent it on a scatter diagram.
      Comment on the relationship, but do not be too disappointed if your scatter diagrams
      do not show good correlation. Statistical data rarely matches perfectly as the figures
      are often affected by other factors as well as those you are measuring.
      Here are some suggestions for investigations.

      Heights and weights of children of the same age.
      Heights of mothers and their 16 year old daughters.
      Ages of young children and their bedtimes.
      Heights and arm-spans.
      Exam marks in similar subjects such as Maths and Science, French and German, or
      in different subjects such as Art and Science.
      Times spent learning a piece of work, and marks gained in a test on it.
      Times taken to do a piece of work using (1) normal hand and (2) other hand.
      Shoe sizes and collar (or hat) sizes.
      Amounts of pocket money and amounts saved.

PUZZLES

33.   Here is the table of results, with some gaps, in the local football league, when each team
      had played each other once.

	played	won	drawn	lost	goals for	goals against
Allsorts	2				4	0
Buskers	2	1			5	
Cobblers	2		1		3	

      Find the score in each match.

34.   Draw a rectangle on squared paper, 13 units long and 8 units wide.
      Divide it into 4 pieces as shown.
      Cut the pieces out and rearrange them to form
      two rectangles of width 5 units.
      What was the area of the original rectangle (in
      square units) ?
      What is the sum of the areas of the two new
      rectangles ?
      Where has the extra 1 square unit come from ?
      (Have you noticed that the numbers used
      belong to the Fibonacci sequence ?)

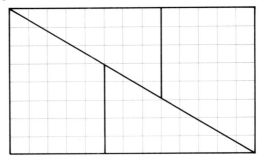

16 Thinking about reflection and

Reflection

Look at the photograph on the right and notice how the water acts as a mirror and reflects the scene.

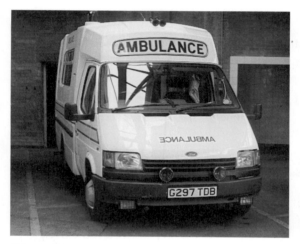

Why is ƎƆИAⅬUＢMA written like this ?

Marie-Antoinette's Hamlet at Versailles

A bit of fun, using a shop window as a mirror

Another bit of fun, using two mirrors

enlargement

Enlargement
Similar figures

Here are three dolls. Although they are similar, they are of different sizes. The larger two are enlargements of the first one.

Photographs

You are used to seeing enlargements of photographs. Everything is enlarged in the same proportion so that the picture is not distorted.

Professor David Bellamy with two visitors to the Shropshire mammoth exhibition

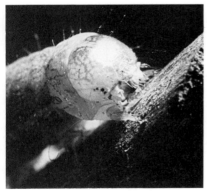 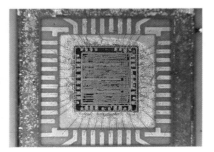 

A caterpillar's head shown in detail

A microchip with over 20 000 interconnected transistors etched onto it

What are these ?

16 Reflection and Enlargement

Reflection

The dotted lines show the reflections of the triangles in the line *AB*, which is an axis of symmetry of the completed figure.

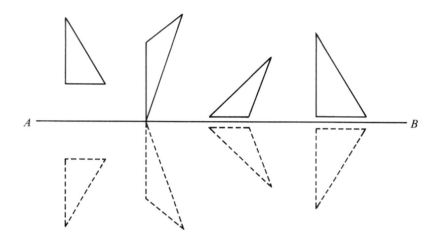

Each dotted triangle is called the **image** of the original triangle.

This diagram shows a point *A* reflected in the line *CD*, into an image point *B*.
The line *AB* meets *CD* at *E*.

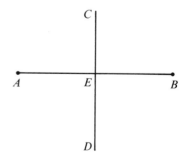

What do you notice about the lengths of *AE* and *EB* ?
What are the sizes of the four angles at *E* ?
In relation to *A* and *B*, what is the description of the line *CD* ?
Which lines would be the reflections of the lines *AC* and *AD* ?

Exercise 16.1

1. Copy this shape, showing half of a house, and reflect it in the dotted line.

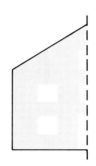

2. The diagram shows a shape and a mirror line. Copy the diagram on squared paper and draw the reflection of the shape.

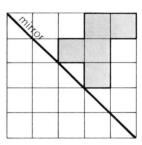

3. Sketch these flags and reflect them in the dotted lines.

   1   **2**   **3**

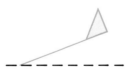
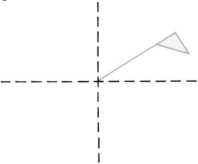

4. In the diagram, P has coordinates $(3, 2)$. What are the coordinates of the image point when P is reflected
   1 in the x-axis,
   2 in the y-axis ?

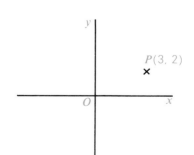

5. Copy the diagram and reflect
    the letter A in line 1,
    the letter B in line 2,
    the letter C in line 3,
    the letter D in line 4.

   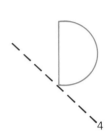

6. The diagram shows the drawing of a face.
    1 Sketch the diagram and show the
    position of the face when it is
    reflected in the x-axis.
    2 Sketch the diagram again and show
    the position of the face when it is
    reflected in the y-axis.

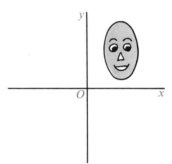

Enlargement

Similar figures have the same shape.
All corresponding angles are equal.
All corresponding lengths are in proportion, i.e. they are in the same ratio as all other
lengths.

Similar triangles

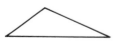 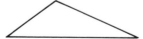 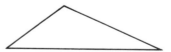

Similar quadrilaterals

  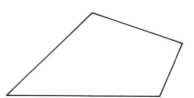

Enlargements

A figure and its enlargement are similar figures.

The **scale factor** of the enlargement is the number of times the original has been enlarged.

e.g. If the scale factor is 2, all lines on the enlargment are twice as long as corresponding lines on the original.

If the scale factor is 3, all lines on the enlargement are three times as long as corresponding lines on the original.

Examples

1 Enlargement with scale factor 2

2 Enlargement with scale factor 3

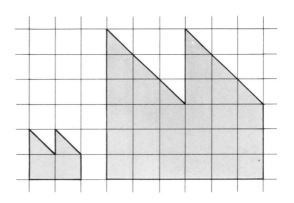

Exercise 16.2

1. Copy these figures and for each one draw an enlargement with scale factor 2.

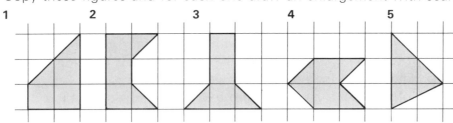

2. What is the scale factor of the
    enlargement which transforms
    figure *A* into figure *B* ?

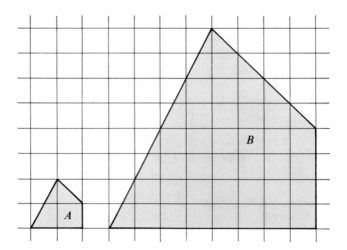

3. Triangle *ABC* has been enlarged into
    triangle *A′B′C′*. What is the scale factor of
    the enlargement ?

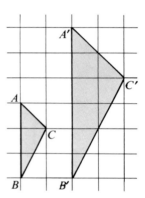

4. Copy these diagrams onto squared paper.
    Using a scale factor of 3, transform triangle *T* into a triangle *T′*.

    1   **2**   **3**

          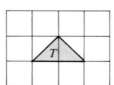   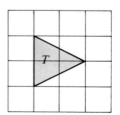

5. A triangle is transformed by enlargement with scale factor 3 into a similar triangle.
    1   One side of the new triangle has length 7.5 cm. What is the length of the
        corresponding side of the original triangle ?
    2   One angle of the new triangle has size 54°. What is the size of the
        corresponding angle of the original triangle ?

6.

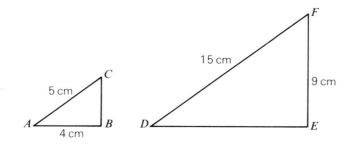

$\triangle DEF$ is an enlargement of $\triangle ABC$.

1   What is the scale factor of the enlargement ?
2   What is the length of DE ?
3   What is the length of BC ?
4   If $\angle A = 36.9°$, what is the size of $\angle D$?

7.   Copy this drawing of a prism on your own
squared paper, then using the squares to
help you, draw an enlargement of your
prism with scale factor 2.

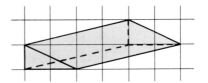

8.   Use squared paper to copy these letters
and then enlarge them with scale factor 2.

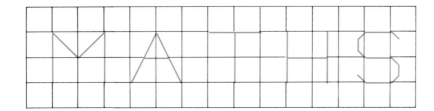

Exercise 16.3   Applications and Activities

1.   Use a mirror to read this question, then find the answer.

A group of people on a coach outing went into a cafe for a snack. The party
leader ordered a cup of tea and a sandwich for everyone and the total bill came to
£28.09. How many people were on the coach ?

2. This square tile has two axes of symmetry
    shown by the dotted lines. Copy the figure
    and complete the rest of the pattern.

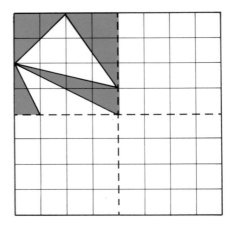

3. On separate diagrams, using squared
    paper, copy the figure and
    1   reflect it in the x-axis,
    2   reflect it in the line $y = x$
           (the line OA).

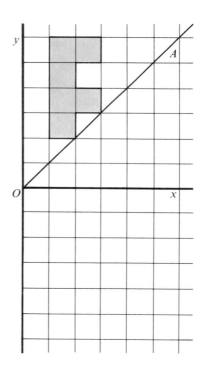

4. Use a mirror to read this advice.

    *When you are doing a question, concentrate completely
    on it, so that you immediately think about the method.
    Start it quickly and continue working it out without a
    pause until you finish it.*

5. State the coordinates of the image point when the point P (4, 2) is reflected

  1 in the x-axis,
  2 in the y-axis,
  3 in the line $y = x$ (the line OA),
  4 in the line $y = -x$ (the line OB).

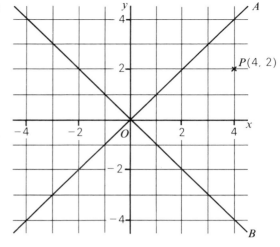

6. Draw axes with x from -4 to 5 and y from -7 to 4, using 1 cm to 1 unit on both axes.

  Plot these points and join each one to the next, to form an arrow.

  $(-2, 3)$, $(-1, 2\frac{1}{2})$, $(-2, 2)$, $(1, 2)$, $(0, 1)$, $(1, 1)$, $(2\frac{1}{2}, 2\frac{1}{2})$, $(1, 4)$, $(0, 4)$, $(1, 3)$, $(-2, 3)$.

  Draw an enlargement of the arrow with scale factor 2, beginning with the point corresponding to the point $(-2, 3)$ at $(-4, -3)$.

7. On squared paper with 1 cm squares draw the quadrilateral $ABCD$ and enlarge it using scale factor 3 into a quadrilateral $PQRS$, where P corresponds to A, etc. Measure in cm and mm the sides of both quadrilaterals and use your calculator to find the values of

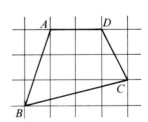

$$\frac{PQ}{AB}, \frac{QR}{BC}, \frac{RS}{CD}, \frac{SP}{DA}.$$

What can you say about the perimeter of $PQRS$ compared to the perimeter of $ABCD$?

What can you say about the diagonal PR compared to the diagonal AC ?

8.   **Enlarging a picture using a grid**

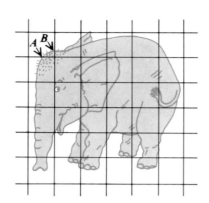
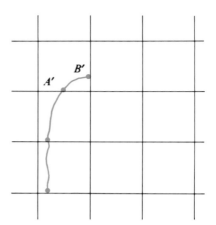

To make the drawing twice as large, notice where the drawing meets the lines of the grid.

e.g. *A* is halfway along the line, so mark *A'* halfway along the corresponding line. *B* is a quarter-way up the line, so mark *B'* a quarter-way up the corresponding line.

Make a larger grid for yourself and mark points on, then by joining the points as on the original, complete the drawing.

A pantograph is an instrument with jointed rods which can be used for drawing enlargements of pictures. If you have one available, use it to draw an enlargement of the picture above.

9. **Areas and Volumes**

With an enlargement scale factor 2,
    length of enlargement : length of original = 2 : 1
This ratio applies to any corresponding lengths on the drawings.
What happens to areas ?

Draw a rectangle 3 cm by 2 cm and enlarge it with scale factor 2.
Find area of enlargement : area of original.
Repeat with an enlargement scale factor 3, and then scale factor 4.
Investigate other shapes to see if the same results about areas apply.
Can you discover a general pattern ?

Does this pattern also apply to surface areas of solid figures ?

If a cuboid with measurements 5 cm by 3 cm by 2 cm is enlarged with scale factor 2, work out
    surface area of enlargement : surface area of original.
Repeat with enlargements using other scale factors.

Can you decide what will happen to volumes of solid figures ?
Work out the volume of the cuboid and its enlargement, using various scale factors.
Find volume of enlargement : volume of original.
What is the general pattern ?

PUZZLES

35. There are 3 boxes. One contains 2 red marbles, one contains 2 blue marbles and the third contains 1 red and 1 blue marble. The boxes are labelled RR, BB and RB to show their contents. But the lids have been switched so that each box is labelled wrongly.
One marble at a time may be removed from any box without looking inside. What is the smallest number of drawings needed to be sure of the contents of each box ?

36. Two boats leave the harbour at Athney at the same time, and sail to Borley. They each spend 3 hours there before returning to Athney. The first goes from Athney to Borley at 30 km/h and returns at 40 km/h. The second boat travels at 35 km/h each way. Which boat gets back first ?
(If you need more information, the distance from Athney to Borley is 84 km.)

37. Jayesh had a number of small cubes of edge 1 cm, and using all of them he made a larger cube of edge 6 cm. How many of the small cubes did he have ?
Then he made the large cube into three smaller cubes, with none of the small cubes left over.
What were the sizes of the three cubes ?

17 Thinking about more equations

Equations

Up to now, equations have been simple ones, based on simple functions. But in today's world, more complicated equations can occur. A few years ago, their solution would take a long time, but nowadays, with calculators and computers to deal with the arithmetic, trial and improvement methods can be used to solve quite complicated equations very quickly.

An example

If a projectile is sent upwards into the air with a speed of 70 m/s at an angle of about 71.6° with the horizontal, then it will go upwards first and then fall downwards, because of the force of gravity acting on it.

Its path can be calculated and, neglecting the effect of air resistance, its height above the starting point, y metres, is connected to the horizontal distance from the starting point, x metres, by the equation
$y = 3x - \frac{1}{100}x^2$.

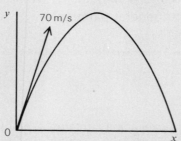

Using the equation

This equation can be used to find how far the projectile has travelled horizontally when it has reached certain heights.

e.g. To find out how far it has travelled horizontally when it reaches a height of 189 m is found by putting $y = 189$ in the equation.

So $189 = 3x - \frac{1}{100}x^2$.

This equation can be rearranged as $x^2 - 300x + 18\,900 = 0$, and solved by trial methods.

There will be 2 solutions, one for the distance when the projectile is going up and one for when it is coming down.

Can you find the solutions ?

Other projectiles

To work out the path of a space rocket and to find when it will reach certain points needs a much more complicated equation, but the idea is similar, and calculations can be made using a computer. Fireworks are also projectiles and their paths follow the same mathematical rules. So are fountains.

The launch of the Soviet space rocket-carrier Proton, in 1989

Shot putt. The winner, Udo Beyer of East Germany, preparing to launch his projectile. Birmingham, 1985.

Fireworks at Lugano, Switzerland

Fountains in Trafalgar Square

17 More Equations

An equation such as $3x + 5 = 41$ is called a **linear** equation. You can solve it easily by now. What is the solution ?

An equation involving a term in x^2, such as $2x^2 + 5x = 33$ is called a **quadratic** equation. Up to now you have not learnt a method for solving quadratic equations, although you will learn one later. So at present you will have to solve it by 'trial and improvement'.

An equation involving a term in x^3, and possibly terms in x^2 and x also, is called a **cubic** equation.
$x^3 = 125$ is quite a simple cubic equation, and you can probably solve it. What is the solution ?
$x^3 - 3x^2 + 7x = 5$ is a more complicated cubic equation, which can be solved by 'trial and improvement'.

There can be equations involving higher powers of x, such as x^4 and x^5.

Simple quadratic equations

Examples

1 Solve the equation $x^2 = 16$.

If we investigate by making a table to work out x^2 for different values of x it looks like this:

x	x^2
0	0
1	1
2	4
3	9
4	16
5	25

We can see that the solution of the equation $x^2 = 16$ is $x = 4$.
In fact, we have found the **square root** of 16.
(There is also the negative solution, $x = -4$, since $(-4)^2 = (-4) \times (-4) = 16$ also.
But at present we will only consider positive solutions.)

2 Solve the equation $x^2 = 1089$.

We are not going to make a table going as far as 1089. The method is similar to the previous example, so we need the square root of 1089.
Use the square root key on your calculator.
Press 1089 $\boxed{\sqrt{}}$ and you will get 33.
So the solution is $x = 33$.

3 Solve the equation $x^2 = 24$.

We need the square root of 24.
We can see from the table in example **1** that it is not a whole number, but it is a number between 4 and 5.
Using the square root key on your calculator gives 4.898979 . . .
We do not need so many decimal places in the answer.
The solution is $x = 4.90$, correct to 2 decimal places.

4 Solve the equation $2x^2 = 7$.

Divide both sides by 2
$$x^2 = 3.5$$
Take the square root of both sides
$$x = 1.87, \text{ correct to 2 decimal places.}$$

Exercise 17.1

1. Solve these equations, giving the positive solution.

1	$x^2 = 64$	**6**	$x^2 = 400$
2	$x^2 = 121$	**7**	$x^2 = 529$
3	$x^2 = 1$	**8**	$x^2 = 1936$
4	$x^2 = 81$	**9**	$x^2 = 9.61$
5	$x^2 = 36$	**10**	$x^2 = 216.09$

2. Solve these equations, giving the positive solutions, correct to 2 decimal places.

1	$x^2 = 17$	**6**	$x^2 = 1000$
2	$x^2 = 30$	**7**	$2x^2 = 81$
3	$x^2 = 75$	**8**	$2x^2 = 220$
4	$x^2 = 6.5$	**9**	$3x^2 = 100$
5	$x^2 = 40$	**10**	$4x^2 = 250$

Simple cubic equations

Examples

1   Solve the equation $x^3 = 125$.

If we investigate by making a table to work out x^3 for different values of x it looks like this:

x	x^3
0	0
1	1
2	8
3	27
4	64
5	125
6	216

We can see that the solution of the equation $x^3 = 125$ is $x = 5$. In fact, we have found the **cube root** of 125.
(There is no negative solution.)

2   Solve the equation $x^3 = 60$.

We need to find the cube root of 60, and we can see from the table above that it is not a whole number, but it is a number between 3 and 4.
If you have a scientific calculator there will be a key labelled y^x and the inverse function on this key is $\sqrt[x]{y}$. If you put $x = 3$, this will give the cube root of number y.
So press 60 $\boxed{\sqrt[x]{y}}$ 3 $\boxed{=}$ and you will get 3.914867 . . .
The solution is $x = 3.91$, correct to 2 decimal places.
(On your calculator the keys may be labelled x^y and $\sqrt[y]{x}$, but the method is the same.)
If you have not got a $\boxed{\sqrt[x]{y}}$ key on your calculator you will have to find the cube root of 60 by a trial and improvement method.
This will remind you of how to do it:

To find the cube root of 60

First, use the table in example **1** to check that it is a number between 3 and 4, and it seems to be much nearer 4 than 3.

So find the value of 3.8^3
$3.8^3 = 3.8 \times 3.8 \times 3.8 = 54.872$
This is smaller than 60, so try 3.9^3
$3.9^3 = 59.319$
This is still too small, so try 3.95^3
$3.95^3 = 61.629 \ldots$; too big.
Now you know that the cube root of 60 lies between 3.9 and 3.95, so correct to 1 decimal place it is 3.9

If you need the answer correct to 2 decimal places, you must carry on further.

Try 3.92^3 (or 3.93^3)
$3.92^3 = 60.236 \ldots$; too big, so the answer lies between 3.9 and 3.92
Try 3.91^3
$3.91^3 = 59.776 \ldots$; too small, so the answer lies between 3.91 and 3.92
Now try 3.915^3
$3.915^3 = 60.006 \ldots$; too big.
So the answer lies between 3.91 and 3.915, and correct to 2 decimal places it is 3.91.

Exercise 17.2

1. Solve these equations
1	$x^3 = 27$		**4**	$x^3 = 1$
2	$x^3 = 512$		**5**	$x^3 = 216$
3	$x^3 = 1000$			

2. Solve these equations, correct to 2 decimal places.
1	$x^3 = 10$		**4**	$x^3 = 275$
2	$x^3 = 121$		**5**	$x^3 = 20.2$
3	$x^3 = 900$			

Other equations with solutions which are positive whole numbers

Examples

1 Solve the equation $2x^2 + 5x = 33$

Make a table to work out the values of $2x^2 + 5x$ for different values of x.
(The columns x^2, $2x^2$, $5x$ are steps in the working out of $2x^2 + 5x$.)

x	x^2	$2x^2$	$5x$	$2x^2 + 5x$
0	0	0	0	0
1	1	2	5	7
2	4	8	10	18
3	9	18	15	33
4	16	32	20	52

From the table you can see the solution $x = 3$.
You can also see that as x gets bigger, $2x^2 + 5x$ keeps increasing, and there will not be any other solution in positive numbers.

2 Solve the equation $x^3 - 3x^2 + 7x = 5$

Make a table to work out the values of $x^3 - 3x^2 + 7x$ for different values of x.

x	x^2	x^3	$3x^2$	$7x$	$x^3 - 3x^2 + 7x$
0	0	0	0	0	0
1	1	1	3	7	5
2	4	8	12	14	10
3	9	27	27	21	21
4	16	64	48	28	44

From the table you can see the solution $x = 1$.
You can also see that as x gets bigger $x^3 - 3x^2 + 7x$ keeps increasing, and there will not be any other solution in positive whole numbers.

Exercise 17.3

Solve these equations by trial. Find for each equation a solution for x which is a positive whole number.

1. $x^2 - 4x = 45$
2. $2x^2 - 5x = 12$
3. $x^2 + 5x = 24$
4. $x^2 - x = 72$
5. $x^2 - 2x = 80$

6. $x^3 - 10x = 24$
7. $x^3 + x = 130$
8. $x^3 - 2x = 56$
9. $x^3 - 15x + 18 = 0$
10. $x^3 + 8x = 1080$

Exercise 17.4   Applications and Activities

1. **Finding a square root without using the square root key on your calculator**

    There are several methods you can use. One is the method used for cube roots on page 269.
    Here is a different way.

    Example To find the square root of 70, correct to 2 decimal places.

    Make a guess, e.g. 8
    Divide 70 by 8, getting 8.75.
    The square root lies between 8 and 8.75.
    Now use a number between 8 and 8.75.
    You can find the exact halfway number, which is $(8 + 8.75) \div 2 = 8.375$, or you can make a rough choice, such as 8.4
    Divide 70 by 8.4, getting 8.333 . . .
    The square root lies between 8.4 and 8.333 . . .
    Choose a number halfway between 8.4 and 8.333 . . .
    A rough choice is 8.37
    Divide 70 by 8.37, getting 8.363 . . .
    The square root lies between 8.37 and 8.363 . . .
    Now try 8.365, to find whether the square root is nearer 8.36 or 8.37
    70 divided by 8.365 gives 8.3682 . . .
    The square root lies between 8.365 and 8.3682 . . . , so correct to 2 decimal places it is 8.37
    Use this method to find the square roots used in Exercise 17.1, question 2, to get practice in the method.

2. **Finding a cube root without using the cube root key on your calculator**

Here is another method to that shown previously.

Example To find the cube root of 60, correct to 2 decimal places.

We use a formula $\dfrac{\text{number} - (\text{estimate})^3}{3 \times (\text{estimate})^2}$ = correction to estimate

Start with an estimate of 4, since we already know that the answer is between 3 and 4, and nearer 4.

Put 4 into the memory of your calculator, and calculate

$$\dfrac{60 - 4^3}{3 \times 4^2} = -0.0833 \ldots$$

This is the correction to the estimate, so while it is still on the calculator, add it to the memory.

The new estimate is 3.9166 . . . and this is the number in the memory.

Work out

$\dfrac{60 - (3.9166 \ldots)^3}{3 \times (3.9166 \ldots)^2}$ making use of the number in the memory.

This is −0.00179 and is the new correction to the estimate, so add it to the memory, getting 3.9148 . . .

If you work out

$\dfrac{60 - (3.9148 \ldots)^3}{3 \times (3.9148 \ldots)^2}$ you get a number so small that it will not alter the first two

decimal places of the estimate.

So the cube root of 60 is 3.91, correct to 2 decimal places.

(In fact, this method has given us the answer already correct to 5 decimal places.)

Use this method to find the cube roots used in Exercise 17.2, question 2, so that you can compare the methods. Of course, you can only use this method if you remember the formula above.

3. A dairy wants to design a carton for milk which is twice as high as the length of a side of its square base, and it has to hold 1 litre of milk.
If the length of a side of the base is x cm, find expressions for its height, and its volume.
How many cm³ are there in 1 litre ?
Write down an equation.
By trial, solve it to find x, correct to 1 decimal place.
What are the measurements of the carton ?

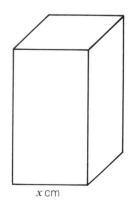

x cm

4. A rectangular lawn has width x metres and
    it is 3 m longer than it is wide.
    Find expressions for its length, and its area.
    If its area is 88 m², write down an equation.
    By trial, solve it to find x.
    What are the measurements of the lawn ?

x
metres

5. The volume of a hemispherical bowl is
    given by the formula $V = 0.262\,d^3$, where
    V is the volume in cm³ and d is the
    diameter of the sphere, in cm.
    If the bowl has to hold 5 litres, how many
    cm³ is this ?
    Write down an equation.
    By trial, solve it to find d, correct to
    1 decimal place.
    What is the diameter of the bowl ?

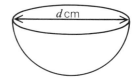

d cm

6. When a stone is dropped down a well, it
    will take t seconds to fall, where the time,
    t seconds, is connected to the depth,
    d metres, of the well by the formula
    $d = 4.9t^2$.
    If the well is 60 m deep, how long will the
    stone take to hit the water at the bottom,
    to the nearest 0.1 second ?

PUZZLE

38. Construct these 3 quadrilaterals and 1 triangle accurately on cardboard.
    For the quadrilaterals, begin by drawing the sides enclosing the right angle, and find the
    4th point using compasses. If you draw them accurately, the angles in the quadrilaterals
    are either 60°, 75°, 105° or 135°.

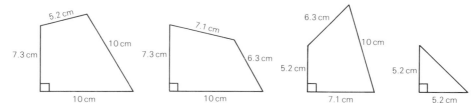

Cut out and rearrange the 4 pieces to form an equilateral triangle. (You may have to turn
some of the pieces over.)

18 Thinking about circles

A circle

What is a circle ?
One girl described it as 'a round square'.
Can you give a more mathematical
description ?

Circles around us

Why are wheels circular ?
Why are coins circular ?
Make a list of objects which include a
circular shape.
Include some very large objects in
your list.
Include some very small objects in
your list.

Pottery

A potter uses his wheel to make
circular pottery. Perhaps you could
arrange a visit to watch him at work.

The Great Laxey Wheel, 22 m diameter. It was built in
1854 to pump out water from the mines, and is the
largest surviving wheel of its kind in the world.

St Paul's Cathedral

20 year-old Christine Turnbull was the first woman to pilot a balloon across the English Channel, in 1969. Here the flight is beginning, at Rye.

An Indian farmer, using a seed drill

An American Indian, photographed in 1909

A display

Hold a display of circular objects. Decide on what things you can include, and arrange them attractively. You can also have posters showing pictures, drawings or photographs of other things. Think of circles in nature, and circles in architecture.
You could also include some patterns based on circles.

Thoughts about circles

'Everything an Indian does is in a circle and that is because the Power of the World always works in circles. The sky is round and I have heard that the earth is round like a ball. The wind, in its great power, whirls. Birds make their nests in circles. Even the seasons form a great circle and always come back again to where they were. The life of a man is a circle from childhood to childhood. Our tepees were round like the nests of the birds and these were always set in a circle.'

This was said by Black Elk, a Plains Indian from North America.

18 Circles

Use your compasses to draw a circle. (Begin by marking the centre point by crossing two thin lines ×)

Here are the names of some parts of a circle.

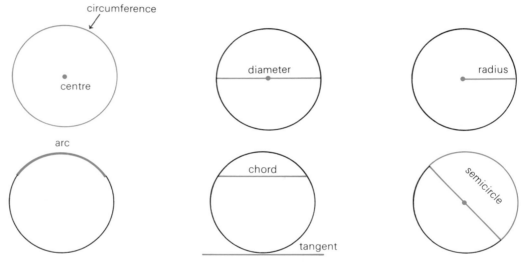

The circumference is often just referred to as the circle.
The word 'radius' can also mean the **distance** between the centre and any point on the circumference.
The plural of radius is radii.
An arc is a part of the circumference.
Here are some other names.

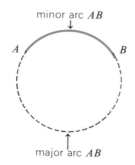

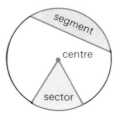

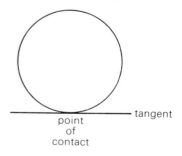

Symmetry

1   The centre of the circle is the point of
    symmetry, and the centre of rotational
    symmetry.
    Every diameter is an axis of symmetry.
    Since there is an infinite number of
    diameters, there is an infinite number of axes
    of symmetry.

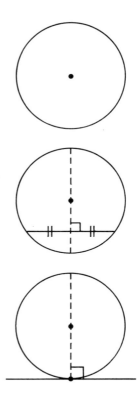

2   Circle and chord.

    The diameter which goes through the mid-
    point of the chord is an axis of symmetry.
    It is also at right angles to the chord, so it is
    the perpendicular bisector of the chord.

3   Circle and tangent.

    The diameter which meets the tangent at the
    point of contact is an axis of symmetry
    (when equal lengths of the tangent are
    drawn either side of the point of contact).
    The diameter is at right angles to the
    tangent.

4   Circle and two tangents meeting at a point
    outside the circle.

    The line OT is an axis of symmetry.
    OT bisects the angle PTQ.
    $PT = QT$

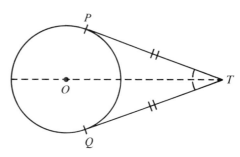

To draw a tangent accurately

Mark the centre C, draw the circle and mark a
point T on the circumference.
Draw the radius CT.
At the point T, draw a line at right angles to
TC.
This is the tangent to the circle, with point of
contact T.

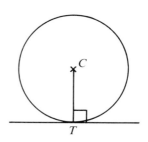

Exercise 18.1

Drawing patterns using compasses

1. If you keep the same radius as used for the circle, you can 'step off' that distance round the circumference exactly six times.

Draw a circle, centre O. Mark a point A on the circumference.

Keeping the same radius throughout, with centre A, draw an arc to cut the circle at B, then,

with centre B, draw an arc to cut the circle at C, with centre C, draw an arc to cut the circle at D, with centre D, draw an arc to cut the circle at E, with centre E, draw an arc to cut the circle at F. Check that with centre F a similar arc would just pass through A. This is a check on the accuracy of your drawing and it is a good idea to practise this construction until your drawing is accurate.

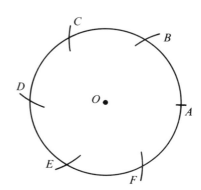

Now by drawing more of the arcs you can make these two patterns.

1 Keep the same radius   **2** Extend to outer circles

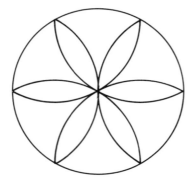

2. All these patterns are based on a hexagon, so you should begin with a circle and 'step off' 6 equally-spaced points on the circumference.

1

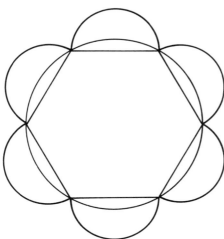

2

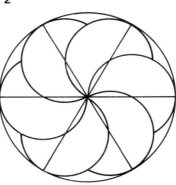

3

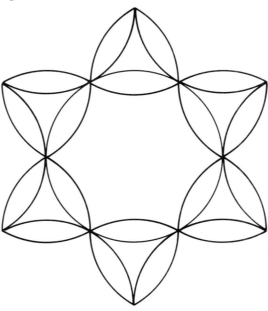

3.   All these patterns are based on a square.
     Draw the square accurately. You can use one drawn on squared paper or graph
     paper as a help, and 'prick through' the points onto your paper.
     Then decide on where the centres of the circles or arcs are, and what the radii
     are, and complete the patterns.

1

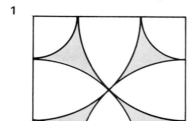

2

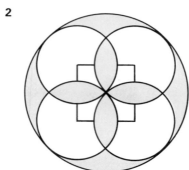

3

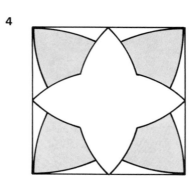

4

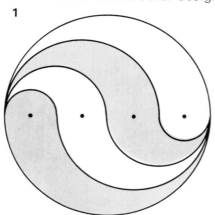

4.   Here are some other patterns to draw.
     You should invent other designs for yourself.

1

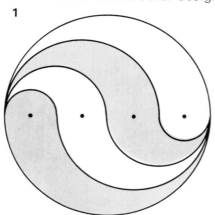

2

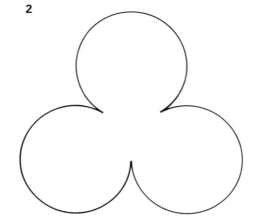

3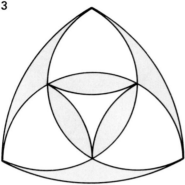

4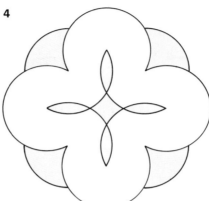

5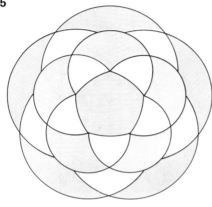

5.   Sketch these diagrams and mark in the axes of symmetry.

1 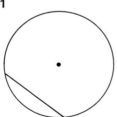   **2**    **3**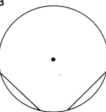

4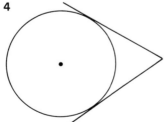

6. Find the marked angles in these circles. (Notice which triangles are isosceles.)
    O is the centre of the circle, and in **4**, PTQ is a tangent touching the circle at T.

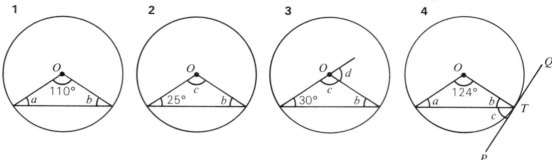

7. Find the marked angles in this diagram.
    O is the centre of the circle and AOC is a
    diameter.
    What is the size of $\angle ABC$?

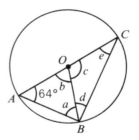

Exercise 18.2 Applications and Activities

1. **Constructions using ruler and compasses**

    1 **To find the mid-point of a line AB or the perpendicular bisector of AB**

    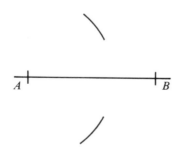

    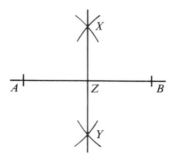

    With centre A and a radius more than   With centre B and the same radius,
    half of AB, draw two arcs.   draw two arcs to cut the first two arcs
                                                   at X and Y.

                                                   Join XY, cutting AB at Z.

                                                   Then Z is the mid-point of AB, and
                                                   XZY is the perpendicular bisector of AB.

2   To bisect an angle *ACB*

With centre *C*, draw arcs to cut *CA*
and *CB* at *X* and *Y*.

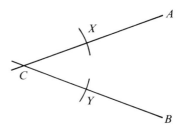

With centres *X* and *Y* in turn, and a
suitable radius, draw arcs to cut at *Z*.
Join *CZ*, which is the bisector of
angle *ACB*.

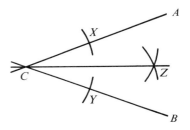

3   To draw a perpendicular to a line *AB* from a point *C*

With centre *C* and a suitable radius,
draw arcs to cut *AB* at *X* and *Y*.

With centres *X* and *Y* in turn, draw
arcs, with the same radius for both, to
cut at *Z*. Join *CZ*, which is
perpendicular to *AB*.

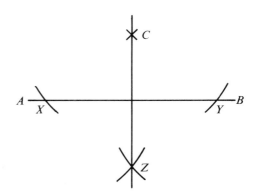

1. **4 To make an angle of 90°, at C, on the line AB,**
   i.e. **To draw a perpendicular to a line AB from a point C on AB**

   With centre C, draw arcs to cut AB at
   X and Y.

   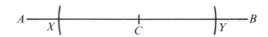

   With centres X and Y in turn, and
   radius slightly larger than before, draw
   arcs to cut at Z. Join CZ, which is
   perpendicular to AB.

   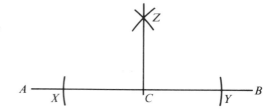

   5 To make an angle of 60°, at P, on the line PQ

   With centre P draw a large arc, to cut
   PQ at Z.
   With centre Z and the same radius,
   draw an arc to cut the other arc at R.
   Join PR.
   Then angle RPQ = 60°

   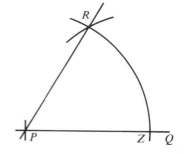

   You can draw an angle of 30° by drawing an angle of 60° and bisecting it.

   You can draw an angle of 45° by drawing a perpendicular line, to make a
   right angle, and bisecting the angle.

   Practise doing constructions using ruler and compasses by doing these questions.

   6 Draw a triangle ABC and find the perpendicular bisectors of AB, BC and CA.
   What do you notice ?
   If the bisectors of AB and BC meet at a point O, draw a circle, centre O,
   which passes through B.
   What do you notice ?
   Repeat with a triangle of a different shape.

7   Draw a triangle *ABC* and find the bisectors of the angles *A*, *B*, *C*.
What do you notice ?
If the bisectors of angles *A* and *B* meet at a point *I*, from *I* construct a line
perpendicular to *AB*, meeting *AB* at *X*.
Draw a circle, centre *I*, radius *IX*.
What do you notice ?
Repeat with a triangle of a different shape.

8   Draw a triangle *ABC*. From *A* draw a line perpendicular to *BC*, from *B* draw a
line perpendicular to *AC*, and from *C* draw a line perpendicular to *AB*.
What do you notice ?
These lines are sometimes called the **altitudes** of the triangle.
Repeat with a triangle of a different shape.

2. **Discovering facts about angles and circles**

1   Angle *AOB* is the angle at the centre and
angle *ACB* is one of the angles at a point
on the circumference, both 'standing' on
the arc *AB*.
Draw an accurate diagram and measure
these angles.
Repeat with other circles, making ∠*AOB*
different sizes.
Can you discover any relationship between
∠*AOB* and ∠*ACB* ?

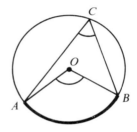

2   In this circle, *AB* is a diameter and *C* is any
point on the circumference.
Draw an accurate diagram and measure
∠*ACB*.
Repeat using other circles.
Can you discover anything about the size of
∠*ACB* ?

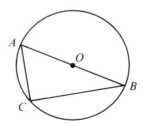

3   *ABCD* is any quadrilateral whose points lie
on the circumference. It is called a **cyclic
quadrilateral**.
Draw an accurate diagram and measure the
angles of the quadrilateral.
Repeat using other circles and different-
shaped quadrilaterals.
Can you discover any relationship between
opposite angles of a cyclic quadrilateral ?

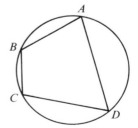

3. **Discovering facts about chords and circles**

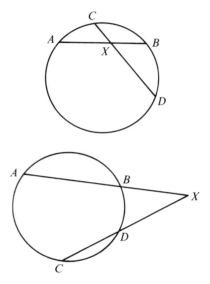

AB and CD are two chords of a circle, which meet at X. X may be inside the circle as in the first diagram, or the chords may have to be produced (extended) to meet outside the circle, as in the second diagram.

Draw an accurate diagram and measure the lengths of AX, BX, CX, DX, to the nearest mm.

Repeat using chords in other circles.

Use your calculator to find the products AX multiplied by BX, and CX multiplied by DX.

Can you discover any relationship ?

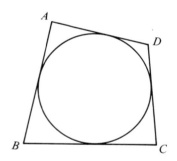

4. **Discovering facts about tangents and circles**

ABCD is a quadrilateral whose sides are all touching the circle (so they are tangents to the circle).

Draw the circle first and then draw the quadrilateral round it. Try to make it irregular, not a square.

Measure the lengths of the sides of the quadrilateral, to the nearest mm.

Repeat using a different circle and quadrilateral.

Can you discover anything about the sum of lengths of opposite sides of the quadrilaterals ?

5. **A mystic rose pattern**

The basic design for this pattern is a circle whose circumference is marked by equally-spaced points. The pattern consists of joining every point to every other point.

This makes an interesting picture if just drawn in one colour, or you can use several different colours. You can also use the pattern for curve stitching or string art.

If you want to draw a simple pattern, choose to have 12 points or 15 points, and a circle with radius 5 cm. If you want a more interesting pattern, use 20 or 24 points, and a larger circle. A radius of 8 cm would be suitable.

The following instructions are for a pattern from 24 points, so change them if you are using more or less points.

You can find the points by drawing radii. For 24 points, the angle between radii is $\frac{360°}{24} = 15°$.

Number the points from 1 to 24.

(If you have an even number of points, the radii will become part of the pattern, but if you choose an odd number of points, or you want to use colour, you will have to rub out the radii once you have found the points. For curve stitching, you could do the drawing on the wrong side of the work.)

To join every point to every other point it is a good idea to work systematically or you may leave some out.

If you are using different colours, then first of all join the opposite points 1 to 13, 2 to 14, etc., in one colour.
Change colour and join the 'nearly opposite' points 1 to 12, 2 to 13, etc., and don't stop until you have used 24 to 11.
Change colour again and join 1 to 11, 2 to 12, etc. finishing with 24 to 10. Continue in this way until you finish by drawing the sides of the 24-sided polygon.

For curve stitching you would take the cotton to the nearest point on the wrong side, so you would begin by doing 1 to 13, then 14 to 2, 3 to 15, 16 to 4, and so on.

For string art it would be better to start with a number of points which is a prime number, such as 23. The angle between the radii is $\frac{360°}{23}$ = approximately $15\frac{1}{2}°$. As the thread has to go round each nail many times, use long nails.

Start by tying the thread onto any nail. Leave an end, to mark the nail and to tie off with at the finish.
Count along 10 nails and go round the 11th, then count along 10 nails from that nail and go round the 11th. Continue doing this until you get back to the nail you started with.
Then count along 9 nails and go round the 10th, and continue doing this until you get back to the nail you started with.

Now count along 8 nails and go round the 9th, and carry on in this way, counting one less every time you get back to the nail you started with.

On some rounds it is advisable to loop round the nail but most times you can just go round the nail. On the last round you are going round every nail in turn. Loop round each nail as this will make the rest secure. When you get back to the starting nail, loop round, weave the thread to the bottom of the nail and tie it to the loose thread.

PUZZLES

39. Here is a piece of cardboard. The lengths of three of its edges are marked in the diagram, but we do not know the length of the edge *AB*. The area of the whole piece of cardboard is 532 cm². How long is the edge *AB* ?

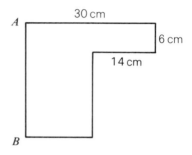

40. **A Cross-figure**

Across

1   *A* is south-west of *C*. *B* is on a bearing of 310° from *C*. Find the size of angle *ACB* (in degrees).

3   The number of diagonals of a six-sided polygon.

4   Begin with the number of hours in a day, double the number, add 8, divide by 7 and add 4. Square that answer, add 25 and take the square root. Add 1. What is the answer ?

5   What is the average height, in cm, of three children who are 1.30 m, 1.35 m and 1.43 m tall ?

7   A girl going on a sponsored walk travels $\frac{5}{8}$ of the distance in the morning and $\frac{2}{3}$ of the remainder in the afternoon. If the total distance to be covered is 16 km, how far has she still to walk after tea ?

Copy this diagram and fill in the answers on your copy.

8 If you threw a die 90 times, how many times would you estimate getting a score of 1 ?

9 The number of mm in 10 cm − the number of cm in 1 m.

10 The x-coordinate where the graph of the function $y = 3x - 12$ meets the x-axis.

11 A man sets out by car and travels at an average speed of 60 mph from 9.30 am to 11.30 am. On the return journey he sets off at 3 pm but does not arrive home until 6 pm. What is his average speed, in mph, on the return journey ?

12 If $13x + 25 = 18x - 15$, what is the value of x ?

13 The number of square tiles of edge 25 cm needed to cover the floor of a corridor 3 m wide and 18 m long.

15 Add together the number of faces, the number of edges and the number of vertices in a triangular prism.

16 The change, in pence, from £1 after buying a loaf at 73p and a cake at 20p.

17 A cube has edges 4 cm long. What is its total surface area (in cm^2) ?

Down

1 What is the number which is less than 100, a multiple of 7, and has digits which add up to 12 ?

2 If the numbers 1 to 9 are placed in a magic square, so that each row, each column and each diagonal adds up to 15, what is the number in the centre square ?

3 Four angles of a pentagon are equal and the fifth one is 168°. What is the size of one of the equal angles (in degrees) ?

4 The value of the largest of (a) 48% of 2500, (b) 2.6 × 4.8 × 100, (c) $\frac{2}{9}$ of 5508.

5 The angles of a quadrilateral are in the ratio 2 : 3 : 9 : 10. What is the size of the largest angle (in degrees) ?

6 A man left £76 000, of which 12% went to charity. The rest was divided between his two children, Andy and Bob, in the ratio 6 : 5. How much more did Andy receive than Bob, in £'s ?

8 The largest value of these expressions when $a = 4$ and $b = 6$.
$2ab,\ a^2 + b^2,\ ab^2,\ (a + b)^2.$

14 A is the point with coordinates (0, 6). B is (2, 2) and C is (8, 3). Find the coordinates of D, where $ABCD$ is a parallelogram, and write them down in order.

15 The value of $2x^2 - 3y$ when $x = 4$ and $y = 2$.

17 27 blocks, each a cube with edge 1 cm, are placed on a table to form a solid cube. The top and the four sides of this large cube are now painted red. How many of the original small cubes have just one face painted red ?

41.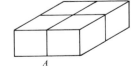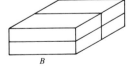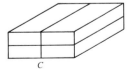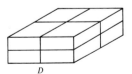

These parcels are exactly the same shape and size.
A needs 114 cm of string, B needs 152 cm and C needs 142 cm.
How much string does D need ? (Ignore the string needed for the knots.)

Miscellaneous Section C

Aural Practice

These aural exercises, C1 and C2, should be read to you, probably by your teacher or a friend, and you should write down the answers only, doing any working out in your head. You should do the 15 questions within 10 minutes.

Exercise C1

1. In the number 37.961, which figure represents the tenths ?

2. How many faces has a pyramid with a square base ?

3. A square has an area of 36 cm². What is the length of one side ?

4. Simplify the expression $x^2 \times x$.

5. If the capital letters O, W, T are reflected in a mirror, what word is shown ?

6. What main compass direction has the bearing 090° ?

7. A drawing is enlarged by a scale factor of 4. How long is a line on the enlargement, if on the original it was 7.5 cm long ?

8. What is the volume of a cuboid 6 cm long, 5 cm wide and 4 cm high ?

9. If the point with coordinates $(-2, 3)$ is reflected in the y-axis, what are the coordinates of the image point ?

10. The average age of three children is 10 years. Two of them are aged 9 and 8. How old is the third child ?

11. A man invests £500 in a business and gets £45 as a share of the profits. What percentage of his investment was this ?

12. In the function $y = 5x - 3$, what is the value of y when $x = 0$?

13. What is the bearing in the opposite direction to the bearing 005° ?

14. A motorist goes 20 miles in $\frac{1}{2}$ hour. What is his average speed in miles per hour ?

15. Find a whole number, less than 10, which is a solution for x in the equation $x^2 + x = 20$.

Exercise C2

1. A rectangular field measures 50 m by 40 m. What is its area ?

2. What is the name for a quadrilateral with 4 equal sides but no right angles ?

3. What is the bearing of the compass direction north-east ?

4. What is the ratio of lengths, in its simplest form, of two model ships which are 20 cm and 25 cm long ?

5. If the point with coordinates (1, 5) is reflected in the x-axis, what are the coordinates of the image point ?

6. A girl buys 3 cans of drinks for 22 pence each. What change should she get from a £1 coin ?

7. A cube has sides of length 3 cm. What is its volume ?

8. Find a whole number, less than 10, which is a solution for x in the equation $x^3 + 2x = 12$.

9. When tossing 2 coins, what is the probability that they will both show heads ?

10. Write down an approximate whole number answer to the question $325 \div 79$.

11. Simplify the expression $a - b + 4b - a$.

12. What is the bearing in the opposite direction to the bearing 200° ?

13. If $p = 6$ and $q = 2$, what is the value of $p^2 + 3q$?

14. A model statue is enlarged by a scale factor of 3. How high is the original, if the enlarged statue is 33 cm tall ?

15. In a pentagon, the sum of the angles is 540°. If 4 of the angles are each 120°, how big is the 5th angle ?

Exercise C3   Oral Practice

Here are some questions to remind you of some of the Mathematical facts you have used in this book.
They are here to give you practice in **talking** about Mathematics.
You can work with friends, answering questions in turn, and joining in to improve the answers when necessary. Do not do the questions all at once, just do a few at any one time.
If you are not sure of the answers then search through the book to find them.

1.   What is an odd number ?
2.   What is a prime number ?
3.   What is a factor of a number ?
4.   What is a multiple of a number ?
5.   What is a square number ?
6.   What is the square root of a number ?

7.   What are the main metric measures of length ? How are they connected with each other ?
8.   What are the main metric measures of weight ? How are they connected with each other ?
9.   What are the main metric measures of capacity ? How are they connected with each other ?
10.   Name some British measures.
11.   In which units do we measure time ? How are these units connected with each other ?

12.   Name some kinds of statistical diagrams and describe them.
13.   How do we find the mean of a set of numbers ?

14.   What is a quadrilateral ?
15.   What do you know about the angles of a quadrilateral ?
16.   What special kinds of quadrilateral do you know ? What is special about each one ?
17.   What is a diagonal of a quadrilateral ?

18.   When we give the probability as a number, what range of numbers do we use ?
19.   What does it mean if the probability of an event happening is $\frac{1}{2}$?

20.   What does it mean if the probability of an event happening is 0.99 ?

21.   How do you calculate the probability of an event happening ?

22.   What is a polygon ?

23.   What is special about a regular polygon ?

24.   What are the names of some polygons ?

25.   What kinds of solid figures do you know ? Describe each one.

26.   What is the net of a solid figure ?

27.   How many faces, edges and vertices (corners) has a cuboid ?

28.   How many faces, edges and vertices has a triangular prism ?

29.   How many faces, edges and vertices has a pyramid on a square base ?

30.   How would you find the perimeter of a rectangle ?

31.   What is the area of a figure ?

32.   How would you find the area of a rectangle ?

33.   How would you find the area of a triangle ?

34.   What is the volume of a solid figure ?

35.   How would you find the volume of a cuboid ?

36.   How would you find the surface area of a cuboid ?

37.   What are the 8 main compass directions ?

38.   How are bearings measured ?

39.   What are similar figures ?

40.   What names of parts of a circle do you know ? Describe each one.

Exercise C4   Revision

1.   Find the surface area of a cube with edges of length 3 cm.

2.   The sizes of the angles of a quadrilateral are in the ratio $2:3:4:6$.
      Calculate the size of the smallest angle of the quadrilateral.

3.   A firm prints photographs on paper of size 10 cm square. They decide to make
      larger prints, 11.5 cm square.
      1   What is the new area ?
      2   The firm has advertised their new prints as being 30% larger. Is this correct ?

4.   In a regular polygon each interior angle is
     5 times the size of each exterior angle.

     1   If the exterior angle has size $x°$, what
             is the size of the interior angle in
             terms of x ?
     2   Write down an equation and solve it
             to find the value of x, and hence
             state the sizes of an exterior angle
             and an interior angle.
     3   What is the sum of the exterior
             angles of a polygon ?
     4   How many exterior angles are there
             in this polygon ?
     5   How many sides has the polygon ?

5.   If the point P with coordinates $(-3, 5)$ is reflected in the y-axis, what are the
     coordinates of its image point ?

6.   Express 75 g : 30 kg as a ratio in its simplest form.

7.   Two fair dice are thrown.
     1   How many equally likely outcomes of scores are there ?
     2   What is the probability of scoring a 1 on both dice ?

8.   From the diagram, state the bearings of
     the directions OA, OB, OC, OD and OF.

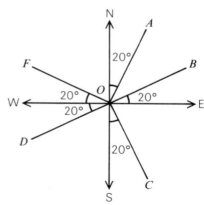

9.   There are two blocks of metal. One contains 1250 cm³ of silver, the other
     contains 1200 cm³ of lead. Which is the heavier block ? (The density of the
     silver is 10.6 g/cm³ and the density of the lead is 11.4 g/cm³.)

10. Hanif reckons that in an exam the probability of him getting grade A is 0.4, the
     probability of getting grade B is 0.3 and the probability of getting grade C is 0.2.
     If he does not get one of these grades he will fail. What is his estimate of the
     probability that he will fail ?

11. What is the scale factor of the
    enlargement which transforms
    1   triangle (1) into triangle (2),
    2   triangle (2) into triangle (3),
    3   triangle (1) into triangle (3) ?

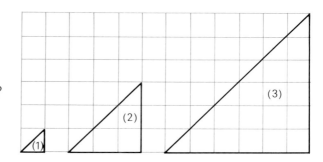

12. On a holiday journey the car mileage indicator readings at certain times were as
    follows:

Time	7.00 am	8.30 am	9.45 am	10.30 am
Mileage reading	10317	10407	10407	10446

(I had stopped for breakfast from 8.30 am to 9.45 am.)

1   What was the average speed for the part of the journey up to 8.30 am ?
2   What was the average speed for the remaining part of the journey from
        9.45 am ?
3   I estimate that my car used 4 gallons of petrol on the journey. What is the
        approximate fuel consumption in miles per gallon ?

13. If $\triangle ABC$ is reflected in the line BC, with A reflected into a point D, what sort of
    quadrilateral is $ABDC$?

1

2

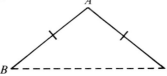

3

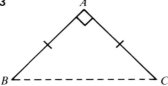

14. On graph paper, using the same scales on both axes, plot the points
    $A (-4, -1)$, $B (0, 2)$, $C (3, -2)$ and join AB and BC. Add a point D such that
    $ABCD$ is a square, and join CD and DA.
    State the coordinates of D.

15. The formula for the sum of numbers from 1 to n is $\dfrac{n(n+1)}{2}$.

Put $n = 40$ in this formula to find the sum of the numbers from 1 to 40.
Put $n = 20$ in the formula to find the sum of the numbers from 1 to 20.
What is the sum of the numbers from 21 to 40 ?

16. Construct $\triangle ABC$, using a ruler and compasses.
Measure $\angle B$.
Construct a point D, such that $ABCD$ is a parallelogram. Join CD and AD.
Measure $\angle D$ ($\angle ADC$).

17. A robot figure weighs 80 g for each centimetre of his height, and the square of his height in cm is 900 greater than his weight in grams.
1 If he is x cm tall, how much does he weigh, in grams ?
2 Write down an equation involving x.
3 By a trial method, solve the equation and hence find his height and weight.

18. The figures show the numbers of tractors and horses used on farms in Great Britain, over a period when farming was becoming mechanized. (The figures are in 10 000's, to the nearest 10 000.)
Plot these figures on a scatter diagram and comment on the relationship between them.
Put 'tractors' on the horizontal axis, using a scale of 1 cm to 5 units, and 'horses' on the vertical axis, using a scale of 1 cm to 10 units.

	1930	1940	1950	1960	1970
Tractors	2	10	33	47	50
Farm horses	80	62	35	6	1

19. In factory A there are 1250 workers and their average weekly wage is £170. In factory B there are 750 workers and their average weekly wage is £210. Find the total wages for all the workers in both factories together.
Find the average wage per worker for the two factories together.

20. The map shows the positions of 3 towns, *A*, *B*, *C*.
The table shows the distances by road between the towns, in km.

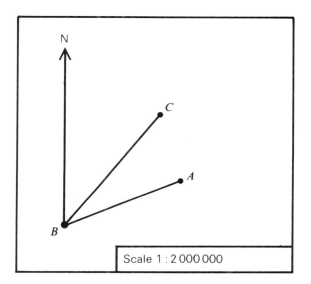

A		
75	*B*	
46	90	*C*

1 A helicopter must fly from *A* to *B* and then on to *C*. By measuring on the map, find the bearings on which it must fly, and the distances from *A* to *B* and from *B* to *C*.

2 How much further is it for a motorist to travel from *A* to *C* via *B* than for the helicopter ?

Exercise C5 Revision

1. In a certain manufacturing process the probability of a component being defective is 0.04. What is the probability of a component being satisfactory ?

2. A metal plate has the measurements shown. If the metal is melted down and recast as a square plate of the same thickness, what is the length of a side of the square ?

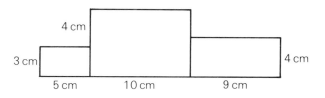

3. Two years ago the cost of an article was £200, made up of charges for labour, materials and other expenses in the ratio $6:3:1$. Since then, labour costs have increased by $\frac{2}{5}$, the price of materials has increased by $\frac{1}{4}$ and the cost of other expenses has increased by $\frac{1}{10}$. What is the cost of the article now ?

4. Village Q is due North of P. Village R is on a bearing of 032° from P. The distances PQ and PR are both 10 km. What is the size of $\angle PQR$? What is the bearing of R from Q ?

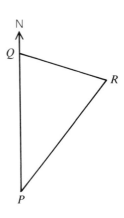

5. On a timed trial the liner Queen Elizabeth averaged a speed of 30.56 knots. What is this speed in km/hour, if 1 knot = 1.853 km/h ?

6. If this trapezium is enlarged with scale factor 5, into trapezium $A'B'C'D'$, what are the lengths of the sides of $A'B'C'D'$?

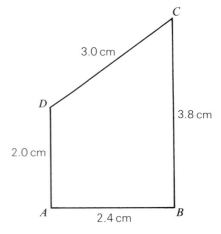

7. A salesman is paid a commission of 8% on the value of goods he sells. If he sells goods worth £1800, what commission does he get ?

8. $ABCD$ is a square and CDE is an equilateral triangle.
    1 Find the size of $\angle ADE$.
    2 Explain why $\triangle ADE$ is isosceles.
    3 Find the size of $\angle AED$.
    4 Find the size of $\angle AEB$.

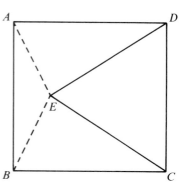

9. **1** Simplify the expression $6(x - 1) + 4(x - 2) - 3(x - 3)$
    2 Solve the equation $6(x - 1) + 4(x - 2) - 3(x - 3) = 30$

10. The diagram shows the drawing of a
letter F and the axes Ox and Oy.

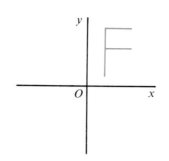

1 Sketch the diagram and also show
the reflection of F in the y-axis.

2 Sketch the original diagram again
and also show the reflection of F in
the x-axis.

11. 8 plots were treated with different amounts of fertilizer and the crop yield
recorded.

Amount of fertilizer (units/m²)	1	2	3	4	5	6	7	8
Yield (in kg)	36	41	58	60	70	76	75	92

Plot a scatter diagram of these results and comment on the relationship between
them.
(Put the 'yield' on the vertical axis and label it from 30 to 100, choosing a
suitable scale.)

12. In the diagram, O is the centre of the
circle.

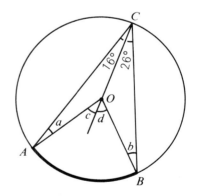

1 What sort of triangles are $\triangle AOC$ and
$\triangle BOC$?

2 Find the sizes of angles a, b, c, d.

3 What is the size of $\angle AOB$?

4 Is there any connection between the
sizes of $\angle AOB$ and $\angle ACB$?

13. A game is played by picking at random a card
from a set of three cards numbered 1, 2, 3 and
then picking at random a second card from a
set numbered 4, 5, 6.
Copy and complete the table showing the
outcomes when the two cards are selected.
What are the probabilities that

1 the sum of the numbers on the cards is 7,

2 at least one of the cards is a 3 or a 6 ?

		1st card		
		1	2	3
2nd card	4	1,4	.	.
	5	.	.	.
	6	.	.	.

14. A rectangular lawn is 30 m longer than it is wide.
    If its length is x metres, find an expression for its width.
    If its area is 1539 m², write down an equation and, by trial, find its solution.
    State the length and width of the lawn.

15. This is a net of a triangular pyramid.

    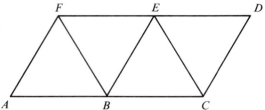

    1 When it is cut out and folded, which
        letter(s) will point A join ?
    2 In the completed solid figure, how
        many faces, edges and vertices are
        there ?

16. A survey is to be made among children of your age about membership of groups
    with regular evening activities, such as youth clubs, sports groups, etc.
    The survey should include girls and boys.
    Details are also wanted about costs, and the times spent on such activities.
    Write out 5 questions suitable for a questionnaire for the survey.

17. A closed metal safe in the shape of a rectangular box has outside measurements
    40 cm by 27 cm by 22 cm and the metal is 1 cm thick.

    1 Find the total volume of the safe.
    2 Find the inside measurements of the
        safe.
    3 Find the volume of the space inside
        the safe.
    4 What is the volume of the metal used
        to make the safe ?

18. A man travelled by car for 30 km at an average speed of 45 km/h and then, on
    the motorway, another 100 km at an average speed of 80 km/h. If he began his
    journey at 9 am, at what time did he finish the journey ?

19. A and B are two harbours, 20 km apart,
    on a straight coastline running west to
    east.
    A ship out at sea is seen from A on a
    bearing of 042° and from B on a bearing
    of 310°.
    Use a scale drawing, with a scale of 1 cm
    to represent 2 km, to find the distance of
    the ship from B, to the nearest 0.2 km.

    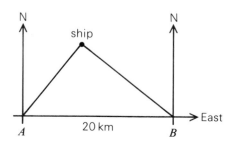

20.   On graph paper draw the x-axis from -2 to 4, taking 2 cm to 1 unit, and draw
        the y-axis from 0 to 45, taking 2 cm to 5 units.
        Write down the coordinates of 3 points which lie on the line with equation
        $y = 20 - 5x$, plot them on the graph, and draw the line, using a ruler.

        Copy and complete this table of values for the graph of the curve $y = \dfrac{42}{5 - x}$.

x	-2	-1	0	1	2	3	4
$5 - x$	7	6	5				1
y	6		8.4				42

        (The last row is obtained by dividing 42 by the value of $5 - x$ in the row
        above.)

        Plot these points and also the point (3.5, 28), and join the points with a smooth
        curve, drawn freehand.
        Find the coordinates of the point of intersection of the line and the curve.

Exercise C6   Activities

1.   **A garden patio**

     You are asked to design a paved patio for a friend's garden. You discover that
     you can buy paving slabs which are equilateral triangles, squares, regular
     hexagons or regular octagons. The lengths of all edges on all these are either
     45 cm for small ones or 60 cm or 90 cm for larger ones. In addition there are also
     rectangular slabs in sizes 90 by 60 cm, 90 by 45 cm or 60 by 45 cm. The slabs can
     be of natural stone colour, pale green or pink.
     Try out different arrangements using shapes cut out of cardboard.
     Choose an arrangement of slabs which would make a pleasing design. Do not
     worry about the exact measurements of the patio, or its shape, since the paved
     area need not have straight edges.

2. **Paper sizes**

The main sizes of paper used to be foolscap (8 inches by 13 inches) and quarto (8 inches by 10 inches) but now there is an international paper size system. You are probably most familiar with the size called A4, which is often used for photocopying and file paper, or A5, which is half as big as A4.

Measure the length and breadth of a sheet of A4 paper, measuring to the nearest mm, and writing them as decimals of a metre. Then calculate the area, in m^2, as a decimal.
How many sheets of A4 paper will cover an area of approximately 1 m^2 ?
Find the ratio length : breadth of the sheet of A4 paper. (Divide the length by the breadth to give this in the form $x : 1$, where x is a number given to 3 decimal places.)

Put 2 A4 sheets of paper together and fasten them with sellotape.
These make a sheet of size A3.
Find the ratio length : breadth of the sheet of A3 paper.
What do you notice ?

Use half a sheet of A4 paper, which makes a sheet of A5 paper.
Find the ratio length : breadth of the sheet of A5 paper. What do you notice ?

The A series of paper starts with size A0. Here is a drawing showing how a piece of A0 paper can be divided continually into halves to make the other sizes.

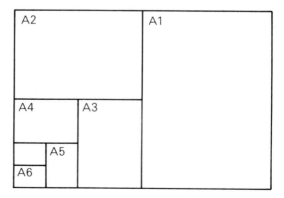

A0 paper has an area of 1 m^2 so you can work out the areas of the other sizes, as fractions of a square metre, and also as decimals.
Check that your answer for the area of A4 paper was correct, although not exactly, due to measurement approximations.

So that the different sizes have the same shape, i.e. A0 is an enlargement of A1, A1 is an enlargement of A2, and so on, the ratio length : breadth = $\sqrt{2} : 1$. This is approximately 1.414 : 1.
Do your results for A4, A3 and A5 papers agree with this ?

In order to get this ratio **and** the area of 1 m², the length of A0 paper has to satisfy the equation (length)² = $\sqrt{2}$ (with length in metres).

Find its length by getting the square root of the square root of 2, from your calculator. Give it to 3 decimal places, which will be to the nearest mm.

Find the breadth by dividing the length by $\sqrt{2}$, and also give this to 3 decimal places.

Check that the area = length × breadth = 1 m² (approximately)

Make a list of the paper sizes from A0 to A6, by halving the longer side each time and ignoring $\frac{1}{2}$'s of mm.

Size	millimetres	Area in m²
A0	1189 × 841	1
A1	841 × 594	$\frac{1}{2}$
. . .		

There are intermediate sizes called the B series. Maybe you can find out their sizes and see how they match the A series.

3. **Buttons**

You can make a mathematical collection of buttons.

If your family has a 'button box' then you will have plenty to look at. If not, you can probably find a few buttons and your friends and neighbours may also have some. You could join with friends to make a combined collection.

Firstly, although most buttons are circular, some are made in different shapes such as triangles, hexagons or squares. Some are cylindrical or spherical.

Then, look at the designs **on** the buttons. You can find different types of symmetry, and you can find many geometrical shapes such as squares, rhombuses, hexagons and circles.

Finally, you can collect different sizes of circular buttons from the smallest to the largest you can find, and measure their diameters.

Make a proper arrangement of your collection, with neat labelling of the different sections. You can sew the buttons onto small pieces of card, and then these can be stuck onto a background to make a poster. Or you can just show the buttons arranged on a table.

4.   **'Roll-a-penny'**

There is a game, often seen on fairgrounds,
where you roll coins onto a board which is
marked with squares.
You can find the probability of winning
at it.
You lose your money if the coin touches
or crosses the black lines dividing the
squares. To win, the coin has to land
completely inside a square. (Usually, some
squares are marked to win more money
than others. Here, we will just work out
the probability of winning something.)

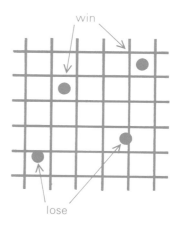

Penny coins are rather small so we will use 2p coins.
Make a grid of squares. You can draw
these on a large sheet of paper and put it
on a table. Mark the squares 5.0 cm wide
and use lines 0.3 cm thick to divide them.

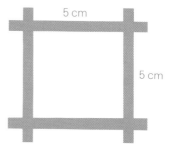

Design and make a gadget for rolling the coins down. You can make this out of
cardboard. (Alternatively, you could put the grid of squares on the floor and
throw the coins onto it, instead of rolling them.)

To carry out the experiment you should carry out a large number of trials, say 500. You can use up to 10 coins at a time, as long as you let them land on different parts of the grid. Count the number of wins out of the total number rolled. (If a coin rolls off the grid or bumps into another, it is best to roll that coin again.)

Before you begin, make a guess of the probability of winning. Then afterwards, work out the experimental result.

$$\text{Probability} = \frac{\text{number of wins}}{\text{total number rolled}}$$

Was your guess a good one ?

Now to work out the theoretical result.

You can assume that the centre of the coin is equally likely to land anywhere on the grid.

For the coin to land within a square, there is a smaller square region inside the square in which its centre must lie.

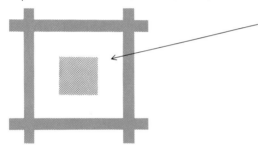
you win if the centre of the coin lies in the shaded region

$$\text{Probability of winning} = \frac{\text{area of the shaded region in any square}}{\text{area of a square}}$$

Calculate the area of a square, including half the thickness of the dividing line on each side. (If you used the measurements suggested here it will be a square 5.3 cm wide.)

Measure the diameter of the 2p coin and hence calculate its radius, r cm.

Use this diagram to find the measurements of the shaded region, and calculate its area.

Then work out the theoretical probability.

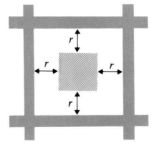

Compare this result with you guess and with the experimental results, and comment about them.

Do you think that the game is a fair one ? Could it be made fairer ?

5. **Reflection using mirrors**

Use a plane mirror to see the reflections of various objects.
Draw half of a symmetrical design and place the mirror along the axis of
symmetry.
You may have done experiments in Science to find out about 'angle of incidence'
and 'angle of reflection'. If not, try this out now.

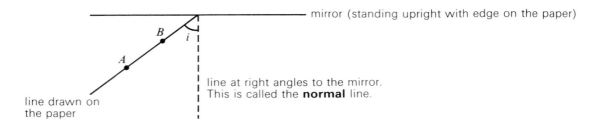

mirror (standing upright with edge on the paper)

B   *i*

A

line at right angles to the mirror.
This is called the **normal** line.

line drawn on
the paper

i is called the angle of incidence. Measure it on your drawing.
Stick 2 pins in the line at *A* and *B*. Look through the mirror until you can see the
reflections of the pins. Now move until the reflection of pin *B* hides that of pin *A*
because they appear to be in a straight line from where you are looking.
Stick in a pin *C* to hide the reflections of pins *B* and *A*, and then another pin *D* to
hide pin *C* and the reflections of pins *B* and *A*.
Then the line joining *D* and *C* will be the line of reflection of the line *AB*.
The angle this line makes with the normal line is called the angle of reflection.
Measure this angle.
Repeat this experiment with a line *AB* making a different angle of incidence.
Repeat again, several times, and list your results for the angles of incidence and
reflection.
Can you discover anything about the angles ?

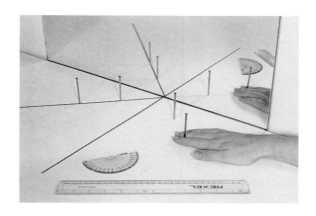

Look at reflections when you hold a mirror
which is nearly parallel to another one.

Discover how mirrors are used in a
kaleidoscope and make some patterns
with one.
Why are curved reflecting surfaces used
in torches and car headlights ?

6. **A maths poster display**

If everyone in the class makes an original poster these form a very effective
display.
The subject of your poster can be any topic connected with mathematics. There
are many ideas in this book and you can get more from library books or maths
magazines.
By keeping to just two sizes it is easier to arrange the posters attractively around
the room, so use a background of sugar paper of size A2, or a half sheet of this.
Design your own poster. Has it a title ? What information should it show ?
Use bright-coloured sticky paper, or plain or lined white paper. Write with felt tips
or use paints. You may want to use photographs, newspaper cuttings, graphs, etc.
Avoid sheets covered with lots of small writing, you are making a poster, not
writing an essay. Place your cut-outs onto the sugar paper background but do
not stick them on until you have got the best arrangement.

Have a date by which all posters should be finished. Arrange them around the
room. Perhaps you will classify them in some logical order or perhaps you will
just show an attractive mixture. Ask someone to judge the posters to decide
which the best ones are, and to point out any important mistakes which must be
put right. Then you can let other classes see your display, and it may also be
possible to have it on show at a Parents' Evening. Before you take down your
display, take photographs so that you keep a record for the future.

7. **Bearings**

    To use a Silva Compass

    e.g. To read a bearing of 040°, turn the dial until 40° is in the direction of the arrow. Hold the compass close to your body, the arrow pointing in front of you. Then turn round slowly until the needle on the compass points to North on the dial. The arrow now points you in the direction you should go. Find a landmark in that direction that you can aim for, and walk towards it. After a while, stop and check the compass again to make sure that you are still going in the right direction.

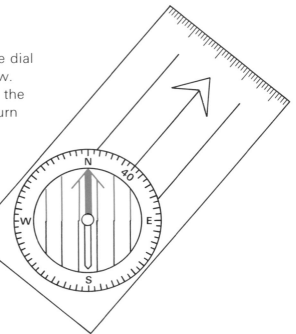

Orienteering is a fairly new sporting activity, based on map reading and finding your way by using compass bearings. Perhaps you can find someone to come to talk to you about orienteering, and arrange for you to have a try at it.

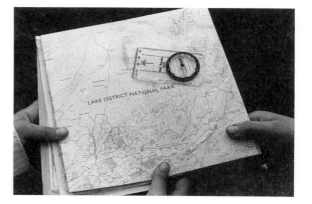

A direction-finding exercise

Instead of finding your way over countryside, here is an exercise where you can mark your way over a piece of graph paper. Use the y-axis and the lines parallel to it as the North direction. Start from the bottom left-hand corner of the sheet. You should measure distances with your ruler so you do not need an x-axis or any scale on the y-axis.

Draw lines to show your track. Start each new instruction from the point you have reached.

1 Go 19.1 cm on a bearing 031°,
2 go 12.3 cm on a bearing 184°,
3 go 7.0 cm on a bearing 043°,
4 go 12.8 cm on a bearing 256°,
5 go 11.4 cm on a bearing 112°,
6 go 9.5 cm on a bearing 328°,
7 go 5.7 cm on a bearing 112°,
8 go 5.3 cm on a bearing 355°,
9 go 17.9 cm on a bearing 220°.

When you finish you should be back at the starting point but there may be errors as is not easy to get this exactly right.

Now if you look at your track you should be able to find a star. Colour it in. Well done!

8. **The Fibonacci Sequence in Nature**

Many natural objects have links with Fibonacci numbers. Count the number of petals on a daisy-type flower. It often turns out to be near to a Fibonacci number such as 21, 34 or 55.

Count the spirals on a pine cone, and then count the spirals going in the opposite direction. Count the spirals on other types of cones, on a pineapple, and in the centre part of a sunflower. The spirals are called equiangular spirals or logarithmic spirals.

The golden section ratio $r : 1$ is such that the number r is the positive number satisfying the equation $r^2 - r = 1$.

You know that r is approximately 1.618

By trial and improvement, find its value correct to 5 decimal places.

Verify that this is the same as the value of $\frac{1}{2}(\sqrt{5} + 1)$, to 5 decimal places.

Golden section spiral

This is an approximation to the equiangular spiral mentioned before and also found in seashells.

Start with a large rectangle with length 1.62 times the breadth. Cut off a square, with the line $A_1 B$. Starting from A, with centre A_1, draw a quarter circle, going to B. Now join XY and $A_1 Z$ as guidelines as a corner of each following square lies on one of these lines.

A nautilus shell

Cut off a square including point B, with the line $B_1 C$.

Starting from B, with centre B_1, which is on $A_1 B$ and on XY, draw a quarter circle, going to C.

Cut off a square including point C, with the line $C_1 D$.

Starting from C, with centre C_1, which is on $B_1 C$ and on $A_1 Z$, draw a quarter circle going to D.

Continue until the squares get too small to go any further. Where does it end ?

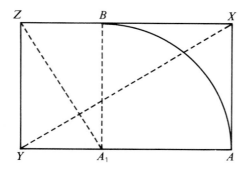

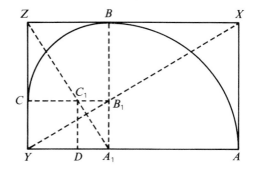

9. **Using the computer**

Here are some more suggestions.

1   The data for scatter graphs can be entered in a suitable program, which will plot them on a scatter graph. Since this is much quicker than drawing your own graph, you can use more pairs of data, and this should make it easier to recognise any sort of correlation.

2   It is much quicker to solve equations by trial methods when a computer is doing the calculations, and this also means that you can get an answer to more decimal places, if that is needed.

3   Reflections, and enlargements, can also be drawn quickly using a computer program.
You can also draw circles, and design many geometrical patterns, some based on symmetry, and others on a random choice generated by the program.

PUZZLES

42.   Angela keeps her books very tidily on her bookshelf. Her mother says that if she keeps acquiring more books at her present rate she will soon have over 50. Exactly 20% of Angela's books are school textbooks and exactly one-seventh were presents she received last Christmas.
How many books has Angela on her shelf ?

43.   A horse dealer left his horses to his sons as follows:- to the first son 1 horse and a tenth of the remainder, to the second son 2 horses and a tenth of those that then remained, to the third son 3 horses and a tenth of those that then remained, and so on with each of the other sons. When all sons had received their shares it was found that all the horses had been distributed, and that all sons had equal shares. How many horses were there, and how many sons shared them ?

44.   'I have found a strange number!' said Robert.
'What is it ?' asked Ian.
'Well,' said Robert, 'if you add 5 to it you get the same answer as when you multiply it by 5.'
What was the number ?

Index

addition in algebra, 26
addition of decimals, 41
addition of fractions, 82
addition of negative numbers, 9
adjacent angles, 53
algebra, 24, 26, 152, 154, 264, 266
alternate angles, 53
angles and lines, 53
angles at a point, 53
angles of quadrilaterals, 51, 52
angles of polygons, 123, 125, 134
angles of triangles, 54
arc of a circle, 276
area, 222, 224
arithmetic mean, 93
average, 93
average speed, 184

bar chart, 91
bar-line graph, 92
bearings, 213, 214, 220, 308
bisecting a line, 282
bisecting an angle, 283
British units, 43

capacity units, 44
chord of a circle, 276
circles, 274, 276
circumference of a circle, 276
collecting information, 88, 90, 95, 251
collecting terms (in algebra), 29
compass directions, 212
computer uses, 113, 211, 311
cone, 168, 176
constructions, 56, 135, 282
convex polygon, 122
coordinates, 152, 156
correlation, 242, 246
corresponding angles, 53
cube, 168, 172, 181, 233
cube numbers, 5
cube roots, 268, 272
cubic equations, 268
cuboid, 168, 173, 233
cylinder, 168, 176

decagon, 125
decimal places, 38, 41
decimals, 36, 38, 72
denominator of a fraction, 72
density, 235
diagonals of quadrilaterals, 53, 66, 68
diagonals of polygons, 203
diagrams (in statistics), 90, 242, 244
diameter of a circle, 276

difference methods, 16
distance, 184
division, 3, 6
division in algebra, 26
division of decimals, 40
division of fractions, 83
division of negative numbers, 11
dodecagon, 132
dodecahedron, 181
drawing perpendicular lines, 283

edges of a solid figure, 171
enlargement, 253, 256
equations, 28, 30, 32, 154, 264, 266
equilateral triangle, 54
expressions (in algebra), 27
exterior angle of a polygon, 122, 126
exterior angle of a triangle, 54

faces of a solid figure, 171
Fibonacci sequence, 15, 18, 49, 206, 309
fractions, 70, 72, 77
fractions in equations, 32
functions, 152, 154

geometric patterns, 130, 278
graphs of functions, 152, 156
graphs (statistical), 90, 242, 244

heptagon, 124
hexagon, 124, 136
hexagonal numbers, 15
hexagonal prism, 168
histogram, 92

icosahedron, 180
independent events, 139, 143
interior angles (between parallel lines), 53
interior angles of a polygon, 125
investigations (in statistics), 88, 95, 257
isosceles triangle, 54

kite, 52, 55, 61, 68

length units, 43
linear equations, 28, 30, 32
line-graph, 90

mapping diagram, 152, 154
mass, 235
mean, 93
measurements, 37, 43
metric system, 43
models of solid figures, 172, 180, 208
multiplication, 2, 6, 20
multiplication in algebra, 26
multiplication of decimals, 40

multiplication of fractions, 73
multiplication of negative numbers, 11
mutually exclusive events, 138, 141

negative numbers, 8
nets of solid figures, 172
networks, 204
nonagon, 125
numbers, 1, 2, 8, 38, 72
numerator of a fraction, 72

octagon, 124, 137
octahedron, 180

parallelogram, 52, 58, 61, 68, 229, 230
pentagon, 124, 135
percentages, 71, 76
perimeter, 52, 222, 224
perpendicular bisector, 282
pictogram, 91
pie chart, 91
plans and elevations, 179
polygons, 122, 124
prime numbers, 3
prism, 168, 173
probability, 138, 140, 202, 304
pyramid, 168, 173

quadratic equations, 266
quadrilateral, 50, 52
questionnaire, 89, 96

radius of a circle, 276
range, 93
ratio, 114, 116
rectangle, 52, 60, 61, 69, 224
rectangular block, 168
rectangular numbers, 14
re-entrant polygon, 122
reflection, 252, 254
regular polygons, 122, 124, 126
regular solid figures, 180
removing brackets, 30
rhombus, 52, 59, 61, 69

scale factor, 257
scatter diagram, 242, 244

scatter graphs, 242, 244
sector of a circle, 276
segment of a circle, 276
sequences of numbers, 1, 13
similar figures, 253, 256
simple interest, 86
solid figures, 166, 168
solving equations, 28, 30, 32, 266
speed, 182, 184
sphere, 168
square, 52, 60, 61, 69, 225
square numbers, 5, 14
square roots, 266, 271
statistical diagrams, 90, 242, 244
statistical graphs, 90, 242, 244
statistical investigations, 88, 95, 251
statistics, 88, 90, 242, 244
substitution (in algebra), 27
subtraction in algebra, 26
subtraction of decimals, 41
subtraction of fractions, 82
subtraction of negative numbers, 9
surface area, 233
symmetry, 62, 277

tables (in arithmetic), 2, 43
tables of functions, 154
tangent to a circle, 276
tessellations, 131
tetrahedron, 175, 180
time, 44, 184, 186
time-series graph, 90
trapezium, 52, 57, 61, 68, 230
trapezium numbers, 15
tree diagram, 144
trial and improvement methods, 266
triangles, 54, 224, 228, 230, 256
triangular numbers, 14
triangular prism, 168, 173
triangular pyramid, 168, 173

VAT, 85
vertex of a solid figure, 171
vertically opposite angles, 53
volume, 223, 233, 235

weight units, 44

Answers

Some answers have been given corrected to reasonable degrees of accuracy, depending on the questions.
There may be variations in answers where questions involve drawings or graphs.

Page 2

1st group

36	33	48	2	21
14	24	28	84	0
0	80	30	108	25
32	10	12	24	7
18	8	7	36	36
99	10	16	56	110
80	30	66	12	60
55	56	21	0	72
49	6	48	4	54
0	42	12	0	36

2nd group

9	12	10	8	39
100	9	15	6	24
4	72	50	37	11
11	21	7	11	0
36	56	8	0	14
9	14	49	9	20
20	6	12	24	35
6	2	100	14	7
3	5	8	40	20
60	5	54	26	18

Page 4   Exercise 1.1

1. **1** 396 241   **6** 96 000
   2 9006   **7** 7022
   3 4 318 092   **8** 70 000
   4 3 003 030   **9** 1001
   5 2 500 000   **10** 250 000

2. **1** 30   **5** 104   **8** 11
   2 11   **6** 90   **9** 15
   3 25   **7** 7   **10** 121
   4 0

3. **1** 7 r 4   **5** 11 r 1   **8** 8 r 0
   2 6 r 2   **6** 3 r 0   **9** 12 r 4
   3 5 r 0   **7** 9 r 5   **10** 5 r 2
   4 7 r 3

4. **1** 8, 3   **4** 10, 3
   2 10, 2   **5** 25, 4
   3 8, 7

5. **1** 8   **2** 5   **3** 4   **4** 9   **5** 4

6. **1** 10   **5** 44   **8** 46
   2 49   **6** 12   **9** 6
   3 54   **7** 9   **10** 300
   4 5

7. **1** 62, 64, 70, 72
   2 65, 70, 75
   3 69, 72, 75

8. **1** 41, 43, 47
   2 67, 97

9. **1** 36, 49, 64   **4** 45, 50, 55
   2 27, 64   **5** 27, 36, 42, 45
   3 23, 31

10. **1** 1   **2** 2

Page 7   Exercise 1.2

(Estimated answers can differ from those given here.)

1. **1** 5600   **5** 14 000   **8** 4
   2 240 000   **6** 8   **9** 700
   3 270 000   **7** 60   **10** 12
   4 500 000

2. **1** 1300   **7** 1400
   2 1000   **8** 24 000
   3 800 (or 700)   **9** 18 000
   4 1500 (or 1600)   (or 21 000)
   5 2500   **10** 3600
   6 3000 (or 4200)

3.   **1** 1332   **5** 2444   **8** 26 240
    2 1046   **6** 4340   **9** 18 200
    3 761   **7** 1387   **10** 3721
    4 1584

4.   **1** 20   **4** 33
    2 47   **5** 400
    3 500

5.   **1** 17   **4** 31
    2 42   **5** 390
    3 520

6.   **1** 20 000, 20 054
    2 500 000, 541 780
    3 1 500 000, 1 492 400
    4 80 000, 88 150
    5 630 000, 613 360

7.   **1** 14, 13.7   **4** 4, 3.7
    2 6 (or 7), 6.7   **5** 26 (or 28), 25.5
    3 100, 102.8

Page 9

1. −3   5. 1   8. −3
2. −9   6. −20   9. −1
3. 1   7. −6   10. 2
4. −3

Page 11 (top)

1. 3   5. 9   8. 7
2. −1   6. −2   9. −1
3. 5   7. 0   10. 3
4. −1

Page 11

1. −24   5. 0   8. 16
2. 30   6. −14   9. 0
3. 8   7. −55   10. −180
4. −63

Page 12   Exercise 1.3

1. **1** 6   **6** −1 **11** 0   **16** −8
   2 1   **7** −5 **12** 1   **17** −3
   3 −1   **8** 9   **13** −1 **18** −4
   4 −3   **9** −5 **14** 3   **19** 0
   5 −4 **10** −11 **15** −4 **20** 1

2. **1** 1   **6** −5 **11** −1 **16** 10
   2 −7   **7** −7 **12** −16 **17** 2
   3 6   **8** −3 **13** 2   **18** 3
   4 0   **9** −1 **14** 5   **19** −7
   5 −2   **10** −6 **15** 3   **20** 4

3. **1** −6   **6** 0   **11** −2 **16** 3
   2 −15 **7** 15   **12** 81   **17** −10
   3 18   **8** −36 **13** −9 **18** −35
   4 −36 **9** 49   **14** 2   **19** 24
   5 −4   **10** −1 **15** 0   **20** −16

Page 13   Exercise 1.4

1. **1** 31, 38, 45
   2 48, 96, 192
   3 243, 729, 2187
   4 −1, −2, −3
   5 −17, −22, −27
   6 $\frac{1}{27}$, $\frac{1}{81}$, $\frac{1}{243}$
   7 0.0003, 0.00003, 0.000003
   8 18, 24, 31

2. **1** 19, 22, 25   **4** 0.01, 0.001, 0.0001
   2 −2, −6, −10 **5** 20, 25, 31
   3 80, 160, 320 **6** 1200, 7200, 50 400

5. **1** 23, 37, 60   **4** 6, 9, 15
   2 26, 42, 68   **5** 31, 50, 81
   3 11, 19, 30

6. **1** 40, 54, 70   **4** 46, 67, 92
   2 31, 40, 50   **5** 40, 53, 68
   3 55, 80, 110

Page 16   Exercise 1.5

1. 1470 miles   6. £164
2. £2200   7. 400
3. 130   8. 1798
4. £18   9. £12 480
5. 20   10. 336 litres

11. **1** Friday **2** 8° **3** 5° **4** −12°C

12. **1** 12°C **2** −13°C **3** 6 pm

15. **1** 420   **10** 3456 **19** 891
   2 180   **11** 6039 **20** 286
   3 1310 **12** 4257 **21** 473
   4 135   **13** 71 181 **22** 517
   5 245   **14** 600   **23** 935
   6 576   **15** 1500 **24** 29 216
   7 783   **16** 1900 **25** 139 568
   8 4284 **17** 350   **26** 35 261
   9 2673 **18** 775

Page 26   Exercise 2.1

1. **1** $5a$ **5** 0 **8** $3k^2$
    2 $2b$ **6** $5fg$ **9** $7m - 7n$
    3 c **7** 0 **10** $p + 1$
    4 $4d$

2. **1** $6a$ **5** $12f^2$ **8** m
    2 0 **6** $7gh$ **9** n^3
    3 c^2 **7** $12jk$ **10** $5p^2$
    4 $5de$

3. **1** 3 **6** $\frac{3}{5}f$ or $\frac{3f}{5}$ **9** $\frac{4p}{q}$
    2 1
    3 $2c$ **7** $\frac{8}{3}g$ or $\frac{8g}{3}$ **10** r
    4 0
    5 $\frac{1}{4}e$ or $\frac{e}{4}$ **8** $\frac{m}{n}$

4. **1** a^3 **5** $20fg$ **8** 2
    2 $2bc$ **6** h **9** $5mn$
    3 $4d$ **7** 0 **10** $p + 2q$
    4 9

Page 28   Exercise 2.2

1. **1** bx pence   **6** $x + 1, x + 2$
    2 $(100c - x)$ pence   **7** $4f$ cm
    3 $100d$ (cm)   **8** $\frac{1}{3}g$ cm or $\frac{g}{3}$ cm
    4 $\frac{1}{1000}d$ or $\frac{d}{1000}$ (km)   **9** $17h$ pence
    5 $e + 5$ **10** $(100 - j)$ cm

2. **1** 19 **5** 5 **8** 27
    2 11 **6** 2 **9** 1
    3 15 **7** 50 **10** 16
    4 0

3. **1** $x = 3$ **8** $x = 20$ **15** $x = 7$
    2 $x = 5$ **9** $x = 14$ **16** $x = 5$
    3 $x = 32$ **10** $x = 45$ **17** $x = 12$
    4 $x = 36$ **11** $x = 1$ **18** $x = 9$
    5 $x = 6$ **12** $x = 15$ **19** $x = 6$
    6 $x = 11$ **13** $x = 5$ **20** $x = 11$
    7 $x = 4$ **14** $x = 4$

Page 32   Exercise 2.3

1. **1** $5a$ **5** $5g - 4h$ **8** $3 - 3p$
    2 $2d$ **6** $3j$ **9** $r + s$
    3 $2e - 2$ **7** $4m - n$ **10** $3t - 3$
    4 $3f + 2$

2. **1** -1 **6** $7g - 18$
    2 $11b + 8$ **7** $2h + 12$
    3 $c - 4d$ **8** $3k^2 + 7k - 6$
    4 $3e - f$ **9** $m^2 + 3m + 8$
    5 -5 **10** $2q - 2r$

3. **1** $x = 3$ **5** $x = 1$ **8** $x = 6\frac{1}{2}$
    2 $x = 2$ **6** $x = 1\frac{2}{5}$ **9** $x = -4$
    3 $x = \frac{1}{2}$ **7** $x = 4$ **10** $x = \frac{1}{3}$
    4 $x = -2$

4. **1** $x = 8$ **4** $x = 11$
    2 $x = 6$ **5** $x = \frac{3}{4}$
    3 $x = \frac{1}{2}$

Page 33   Exercise 2.4

1. £$(10 + 8t)$, $C = 10 + 8t$

2. £$9n$, $P = 9n - 60$

3. $150 - b$, £$(b + 300)$, $b = 64$; 64 bears

4. **1** $a + b + c = 180$
    2 $e + f = 180$
    3 $g + h = 180$

5. £$(11x - 12)$, $x = 5$; adult £5, child £3

6. £50

7. 260

8. $34 - x$, $102 - 2x$, $x = 4$; won 30, drew 4

9. **1** $(3x + 3)$ m
    2 $(x + 7)$ m
    3 1 m

10. **1** $15°$
    2 $131°$

Page 42   Exercise 3.1

1. **1** seventy
    2 7 tenths
    3 7 thousandths
    4 7 hundredths
    5 7 hundred thousand

2. **1** 10   **4** 1000
    2 100   **5** 100
    3 1000

3. **1** 0.06   **4** 0.79
    2 0.33   **5** 0.899
    3 0.001

4. **1** 3.505, 3.52, 3.6
   2 0.048, 0.24, 1.208
   3 0.6, 0.666, 0.67
   4 0.2, 0.22, 0.222
   5 0.005, 0.03, 0.035

6. **1** 0.04, 0.004   **4** 1.0, 0.9
   2 0.09, 0.11   **5** 0.6, 0.3
   3 5, 50

7. **1** 2.45   **4** 1.22
   2 14.14   **5** 3.32
   3 4.36

8. **1** 3.85   **4** 23.04
   2 17.99   **5** 2.96
   3 4.73

9. **1** 3, 3, 9, 8.792
   2 22, 2, 11, 9.95

10. 4

Page 46   Exercise 3.2

1. **1** 500   **8** 30   **15** 365
   2 180   **9** 7000   **16** 4000
   3 150   **10** 20   **17** 240
   4 3000   **11** 70   **18** 2000
   5 2000   **12** 4000   **19** 8000
   6 52   **13** 500   **20** 14
   7 5   **14** 600

2. **1** 1.26 kg   **5** 70 cm   **8** 7.8 cm
   2 59 mm   **6** 750 g   **9** 3.04 m
   3 0.3 m   **7** 1.6 ℓ **10** 2100 g
   4 2600 ml

3. (Other answers possible)
   1 metres and cm   **6** km
   2 kg and g   **7** tonnes
   3 metres   **8** ml
   4 grams   **9** grams
   5 litres   **10** m or cm

4. (Other answers possible)
   1 8.7 m   **6** 5.5 m
   2 270 g (or 275 g) **7** £2.05
   3 420 000 ℓ **8** $\frac{1}{3}\ell$ or 0.3 ℓ
   4 373 m   **9** $2\frac{1}{4}$ hours
   5 10 yrs 2 mths   **10** 5.4 tonnes

Page 47   Exercise 3.3

1. 227

2. 3.6 kg

3. 40 ℓ

4. 68, nearly 14

5. 7

6. **1** 2526   **2** £162.33

7. 80 cm

Page 54   Exercise 4.1

1. Number of axes, in order, 0, 0, 1, 1, 0, 2, 2, 4, Points, in order, no, no, no, no, yes, yes, yes, yes

2. **1** 122°
   2 85°
   3 90°, rectangle, square

3. **1** 73°
   2 $b = 81°$, $c = 72°$
   3 $d = 280°$, $e = 18°$

4. **1** $a = 63°$, $b = 105°$, $c = 56°$
   2 $d = 105°$, $e = 75°$, $f = 50°$

5. $\angle A = \angle C = 93°$, $\angle B = 120°$, $\angle D = 54°$, sum = 360°

6. Isosceles triangle, they are congruent.

7. $\angle A = \angle C = 124°$

8. $\angle A = \angle C = 10°$

9. $\angle D = 110°$, $\angle C = 126°$

10. AD and BC are not equal.

11. 114°

12. $\angle B = 66°$, $\angle C = \angle D = 114°$

13. $\angle A = \angle C = 65°$, $\angle B = \angle D = 115°$, sum = 360°
    $AB = CD = 6.1$ cm, $AD = BC = 4.4$ cm, perimeter = 21.0 cm

14. $\angle B = \angle D = 132°$, $\angle C = 48°$, $BC = 5.6$ cm, $DC = 9.2$ cm

15. A diamond

16. $\angle B = \angle D = 108°$, $\angle C = 72°$, $BC = CD = 6.8$ cm

17. A square

18. An oblong

19. $\angle B = \angle C = \angle D = 90°$, $BC = 5.6$ cm, $CD = 9.2$ cm

20. A square

Page 62   Exercise 4.2

1. **1** $a = 76°$, $b = 64°$
   2 $c = e = 52°$, $d = 28°$

2. 105°

3. **1** $a = c = 112°$, $b = 68°$
   2 $d = f = 23°$, $e = h = 134°$, $g = 46°$

4. $a = c = 37°$, $b = 106°$

5. $a = b = 45°$, $c = 53°$, $d = 82°$

6. 150°

7. $b = c = 62°$, $d = 28°$

8. **1** parallelogram, rectangle
   2 kite
   3 trapezium
   4 rhombus, square

9. **1** kite
   2 rhombus
   3 parallelogram
   4 rectangle
   5 $(8, -2)$

10. **1** 83°   **2** 12.9 cm

11. **1** 29°   **2** 10.5 cm

12. $SR = 3.7$ cm, $QR = 6.4$ cm

13. **1** parallelogram, rhombus
    2 trapezium
    3 rhombus
    4 rectangle
    5 parallelogram

14. **1** isosceles triangle
    2 right-angled triangle
    3 isosceles right-angled triangle

Page 65   Exercise 4.3

1. $a = c = 18°$, $b = 144°$, $d = 82°$

2. **1** $a = 72°$, $b = 54°$ **2** isosceles

3. **1** $a = 60°$, $b = 30°$
   2 22 cm, 12 cm

4. **1** Both equal to DC
   2 $a = 90°$, $b = 64°$, $c = 13°$, $d = 103°$

5. **1** $x = 24$; 48°, 72°, 96°, 144°
   2 $y = 360 - 7x$

6. $AB = 5.8$ cm, $\angle ABC = 118°$

7. **1** $AC = 8.1$ cm, $BD = 13.0$ cm, no
   2 $AX = CX = 4.1$ cm,
     $BX = DX = 6.5$ cm, yes
   3 115°, no

8. **1** $AC = BD = 10.8$ cm, yes
   2 $AX = CX = BX = DX = 5.4$ cm, yes
   3 113°, no

9. **1** $AC = 6.2$ cm, $BD = 10.3$ cm, no
   2 $AX = CX = 3.1$ cm,
     $BX = DX = 5.1$ cm, yes
   3 90°, yes

10. **1** $AC = BD = 8.5$ cm, yes
    2 $AX = CX = BX = DX = 4.2$ cm, yes
    3 90°, yes
    4 45°

11. **1** all
    2 rhombus, square
    3 rectangle, square

12. **1** $a = 58°$, $b = 43°$, $c = 63°$
    2 $d = 42°$, $e = 84°$
    3 $f = g = 45°$, $h = 90°$

13. $AB = 8.2$ cm, $AD = 3.9$ cm
    (or $AB = 3.9$ cm, $AD = 8.2$ cm),
    $\angle DAB = 74°$

14. Yes, 2, 2, 2, 4

Page 75   Exercise 5.1

1. 0.25, 0.75, 0.2, 0.4, 0.6, 0.8, 0.125, 0.375, 0.625, 0.875

2. **1** 0.06   **5** 0.12   **8** 0.95
   2 0.3125   **6** 0.0875   **9** 0.98
   3 0.008   **7** 0.036   **10** 0.825
   4 0.28125

3. **1** 0.444   **5** 0.385   **8** 0.059
   2 0.833   **6** 0.571   **9** 0.167
   3 0.091   **7** 0.818   **10** 0.889
   4 0.286

4. **1** 3.75   **5** 4.2   **8** 10.8
   2 2.7   **6** 16.875   **9** 14.025
   3 13.5   **7** 2.86   **10** 5.0625
   4 4.8

5. **1** $\frac{3}{7}$ **5** $13\frac{1}{3}$ **8** 8
   2 $3\frac{1}{3}$ **6** $6\frac{2}{3}$ **9** $22\frac{2}{3}$
   3 $3\frac{1}{3}$ **7** $3\frac{6}{7}$ **10** $9\frac{1}{3}$
   4 $8\frac{1}{10}$

6. **1** $3\frac{1}{2}$ **5** 28   **8** $11\frac{1}{9}$
   2 10   **6** 3   **9** $2\frac{1}{2}$
   3 $17\frac{1}{2}$ **7** $23\frac{1}{4}$ **10** $66\frac{2}{3}$
   4 $16\frac{1}{2}$

7. **1** 42   **5** 49   **8** $14\frac{2}{5}$
   2 24   **6** 75   **9** $22\frac{2}{5}$
   3 120   **7** $56\frac{1}{4}$ **10** 74.67
   4 22

Page 79   Exercise 5.2

1. **1** $\frac{7}{10}$ **4** $\frac{7}{40}$
   2 $\frac{1}{4}$ **5** $\frac{4}{30}$
   3 $\frac{17}{20}$

2. **1** 0.62   **4** 0.115
   2 0.35   **5** 0.99
   3 0.1675

3. **1** 60%   **4** $66\frac{2}{3}$%
   2 $87\frac{1}{2}$%   **5** $16\frac{2}{3}$%
   3 15%

4. **1** £4.50   **4** 0.2ℓ (200 ml)
   2 4.5 m   **5** 54 min
   3 480 g

5. **1** 2.7 kg   **4** £270
   2 1.089 m   **5** 300 mg
   3 2475

6. **1** 48%   **5** 150%   **8** $\frac{1}{2}$%
   2 $6\frac{1}{4}$%   **6** $62\frac{1}{2}$%   **9** $116\frac{2}{3}$%
   3 80%   **7** $37\frac{1}{2}$%   **10** 32%
   4 $32\frac{1}{2}$%

Page 80   Exercise 5.3

1. 2.2, 11 lb
2. 1.75, greater, $\frac{3}{4}$ pint
3. 1.76 m, 880 m
4. 7.5 g
5. **1** $\frac{3}{8}$ **2** £6937.50
6. $20\frac{12}{2} = 420\frac{1}{4}$
7. $\frac{2}{7}, \frac{3}{10}, \frac{1}{3}, \frac{3}{8}, \frac{2}{5}$
8. 35 min
9. 70
10. £980, £700, £770
11. £1950
12. 80%, 27
13. £2.50
14. 8%
15. 220%
16. £90, £135
17. **1** 113.4 g   **2** yes
18. 12%
19. **1** £17.50   **2** $12\frac{1}{2}$%   **3** £18
20. **1** $1\frac{1}{12}$ **5** $3\frac{5}{8}$ **8** $\frac{11}{12}$
   2 $4\frac{19}{20}$ **6** $1\frac{1}{2}$ **9** $1\frac{1}{2}$
   3 $1\frac{1}{2}$ **7** $2\frac{4}{5}$ **10** $3\frac{3}{4}$
   4 $6\frac{1}{6}$
22. **1** $\frac{5}{6}$ **5** 3   **8** $\frac{2}{3}$
   2 $1\frac{1}{20}$ **6** $\frac{3}{4}$ **9** $\frac{1}{10}$
   3 $3\frac{8}{9}$ **7** $1\frac{7}{8}$ **10** $1\frac{7}{8}$
   4 $\frac{3}{4}$
24. **1** £87.40
   2 £280, £42
   3 60p, £31.20
25. **1** £72   **2** £396   **3** £138

Page 94   Exercise 6.1

1. **1** 38.25, 10   **4** £130, £41
   2 21°C, 6°C   **5** 12 y 11 m, 1 y 9 m
   3 56.9 kg, 20 kg

Page 98 Exercise 6.2

1. men, 320, 308, 276; women, 180, 172, 164; total 500, 480, 440; 12%

2. RS 15, GS 5, BS9, RD16, GD 8, BD 7, Totals R 31, G 13, B 16, S 29, D 31; 60

Page 102 Exercise A1

1. 70, 64
2. £60
3. 1600
4. 60°
5. 4 hundredths
6. £5.20
7. 30ab
8. 12
9. 11
10. 25
11. 60°
12. 77p
13. 1.20 pm
14. 75
15. £2.00

Page 103 Exercise A2

1. 4 000 014
2. 6
3. 25%
4. 18
5. 4°C
6. 17, 33
7. trapezium
8. 100d cm
9. 95°
10. £4.95
11. 0.18
12. 1st Oct
13. 130 m
14. 0.6
15. 35

Page 104 Exercise A3

1. 167 281

2. 144°

3. $\frac{1}{50}$

4. $1\frac{1}{2}$

5. £9

6. **1** 1 **2** 3 **3** 0 **4** 2 **5** 4

7. 9

8. £5720

9. **1** 70° **2** 110° **3** 35° **4** 35°

10. £15 900, £16 536

11. **1** 7° **2** −1°C

12. 1094 yards

13. $7\frac{1}{2}$ lb

14. **1** 25x pence **2** £$\frac{x}{4}$

15. **1** 66 is 68 **4** 1 is 0
    2 9 is 10 **5** 6 is 8
    3 15 is 16

16. 25%, $16\frac{2}{3}$%

17. 5 kg

19. 3x years, Brother (x + 6) yrs, Peter (3x + 6) yrs or 2(x + 6) yrs; x = 6. Peter is 18 yrs, brother is 6 yrs.

20. 9.5 cm

Page 118 Exercise 7.1

1. **1** 4 : 9 **4** 2 : 3
   2 7 : 5 **5** 4 : 1
   3 1 : 6

2. **1** 24p, 60p **4** 84p, 48p
   2 41p, £1.23 **5** £2.50, £3.50
   3 £175, £105

3. **1** £440 **4** £275
   2 £69 **5** £54
   3 £96

4. **1** 90 cm **4** 5 pints
   2 10 kg **5** 26p
   3 2 hours

5. **1** 5 : 8 : 12 **4** 5 : 7 : 8
   2 12 : 15 : 20 **5** 5 : 9 : 11
   3 1 : 2 : 3

6. **1** £60, £90, £120
   2 0.5 m, 2.0 m, 3.0 m
   3 0.4ℓ, 0.6ℓ, 1.0ℓ
   4 1.0 kg, 1.4 kg, 1.6 kg
   5 30p, 45p, 50p

7. 4 : 5

8. 9 cm, 15 cm; 45 cm

9. 2.4 cm

10. 55 km

11. £14.70

12. 1 : 200 000

13. 48 cm

14. 3 : 8

15. $\frac{3}{40}$

16. 8.4 cm

17. £21, £24, £30

18. 45°, 60°, 75°

Page 120   Exercise 7.2

1. 10 kg tin, 4 kg zinc

2. 450 g flour, 300 g butter, 150 g sugar, 100 g nuts

3. 0.5 m³ cement, 1 m³ sand

4. £5000

5. 12 boys, 16 girls; 4 : 5

6. 20%

7. 1 : 4, 10ℓ, 3.2ℓ

8. 3 : 5 : 4, £60 to A, £100 to B, £80 to C

9. £21

10. 4 : 5, £3.50

Page 127   Exercise 8.1

1. **1** $\angle A = 112°$, $\angle B = 89°$, $\angle C = 134°$, $\angle D = 110°$, $\angle E = 95°$, sum = 540°
    2 $AB = 5.5$ cm, $BC = 4.6$ cm, $CD = 5.5$ cm, $DE = 4.3$ cm, $EA = 6.9$ cm, perimeter 26.8 cm

3. octagon, rhombus, hexagon

4. axes: 3, 4, 5, 6, 7, 8; points: no, yes, no, yes, no, yes; order: 3, 4, 5, 6, 7, 8

5. **1** 540°, 86°   **4** 90°
    2 720°, 150°   **5** 170°
    3 1080°, 165°

6. **1** 36°, 144°   **4** 45°, 8
    2 172°   **5** 20
    3 12

7. **1** 360°, 50°   **4** 40°
    2 30°, 90°, 90°   **5** 50°
    3 $a = 72°$, $\angle P = 36°$

8. **1** 108°
    2 isosceles (obtuse-angled)
    3 $a = 36°$, $c = 72°$

9. **1** 108°   **2** 168°

10. **1** 120°
    2 $a = b = c = 60°$
    3 equilateral
    4 rhombus
    5 isosceles trapezium

Page 132   Exercise 8.2

1. **1** isosceles trapezium
    2 rectangle
    3 isosceles (obtuse-angled)
    4 right-angled
    5 equilateral

2. **1** 45°   **2** 135°   **3** square

3. **1** isosceles (obtuse-angled)
    2 162°
    3 9°

4. 20°

5. $x = 40$; $\angle A = 80°$, $\angle B = 120°$, $\angle C = 120°$, $\angle D = 160°$

6. $x = 40$; $\angle A = 80°$, $\angle B = 110°$, $\angle C = 140°$, $\angle D = 100°$, $\angle E = 110°$

7. (20-sided polygon) 3240°

8. **1** 12   **2** 60°   **3** 150°

10. **1** $AD = 9.7$ cm   **2** $AB = 5.9$ cm

Page 141   Exercise 9.1

1. **1** $\frac{1}{5}$ **2** $\frac{4}{5}$

2. **1** $\frac{7}{16}$ **2** $\frac{9}{16}$ **3** $\frac{1}{4}$ **4** $\frac{3}{4}$

3. 0.1

4. $\frac{3}{7}$

5. $\frac{1}{6}$

6. **1** $\frac{1}{17}$ **2** $\frac{16}{17}$ **3** $\frac{4}{17}$ **4** $\frac{13}{17}$

7. 0.48

8. 0.1

9. **1** $\frac{6}{7}$　　**2** $\frac{5}{7}$　　**3** $\frac{4}{7}$

10. $\frac{1}{5}$, $\frac{4}{5}$

11. 0.997

12. $\frac{99999}{100000}$

Page 146　　Exercise 9.2

2. **1** $\frac{1}{4}$　　　**2** $\frac{1}{4}$　　　**3** $\frac{1}{2}$

4. **1** $\frac{1}{9}$　　　**2** $\frac{1}{3}$　　　**3** $\frac{5}{9}$

6. 30 outcomes,　**1** $\frac{1}{30}$　**2** $\frac{1}{6}$　**3** $\frac{2}{15}$　**4** $\frac{1}{6}$

Page 148　　Exercise 9.3

1. **1** $\frac{1}{6}$　　　**2** $\frac{5}{6}$

2. **1** $\frac{1}{20}$　　**2** $\frac{19}{20}$　　**3** $\frac{5}{99}$　　**4** $\frac{94}{99}$

3. 0.995

4. 30 outcomes, P(1) = $\frac{1}{5}$, P(1 twice) = $\frac{1}{25}$

5. **1** $\frac{1}{12}$　　**2** $\frac{1}{2}$　　　**3** $\frac{5}{12}$

6. **1** $\frac{1}{36}$　　**2** 7, $\frac{1}{6}$　　**3** $\frac{1}{6}$　　**4** $\frac{5}{6}$

7. **1** 8　**2** $\frac{1}{8}$　**3** $\frac{3}{8}$　**4** $\frac{3}{8}$　**5** $\frac{1}{8}$　**6** $\frac{7}{8}$

8. **1** $\frac{1}{10}$　　**2** $\frac{9}{10}$　　　**3** 10

Page 155　　Exercise 10.1

1. (3) **1**　(1, 3), (2, 6), (3, 9), (4, 12), (5, 15)
    　　2　(1, 1), (2, 6), (3, 11), (4, 16), (5, 21)
    　　3　(1, 1), (2, 4), (3, 9), (4, 16), (5, 25)
    　　4　(1, 4), (2, 6), (3, 8), (4, 10), (5, 12)
    　　5　(1, 9), (2, 8), (3, 7), (4, 6), (5, 5)

2. **1** $y = 4x$　　　　**4** $y = 5x$
    2 $y = 3x + 1$　　**5** $y = x^3$
    3 $y = 20 - 2x$

3. y-values:
    1　2, 7, 12, 17, 22
    2　10, 12, 14, 16, 18
    3　12, 9, 6, 3, 0
    4　0, $\frac{1}{2}$, 1, $1\frac{1}{2}$, 2
    5　0, 2, 8, 18, 32

4. **1** $y = 9 - x$　　　**4** $y = x^2 - 1$
    2 $y = 2x + 3$　　　**5** $y = \dfrac{12}{x}$
    3 $y = x^2$

5. **1**　6, $y = x + 4$　　**4**　5, $y = 12 - x$
    2　0, 9, $y = x^2$　　**5**　10, $y = 50 - 2x$
    3　21, $y = 5x + 1$

Page 158　　Exercise 10.2

3. y-values: 0, 3, 6, 9, 12, 15, 18

4. y-values: -7, -5, -3, -1, 1, 3, 5, 7

5. y-values: 7, 6, 5, 4, 3, 2, 1, 0, -1

6. y-values:
    1　-10, -5, 0, 5, 10, 15, 20, 25, 30
    2　4, 1, -2, -5, -8, -11, -14, -17, -20
    3　3, 4, 5, 6, 7, 8, 9, 10, 11
    4　7, 5, 3, 1, -1, -3, -5
    5　-9, -5, -1, 3, 7, 11, 15, 19, 23

Page 160　　Exercise 10.3

2. **1**　(1) $y = 3$　　(2) $x = 2$
    2　(3) $y = x$　　(4) $y = 1\frac{1}{2}x + 3$
    　　(5) $y = 3 - x$　　(6) $y = -\frac{1}{2}x$
    3　(1.5, 1.5)

Page 169　　Exercise 11.1

4. **1**　cuboid　　　　**4**　cube
    2　cylinder　　　**5**　cone
    3　triangular prism

6. F, V, E for each figure:
    6, 8, 12; 5, 6, 9; 7, 10, 15; 4, 4, 6; 5, 5, 8

7. 7 faces, 7 vertices, 12 edges

8. 14 faces, 24 vertices, 36 edges

Page 174　　Exercise 11.2

1. **1, 2, 4**

2. E and J

4. **1, 3**

5. pyramid with rectangular base

6. **1**　triangular prism
    2　pyramid with square base

Page 177　　Exercise 11.3

1. 49 cm by 35 cm by 12 cm

2. e.g. cone

3. 3

Page 187   Exercise 12.1

1. **1** 40 mph   **4** 36 mph
    2 66 km/h   **5** 30 km/h
    3 10 m/s

2. **1** 35 miles   **4** $7\frac{1}{2}$ miles
    2 65 km   **5** 75 m
    3 880 km

3. **1** $3\frac{1}{2}$ h   **4** 3 h
    2 $1\frac{3}{4}$ h   **5** $3\frac{1}{2}$ h
    3 $\frac{1}{2}$ h

4. **1** 2.5 h   **4** 1.6 h
    2 0.1 h   **5** 0.9 h
    3 3.8 h

5. **1** $\frac{1}{6}$ h   **4** $\frac{7}{12}$ h
    2 $1\frac{5}{6}$ h   **5** $2\frac{1}{12}$ h
    3 $3\frac{5}{12}$ h

6. **1** 3 h 15 min   **6** 3 h 20 min
    2 2 h 24 min   **7** 1 h 35 min
    3 1 h 45 min   **8** 5 h 10 min
    4 3 min   **9** 1 h 40 min
    5 2 h 42 min   **10** 2 h 50 min

7. **1** 54 km/h   **4** 4 km
    2 4 miles   **5** 100 m
    3 4 min

Page 189   Exercise 12.2

1. $1\frac{1}{2}$ km

2. $\frac{1}{2}$ h

3. Yes, cannot tell

4. 18 min

5. 54 km

6. **1** 138 km   **2** $1\frac{1}{2}$ h   **3** 92 km/h

7. **1** 54 km   **2** 4 h   **3** 13.5 km/h

8. 30 mph

9. $7\frac{1}{4}$ h, 7 h

10. $8\frac{1}{3}$ minutes

11. 1200, 15 h

Page 192   Exercise B1

1. £40   9.   0.3
2. 7   10. 3 : 4
3. 7   11. 30
4. 2 h 30 min   12. 400
5. 36   13. regular
6. 120°   14. 25 runs
7. 150 miles   15. £18
8. 12

Page 193   Exercise B2

1. sphere   9.   6
2. 14c   10. 20 cm
3. 450 g   11. 14
4. 2   12. 40 cm
5. 0.8 or $\frac{4}{5}$ 13. 464
6. 8   14. $\frac{1}{2}x + 3 = 11$
7. $1\frac{1}{2}$ h   15. 1.04 m
8. 81

Page 194   Exercise B3

1. 60

2. **1** 6, 8, 12   **3** 5, 6, 9
    2 5, 5, 8   **4** 8, 12, 18

4. 4 kg, 1.6%

5. **1** $a = 30°$
    2 isosceles
    3 $b = 75°$
    4 $c = 150°$

6. 30 g

7. $\frac{2}{3}$

8. $x = 20$, $\angle A = 48°$, $\angle B = 72°$, $\angle C = 96°$

9. It divides by 7 and 11.

10. **1** equilateral
    2 isosceles (obtuse-angled)
    3 right-angled

11. 14 : 1

12. C and E

13. parallelogram, $(-0.5, 0.5)$

14. 36 mph

15. Total vehicles sold = 874

16. 16 outcomes, $\frac{3}{16}$

17. 2 : 3 : 5; £240, £360, £600

18. y-values: $-9, -7, -5, -3, -1, 1, 3$;
    $y = -3x$, $(0.6, -1.8)$

19. **1** 360° **2** 12°, 168°

20. **1** 4 m **2** 3.2 m **3** 2.56 m

Page 215   Exercise 13.1

1. **1** 032° **4** 155°
   2 317° **5** 225°
   3 255°

3. **1** 212° **4** 335°
   2 137° **5** 045°
   3 075°

4. **1** 148° **4** 337°
   2 226° **5** 010°
   3 052°

5. **1** 225° **4** 045°
   2 090° **5** 270°
   3 315°

6. **1** 240° **4** 205°
   2 325° **5** 303°
   3 040°

7. **1** 070°, 350° **4** 320°
   2 025°, 110° **5** 038°, 314°
   3 95°

8. **1** 124° **2** 304°

Page 218   Exercise 13.2

1. 238°

2. **1** 110°, 100 km **4** 095°, 260 km
   2 230°, 120 km **5** 080°, 180 km
   3 305°, 100 km

3. 028°, 7.4 km

4. **1** 314° **4** 208°
   2 252° **5** 113°
   3 011°

5. 95 km, 314°, $4\frac{3}{4}$ hours

6. 35 km

7. 41 km, 27 km

8. **1** N 75° W **4** S 50° E
   2 S 20° W **5** N 38° W
   3 N 63° E

Page 226   Exercise 14.1

1. **1** 48 cm, 144 cm² **2** 34 cm, 70 cm²

2. **1** 19 cm, 10.5 cm² **2** 19 cm, 9.5 cm²

3. 30 m², 22 m

4. **1** 121 cm² **2** 120 cm

5. 46 cm², 40 cm

6. 38 m²

7. **1** 8.75 cm², 12 cm
   2 8 cm², 15 cm
   3 9.5 cm², 21 cm

8. 15 m², £300

9. 700

10. £2720

11. **1** 2 cm **2** 7 cm **3** 9 cm **4** 11 cm

12. 2 cm by 15 cm, 3 cm by 10 cm, 5 cm by 6 cm; 5 cm by 6cm; 7.5 cm, 23 cm

13. 150 cm²

14. **1** 14 cm²
    2 $\frac{1}{2}$, 14 cm²
    3 20 cm², 6 cm², 14 cm²

Page 231   Exercise 14.2

1. **1** 30 cm² **2** 45 cm² **3** 72 cm²

2. **1** 7.5 cm² **3** 7.5 cm²
   2 6 cm² **4** 3 cm²

3. 5.0 cm²

4. **1** 18 cm^2 **2** 8 cm^2

5. **1** 6 cm^2 **2** 7 cm^2 **3** 7.5 cm^2

6. 98 cm^2

7. 17 cm^2

Page 234   Exercise 14.3

1. **1** 8 cm^3 **2** 40 cm^3

2. **1** 660 cm^3 **4** 45 cm^3
    2 216 cm^3 **5** 46 800 cm^3
    3 75 m^3

3. **1** 216 cm^2 **2** 96 cm^2

4. 7 cm, 343 cm^3

5. 5 cm, 342 cm^2

6. 5

Page 236   Exercise 14.4

1. 10.6 g/cm^3

2. 0.6 g/cm^3

3. 5000 cm^3, 39 kg

4. 12.096 tonnes

5. 8 cm^3, 2 cm

Page 237   Exercise 14.5

1. **1** 5 m by 4 m   **2** 20 m^2 **3** £480

2. 500 tiles, 20 boxes, £160

3. 34 000 cm^2

4. 180 m^2, carpet 13 m by 10 m, 130 m^2;
    tiled area 50 m^2

5. 2.7 kg, 45 g

6. 50

7. areas (m^2): 350, 600, 750, 800, 750, 600,
    350; largest area 800 m^2, 40 m by 20 m

8. **1** 144 cm^2 **4** 24 cm^2
    2 28 cm^2 **5** 62 cm^2
    3 30 cm^2

9. **1** 24 cm^2 **2** 23.0 cm^2 **3** 24.5 cm^2;
    largest is the rectangle, smallest is the
    square.

10. 35 m^2

11. **1** 8 cm^2 **4** 8 cm^2
    2 6 cm^2 **5** 8 cm^2
    3 4 cm^2

12. **1** 294 m^2 **2** 68 m^2

13. 500 m^3

14. 5 ℓ

15. 1.5 m^3

16. 264 cm^3

17. **1** 60   **2** 3   **3** 180

18. **1** 272 g   **2** 13.6

19. 20 m^3, 18 tonnes

Page 248   Exercise 15.1

5. Table: 130, 110, 75, 120, 60, 0; perfect
    negative correlation

6. **1** positive   **4** positive
    2 negative   **5** negative
    3 zero

7. **1** negative correlation
    2 no correlation
    3 positive correlation
    4 perfect negative correlation
    5 perfect positive correlation

Page 255   Exercise 16.1

4. **1** (3, −2)   **2** (−3, 2)

Page 257   Exercise 16.2

2. 4

3. 2

5. **1** 2.5 cm   **2** 54°

6. **1** 3   **2** 12 cm   **3** 3 cm   **4** 36.9°

Page 259   Exercise 16.3

1. 53

5. **1** (4, −2)   **3** (2, 4)
    2 (−4, 2)   **4** (−2, −4)

Page 267   Exercise 17.1

1. **1** $x = 8$ **5** $x = 6$ **8** $x = 44$
   2 $x = 11$ **6** $x = 20$ **9** $x = 3.1$
   3 $x = 1$ **7** $x = 23$ **10** $x = 14.7$
   4 $x = 9$

2. **1** $x = 4.12$ **6** $x = 31.62$
   2 $x = 5.48$ **7** $x = 6.36$
   3 $x = 8.66$ **8** $x = 10.49$
   4 $x = 2.55$ **9** $x = 5.77$
   5 $x = 6.32$ **10** $x = 7.91$

Page 269   Exercise 17.2

1. **1** $x = 3$ **4** $x = 1$
   2 $x = 8$ **5** $x = 6$
   3 $x = 10$

2. **1** $x = 2.15$ **4** $x = 6.50$
   2 $x = 4.95$ **5** $x = 2.72$
   3 $x = 9.65$

Page 271   Exercise 17.3

1. $x = 9$ 5. $x = 10$ 8. $x = 4$
2. $x = 4$ 6. $x = 4$ 9. $x = 3$
3. $x = 3$ 7. $x = 5$ 10. $x = 10$
4. $x = 9$

Page 271   Exercise 17.4

3. $2x$ cm, $2x^3$ cm^3, 1000 cm^3, $x = 7.9$;
   7.9 cm by 7.9 cm by 15.8 cm (or 15.9 cm)

4. $(x + 3)$ m, $x(x + 3)$ m^2, $x = 8$, 11 m by 8 m

5. 5000 cm^3, $d = 26.7$, diameter = 26.7 cm

6. 3.5 seconds

Page 278   Exercise 18.1

6. **1** $a = b = 35°$
   2 $b = 25°$, $c = 130°$
   3 $b = 30°$, $c = 120°$, $d = 60°$
   4 $a = b = 28°$, $c = 62°$

7. $a = 64°$, $b = 52°$, $c = 128°$, $d = e = 26°$,
   $\angle ABC = 90°$

Page 290   Exercise C1

1. 9
2. 5
3. 6 cm
4. x^3
5. TWO
6. East
7. 30 cm
8. 120 cm^3
9. (2, 3)
10. 13 years
11. 9%
12. -3
13. 185°
14. 40 mph
15. 4

Page 291   Exercise C2

1. 2000 m^2
2. rhombus
3. 045°
4. 4 : 5
5. (1, -5)
6. 34p
7. 27 cm^3
8. 2
9. $\frac{1}{4}$
10. 4
11. $3b$
12. 020°
13. 42
14. 11 cm
15. 60°

Page 293   Exercise C4

1. 54 cm^2

2. 48°

3. **1** 132.25 cm^2 **2** yes

4. **1** $5x°$ or $(180 - x)°$
   2 $x = 30$; 30°, 150°
   3 360°
   4 12
   5 12

5. (3, 5)

6. 1 : 400

7. **1** 36   **2** $\frac{1}{36}$

8. OA, 020°; OB, 070°; OC, 160°;
   OD, 250°; OF, 290°

9. Silver block weighs 13.25 kg, lead block
   weighs 13.68 kg, lead is heavier.

10. 0.1

11. **1** 3   **2** 2   **3** 6

12. **1** 60 mph
    2 52 mph
    3 32 miles per gallon

13. **1** kite   **2** rhombus   **3** square

14. D $(-1, -5)$

15. 820, 210, 610

16. $\angle B = \angle D = 42°$

17. **1** $80x$ grams
    2 $x^2 - 80x = 900$
    3 $x = 90$, height 90 cm, weight 7.2 kg

19. £370 000, £185

20. **1** A to B, 248°, 66 km;
    B to C, 040°, 80 km
    2 19 km

Page 297   Exercise C5

1. 0.96

2. 11 cm

3. £265

4. 74°, 106°

5. 56.63 km/h

6. $A'B' = 12.0$ cm, $B'C' = 19.0$ cm,
   $C'D' = 15.0$ cm, $D'A' = 10.0$ cm

7. £144

8. **1** 30°   **3** 75°   **4** 150°

9. **1** $7x - 5$ **2** $x = 5$

12. **1** isosceles (obtuse-angled)
    2 $a = 16°$, $b = 26°$, $c = 32°$, $d = 52°$
    3 84°

13. **1** $\frac{1}{3}$ **2** $\frac{5}{9}$

14. width $(x - 30)$ m, $x = 57$, 57 m by 27 m

15. **1** C **2** 4, 6, 4

17. **1** 23 760 cm^3
    2 38 cm by 25 cm by 20 cm
    3 19 000 cm^3
    4 4760 cm^3

18. 10.55 am

19. 14.8 km

20. values for y: 6, 7, 8.4, 10.5, 14, 21, 42;
    (1.6, 12.2)